Advanced PHYSICS

REVISION HANDBOOK

Stephen Pople

Oxford University Press

Oxford University Press, Great Clarendon Street, Oxford OX2 6DP

Oxford New York
Athens Auckland Bangkok Bogota Bombay
Buenos Aires Calcutta Cape town Dar es Salaam Delhi
Florence Hong Kong Istanbul Karachi
Kuala Lumpur Madras Madrid Melbourne
Mexico City Nairobi Paris Singapore
Taipei Tokyo Toronto

and associated companies in
Berlin Ibadan

Oxford is a trade mark of Oxford University Press

First published 1996
Reprinted 1997

ISBN 0 19 914641 1 School edition
0 19 914640 3 Bookshop edition

Typesetting, design and illustration by Hardlines, Charlbury, Oxford
Printed in Great Britain

CONTENTS

Pathways (concept maps) 4

SECTION A: FOUNDATIONS

A brief review of concepts you may have covered before starting advanced work.

A1 Motion, mass, and forces 6
A2 Work, energy, and power 8
A3 Atoms and molecules in motion 10
A4 Charges and circuits 12
A5 Magnets and currents 14
A6 Waves and rays 16

SECTION B: KEY TOPICS

The main concepts in advanced work.

B1 Units and dimensions 18
B2 Measurement, uncertainties, and graphs 20
B3 Analysing motion 22
B4 Vectors 24
B5 Moments and equilibrium 26
B6 Motion and momentum 28
B7 Work, energy, and momentum 30
B8 Circular motion 32
B9 Gravitation 34
B10 Circular orbits... ...and rotation 36
B11 Cycles, oscillations, and SHM 38
B12 More motion graphs 40
B13 Electric charges and fields 42
B14 Capacitors and fields 44
B15 Current and resistance 46
B16 Analysing circuits 48
B17 Magnetic fields and forces 50
B18 Electromagnetic induction 52
B19 Alternating current – 1 54
B20 Alternating current – 2 56
B21 Charged particles in motion 58
B22 Moving waves 60
B23 Combining waves 62
B24 Using mirrors and lenses 64
B25 Solids, stresses, and strains 66
B26 Liquid and gas pressure 68
B27 Temperature 70
B28 Internal energy, heat, and work 72
B29 The behaviour of gases 74
B30 Kinetic theory 76
B31 Heat transfer 78
B32 The nuclear atom 80
B33 Radiation and decay 82
B34 Nuclear energy 84
B35 Quantum theory 86

SECTION C: FURTHER TOPICS

Options and applications

C1 Particle physics –1 88
C2 Particle physics – 2 90
C3 Astrophysics – 1 92
C4 Astrophysics – 2 94
C5 Cosmology 96
C6 Materials – 1 98
C7 Materials – 2 100
C8 Fluid flow 102
C9 Medical physics – 1 104
C10 Medical physics – 2 106
C12 Energy and the environment – 1 110
C13 Energy and the environment – 2 112
C14 Cars and aircraft in motion 114
C15 Electronics – 1 116
C16 Electronics – 2 118
C17 Telecommunications 120
C18 Turning points 122

Index 124
Physical data 128

Pathways

Concepts covered in Sections A and B: where to find them, and the links between them.

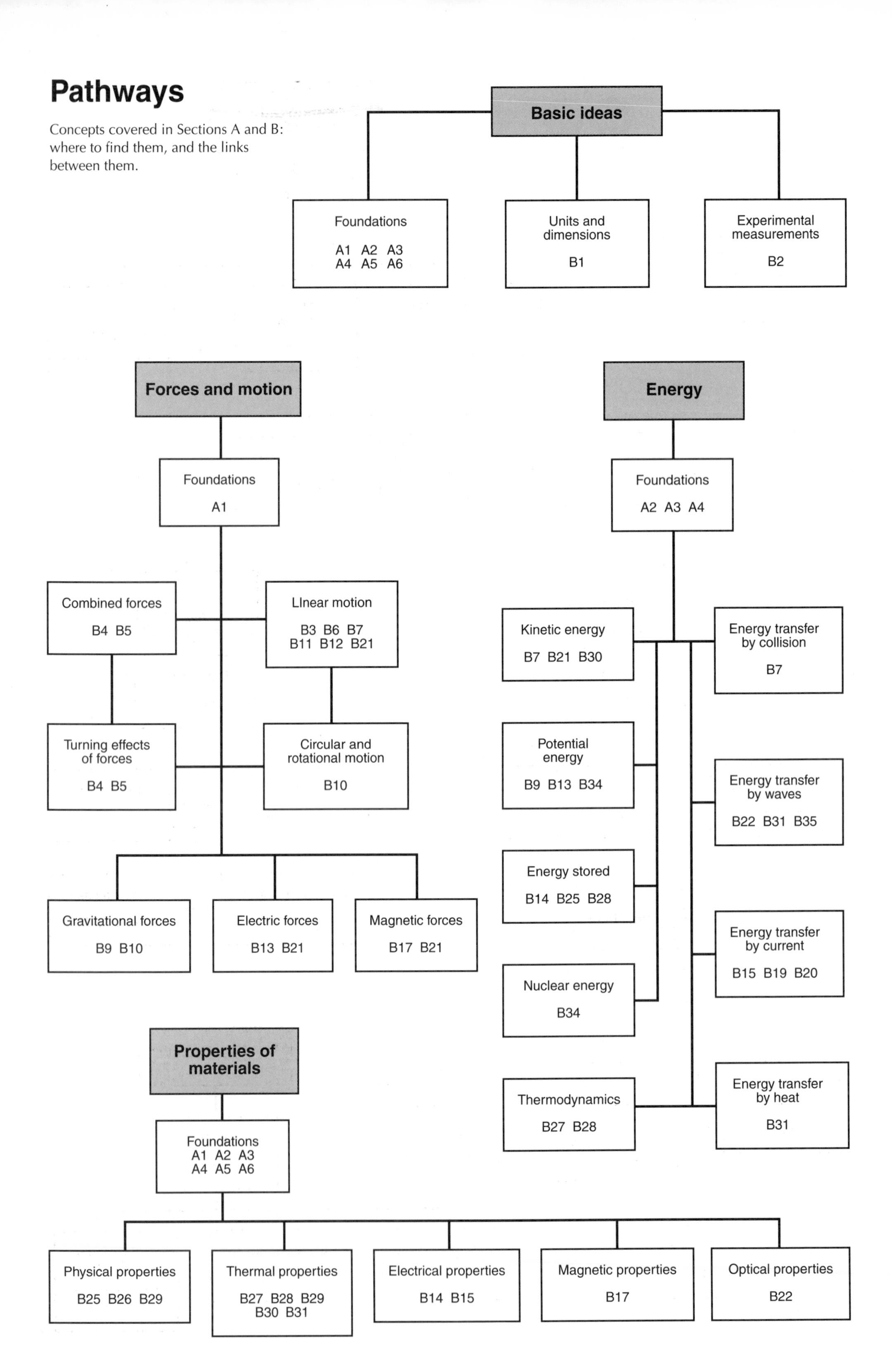

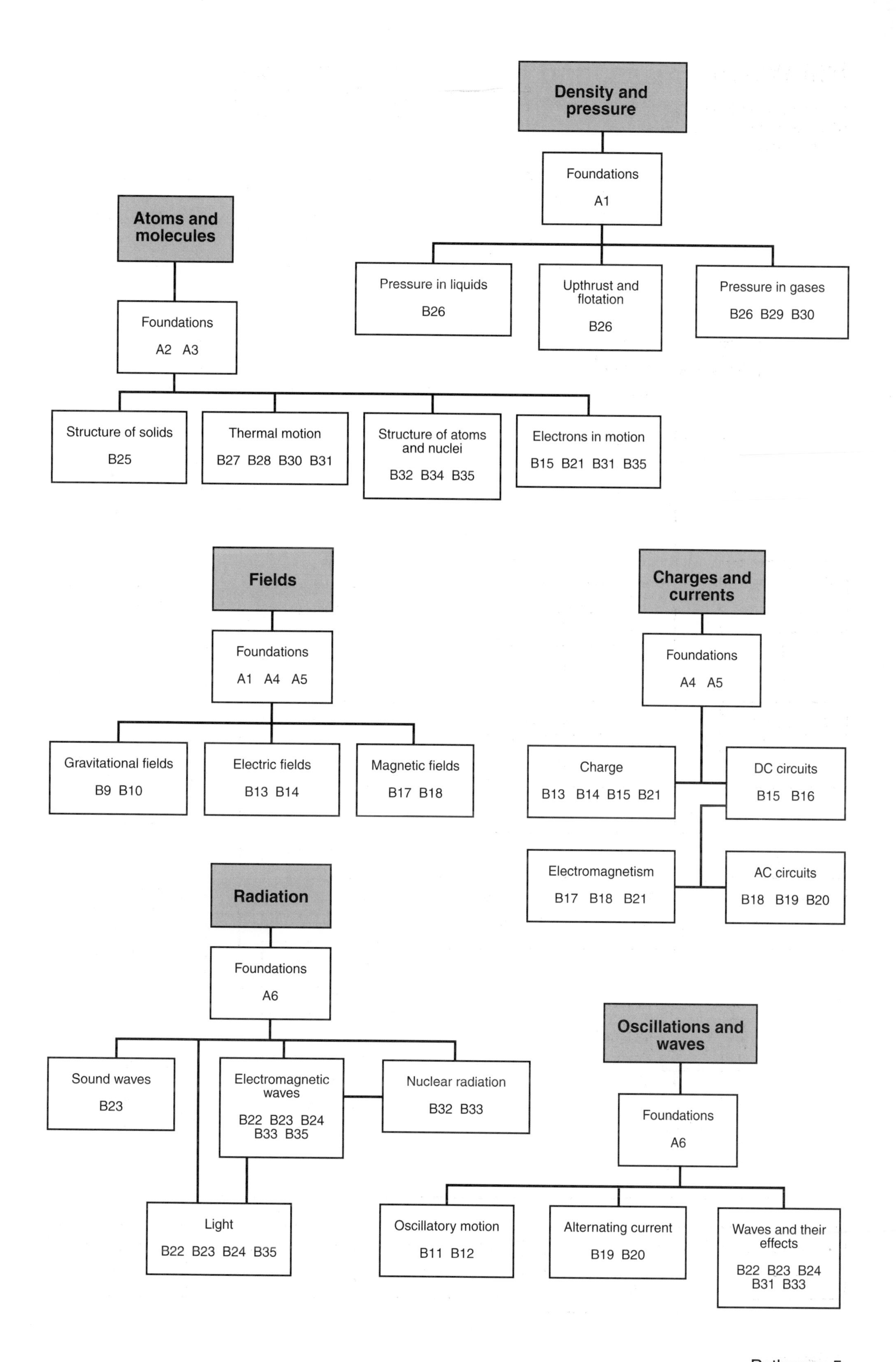

Density and pressure
Foundations
A1
Pressure in liquids
B26
Upthrust and flotation
B26
Pressure in gases
B26 B29 B30
Atoms and molecules
Foundations
A2 A3
Structure of solids
B25
Thermal motion
B27 B28 B30 B31
Structure of atoms and nuclei
B32 B34 B35
Electrons in motion
B15 B21 B31 B35
Fields
Foundations
A1 A4 A5
Gravitational fields
B9 B10
Electric fields
B13 B14
Magnetic fields
B17 B18
Charges and currents
Foundations
A4 A5
Charge
B13 B14 B15 B21
DC circuits
B15 B16
Electromagnetism
B17 B18 B21
AC circuits
B18 B19 B20
Radiation
Foundations
A6
Sound waves
B23
Electromagnetic waves
B22 B23 B24 B33 B35
Nuclear radiation
B32 B33
Light
B22 B23 B24 B35
Oscillations and waves
Foundations
A6
Oscillatory motion
B11 B12
Alternating current
B19 B20
Waves and their effects
B22 B23 B24 B31 B33

A1 Motion, mass, and forces

Units of measurement

Scientists make measurements using SI units such as the metre, kilogram, second, and newton. These and their abbreviations are covered in detail in B1. However, you may find it easier to appreciate the links between different units after you have studied the whole of section A.

For simplicity, units will be excluded from some stages of the calculations in this book, as in this example:

total length = 2 + 3 = 5 m

Strictly speaking, this should be written:

total length = 2 m + 3 m = 5 m

Displacement

Displacement is distance moved in a particular direction. The SI unit of displacement is the ***metre*** (m).

Quantities, such as displacement, which have both magnitude (size) and direction, are called ***vectors***.

Dist= Scaler
Disp= vec

A —— 12 m ——> B

The arrow above represents the displacement of a particle which moves 12 m from A to B. However, with horizontal or vertical motion, it is often more convenient to use a '+' or '–' to show the vector direction. For example:

Movement of 12 m *to the right*: displacement = +12 m
Movement of 12 m *to the left*: displacement = –12 m

Displacement is not necessarily the same as distance travelled. For example, when the ball below has returned to its starting point, its vertical displacement is zero. However, the distance travelled is 10 m.

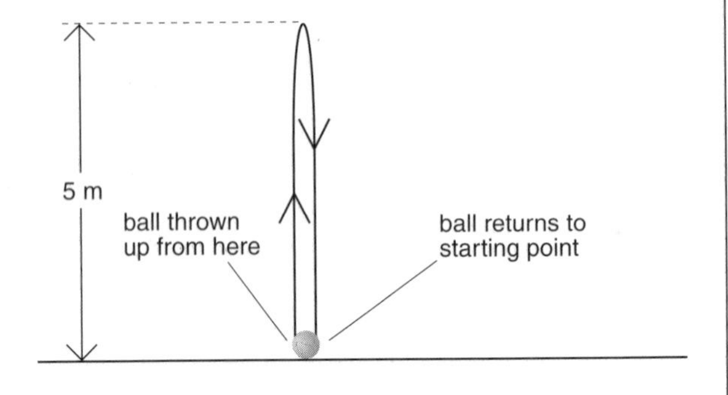

Speed and velocity

Average speed is calculated like this:

$$\text{average speed} = \frac{\text{distance travelled}}{\text{time taken}}$$

The SI unit of speed is the metre/second, abbreviated as m s^{-1}. For example, if an object travels 12 m in 2 s, its average speed is 6 m s^{-1}.

Average velocity is calculated like this:

$$\text{average velocity} = \frac{\text{displacement}}{\text{time taken}}$$

The SI unit of velocity is also the m s^{-1}. But unlike speed, velocity is a vector.

6 m s^{-1} ——>

The velocity vector above is for a particle moving to the right at 6 m s^{-1}. However, as with displacement, it is often more convenient to use a '+' or '–' for the vector direction.

Average velocity is not necessarily the same as average speed. For example, if a ball is thrown upwards and travels a total distance of 10 m before returning to its starting point 2 s later, its average speed is 5 m s^{-1}. But its average velocity is zero, because its displacement is zero.

Acceleration

Average acceleration is calculated like this:

$$\text{average acceleration} = \frac{\text{change in velocity}}{\text{time taken}}$$

The SI unit of acceleration is the m s^{-2} (sometimes written m/s^2). For example, if an object gains 6 m s^{-1} of velocity in 2 s, its average acceleration is 3 m s^{-2}.

3 m s^{-2} ——>>

Acceleration is a vector. The acceleration vector above is for a particle with an acceleration of 3 m s^{-2} to the right. However, as with velocity, it is often more convenient to use a '+' or '–' for the vector direction.

If velocity *increases* by 3 m s^{-1} every second, the acceleration is +3 m s^{-2}. If it *decreases* by 3 m s^{-1} every second, the acceleration is –3 m s^{-2}.

Mathematically, an acceleration of –3 m s^{-2} *to the right* is the same as an acceleration of +3 m s^{-2} *to the left*.

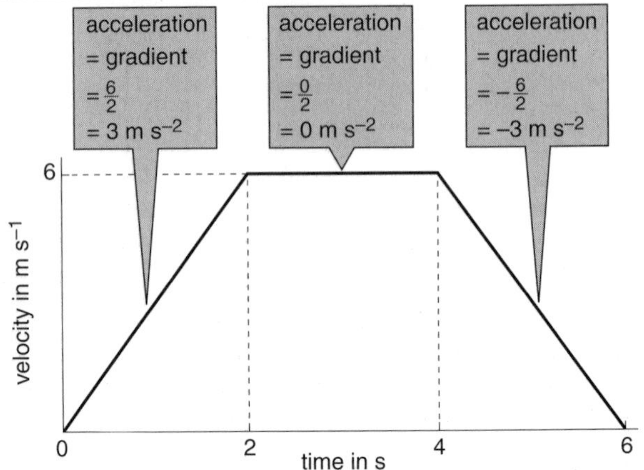

On the velocity-time graph above, you can work out the acceleration over each section by finding the *gradient* of the line. The gradient is calculated like this:

$$\text{gradient} = \frac{\text{gain along } y\text{-axis}}{\text{gain along } x\text{-axis}}$$

Force

Force is a vector. The SI unit is the ***newton*** (**N**).

If two or more forces act on something, their combined effect is called the ***resultant force***. Two simple examples are shown below. In the right-hand example, the resultant force is zero because the forces are ***balanced***.

A resultant force acting on a mass causes an acceleration. The force, mass, and acceleration are linked like this:

resultant force = mass × acceleration $F = ma$

For example, a 1 N resultant force gives a 1 kg mass an acceleration of 1 m s^{-2}. (The newton is defined in this way.)

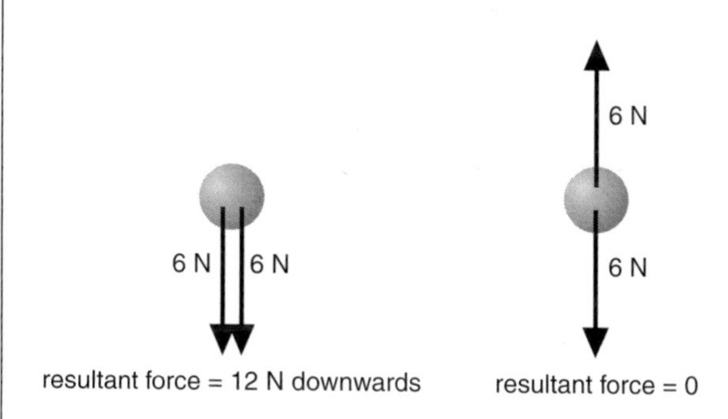

The more mass something has, the more force is needed to produce any given acceleration.

When balanced forces act on something, its acceleration is zero. This means that it is *either* stationary *or* moving at a steady velocity (steady speed in a straight line).

Weight and *g*

On Earth, everything feels the downward force of gravity. This gravitational force is called ***weight***. As for other forces, its SI unit is the newton (N).

Near the Earth's surface, the gravitational force on each kg is about 10 N: the ***gravitational field strength*** is 10 N kg^{-1}. This is represented by the symbol g.

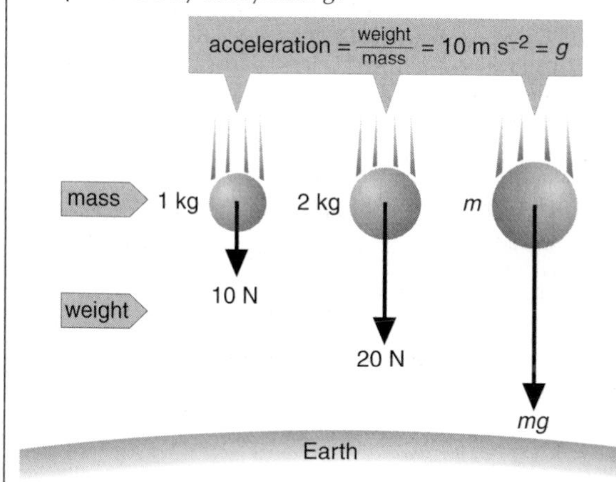

In the diagram above, all the masses are falling freely (gravity is the only force acting). From $F = ma$, it follows that all the masses have the same downward acceleration, g. This is the ***acceleration of free fall***.

You can think of g:

either as a gravitational field strength of 10 N kg^{-1}

or as an acceleraton of free fall of 10 m s^{-2}

In more accurate calculations, the value of g is normally taken to be 9.81, rather than 10.

Moments and balance

The turning effect of a force is called a ***moment***:

moment of force about a point = force × perpendicular distance* from point

* measured from the line of action of the force.

The dumb-bell below balances at point O because the two moments about O are equal but opposite.

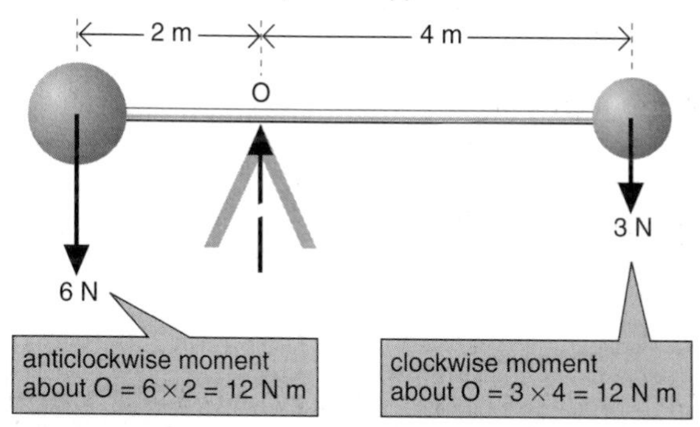

The dumb-bell is made up of smaller parts, each with its own weight. Together, these are equivalent to a single force, the total weight, acting through O. O is the ***centre of gravity*** of the dumb-bell.

Density

The density of an object is calculated like this:

$$\text{density} = \frac{\text{mass}}{\text{volume}}$$

The SI unit of density is the kilogram/cubic metre (kg m^{-3}).

For example, 2000 kg of water occupies a volume of 2 m^3. So the density of water is 1000 kg m^{-3}.

Density values, in kg m^{-3}

alcohol	800	iron	7 900
aluminium	2 700	lead	11 300

Pressure

Pressure is calculated like this:

$$\text{pressure} = \frac{\text{force}}{\text{area}}$$

The SI unit of pressure is the newton/square metre, also called the ***pascal*** (**Pa**). For example, if a force of 12 N acts over an area of 3 m^2, the pressure is 4 Pa.

Liquids and gases are called ***fluids***.

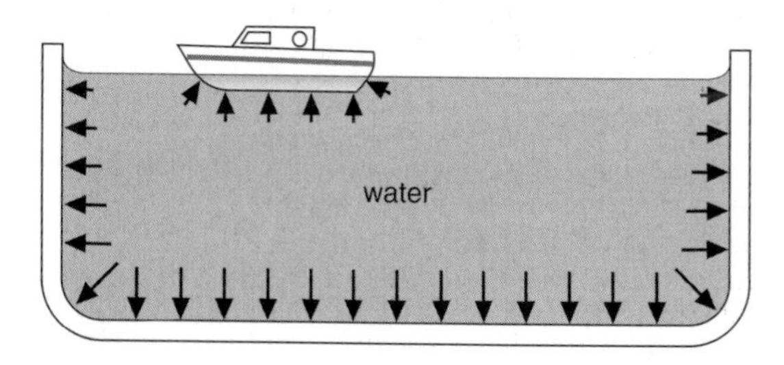

In a fluid:

- Pressure acts in all directions. The force produced is always at right-angles to the surface under pressure.
- Pressure increases with depth.

A2 Work, energy, and power

Work

Work is done whenever a force makes something move.
It is calculated like this:

work done = force × distance moved in direction of force

The SI unit of work is the ***joule*** (J). For example, if a force of 2 N moves something a distance of 3 m, then the work done is 6 J.

Energy

Things have energy if they can do work. The SI unit of energy is also the joule (J). You can think of energy as a 'bank balance' of work which can be done in the future.

Energy exists in different forms:

Kinetic energy This is energy which something has because it is moving.

Potential energy This is energy which something has because of its position, shape, or state. A stone about to fall from a cliff has ***gravitational*** potential energy. A stretched spring has ***elastic*** potential energy. Foods and fuels have ***chemical*** potential energy. Charge from a battery has ***electrical*** potential energy. Particles from the nucleus (centre) of an atom have ***nuclear*** potential energy.

Internal energy Matter is made up of tiny particles (e.g. atoms or molecules) which are in random motion. They have kinetic energy because of their motion, and potential energy because of the forces of attraction trying to pull them together. An object's internal energy is the total kinetic and potential energy of its particles.

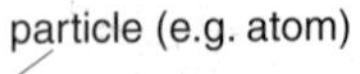

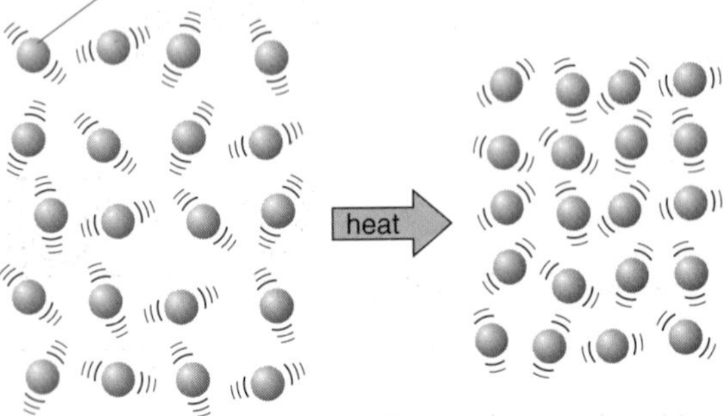

Heat (thermal energy) This is the energy transferred from one object to another because of a temperature difference. Usually, when heat is transferred, one object loses internal energy, and the other gains it.

Radiant energy This is often in the form of waves. Sound and light are examples.

Note:

- Kinetic energy, and gravitational and elastic potential energy are sometimes known as ***mechanical energy***. They are the forms of energy most associated with machines and motion.
- Gravitational potential energy is sometimes just called potential energy (or PE), even though there are other forms of potential energy as described above.

Energy changes

According to the ***law of conservation of energy***:

Energy cannot be made or destroyed, but it can be changed from one form to another.

The diagram below shows the sequence of energy changes which occur when a ball is kicked along the ground. At every stage, energy is lost as heat. Even the sound waves heat the air as they die away. As in other energy chains, all the energy eventually becomes internal energy.

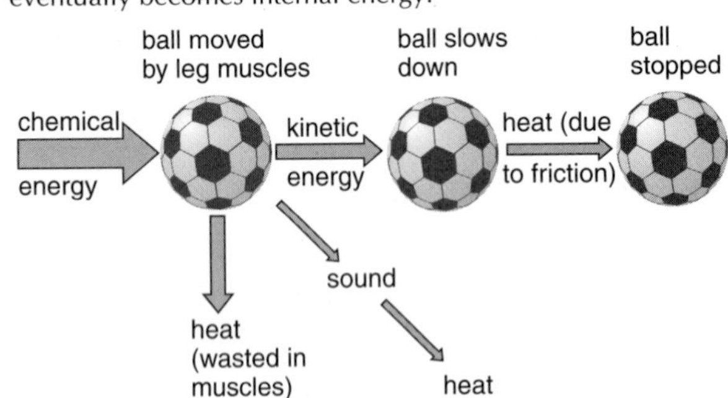

Whenever there is an energy change, work is done – although this may not always be obvious. For example, when a car's brakes are applied, the car slows down and the brakes heat up, so kinetic energy is being changed into internal energy. Work is done because tiny forces are making the particles of the brake materials move faster.

An energy change is sometimes called an energy transformation. Whenever it takes place:

work done = energy transformed

So, for each 1 J of energy transformed, 1 J of work is done.

Calculating potential energy (PE)

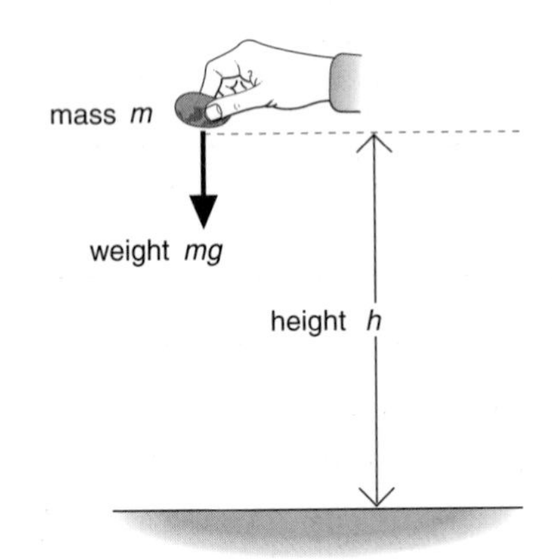

The stone above has potential energy. This is equal to the work done in lifting it to a height h above the ground.

The stone, mass m, has a weight of mg.
So the force needed to overcome gravity and lift it is mg.

As the stone is lifted through a height h:

work done = force × distance moved = $mg \times h$

So potential energy = mgh

For example, if a 2 kg stone is 5 m above the ground, and g is 10 N kg^{-1}, then the stone's PE = $2 \times 10 \times 5 = 100$ J.

Calculating kinetic energy (KE)

The stone on the right has kinetic energy. This is equal to the work done in increasing the velocity from zero to v.

B7 shows you how to calculate this. The result is:

$$\text{kinetic energy} = \tfrac{1}{2}mv^2$$

For example, if a 2 kg stone has a speed of 10 m s^{-1}, its KE $= \frac{1}{2} \times 2 \times 10^2 = 100$ J

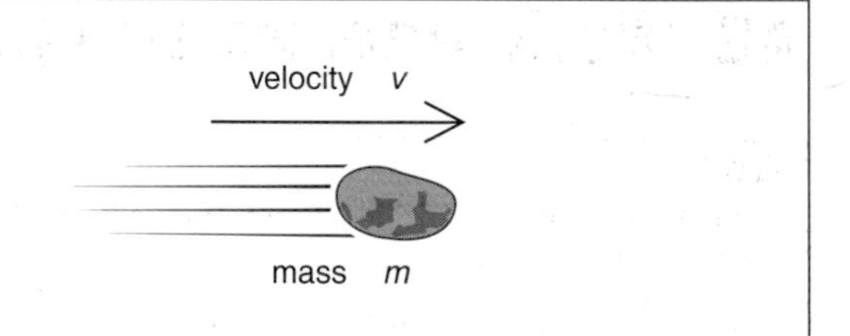

PE to KE

The diagram on the right shows how PE is changed into KE when something falls. The stone in this example starts with 100 J of PE. Air resistance is assumed to be zero, so no energy is lost to the air as the stone falls.

By the time the stone is about to hit the ground (with velocity v), all of its potential energy has been changed into kinetic energy. So:

$$\tfrac{1}{2}mv^2 = mgh$$

Dividing both sides by m and rearranging:

$$v = \sqrt{2gh}$$

In this example, $v = \sqrt{2 \times 10 \times 5} = 10$ m s^{-1}.

Note that v does not depend on m. A heavy stone hits the ground at exactly the same speed as a light one.

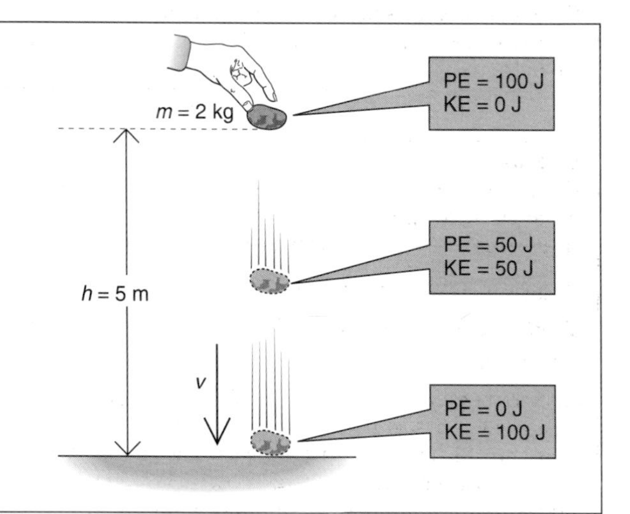

Vectors, scalars, and energy

Vectors have magnitude and direction. When adding vectors, you must allow for their direction. In A1, for example, there are diagrams showing two 6 N forces being added. In one, the resultant is 12 N. In the other, it is zero.

Scalars are quantities which have magnitude but no direction. Examples include mass, volume, energy, and work. Scalar addition is simple. If 6 kg of mass is added to 6 kg of mass, the result is always 12 kg. Similarly, if an object has 6 J of PE and 6 J of KE, the total energy is 12 J.

As energy is a scalar, PE and KE can be added without allowing for direction. The stone on the right has the same total PE + KE throughout its motion. As it starts with the same PE as the stone in the previous diagram, it has the same KE (and speed) when it is about to hit the ground.

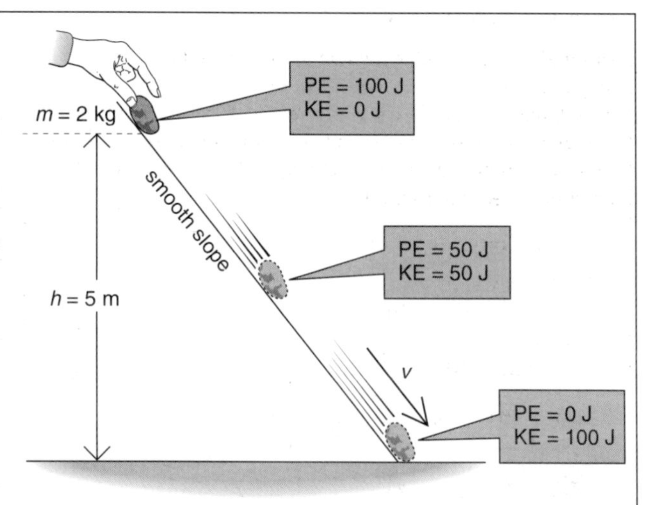

Power

Power is calculated like this:

$$\text{power} = \frac{\text{energy transferred}}{\text{time taken}} \quad \text{or} \quad \text{power} = \frac{\text{work done}}{\text{time taken}}$$

The SI unit of power is the **watt** (W). A power of 1 W means that energy is being transformed at the rate of 1 joule/second (J s^{-1}), so work is being done at the rate of 1 J s^{-1}.

Below, you can see how to calculate the power output of an electric motor which raises a mass of 2 kg through a height of 12 m in 3 s:

$$\begin{aligned} \text{PE gained} &= mgh \\ &= 2 \times 10 \times 12 = 240 \text{ J} \\ \text{power} &= \frac{\text{energy transferred}}{\text{time taken}} \\ &= \frac{240}{3} = 80 \text{ W} \end{aligned}$$

motor

Efficiency

Energy changers such as motors waste some of the energy supplied to them. Their ***efficiency*** is calculated like this:

$$\text{efficiency} = \frac{\text{useful energy output}}{\text{energy input}} = \frac{\text{useful power output}}{\text{power input}}$$

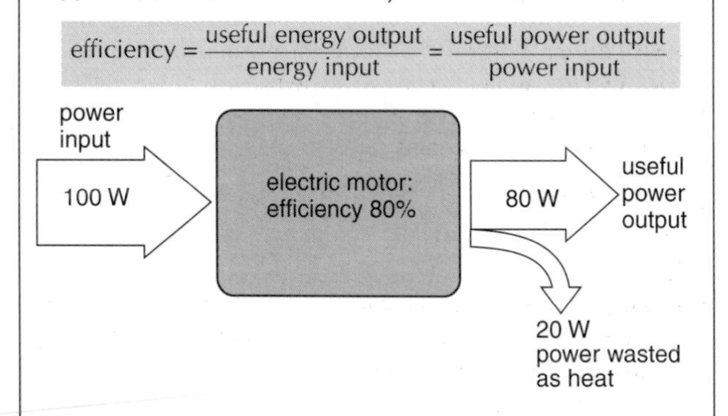

For example, if an electric motor's power input is 100 W, and its useful power output (mechanical) is 80 W, then its efficiency is 0.8. This can be expressed as 80%.

A3 Atoms and molecules in motion

Atoms

All matter is made from ***atoms***. It would take more than a million million atoms to cover this full stop.

An atom has a tiny central ***nucleus*** made of ***protons*** and ***neutrons*** (apart from the simplest atom, hydrogen, whose nucleus is a single proton). Orbiting the nucleus are much lighter particles called ***electrons***.

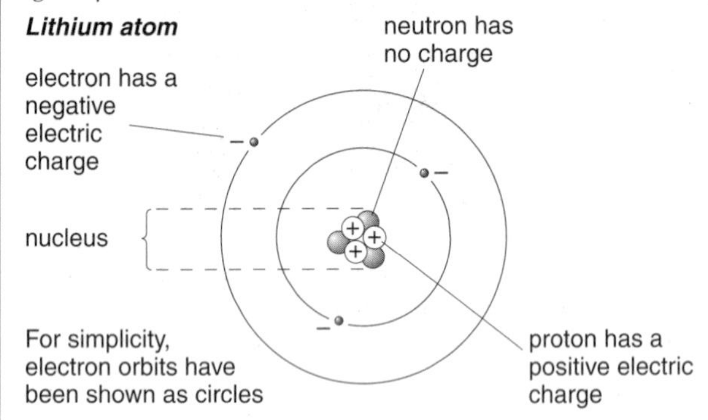

An atom has the same number of electrons as protons, so the amounts of negative and positive charge balance.

Unlike charges (– and +) attract each other. This ***electric force*** holds electrons in orbit around the nucleus.

Like charges (– and –, also + and +) repel each other. However, the particles in the nucleus are held together by a ***strong nuclear force***, which is strong enough to overcome the repulsion between the protons.

Atoms can stick together, in solids for example. The forces that bind them are attractions between opposite charges.

Moving electrons In metals, some of the electrons are only loosely held to their atoms. These ***free electrons*** can drift between the atoms. The electric current in a wire is a flow of free electrons.

If an atom gains or loses electrons, it is left with an overall – or + charge. Charged atoms are called ***ions***.

Elements and isotopes

Everything is made from about 100 substances called ***elements***. Each element has a different number of protons (and therefore electrons) in its atoms.

Elements exist in different versions, called ***isotopes***, each with a different number of neutrons in its atoms. Examples are shown below (italic numbers are for rarer isotopes).

Element	Electrons	Protons	Neutrons
hydrogen	1	1	0 or *1* or *2*
helium	2	2	*1* or 2
lithium	3	3	*3* or 4
carbon	6	6	6 or *7* or *8*
uranium	92	92	*142* or *143* or 146

The total of protons plus neutrons in an atom is called the ***nucleon number***. It is used when naming different isotopes, for example: carbon-12, carbon-13, carbon-14.

Radioactive isotopes These have atoms with unstable nuclei. The nuclei break up, emitting ***nuclear radiation***. The three main types of nuclear radiation are ***alpha*** particles, ***beta*** particles and ***gamma*** waves (see A6).

Solids, liquids and gases

According to the ***kinetic theory***, matter is made up of tiny, randomly moving particles. Each particle may be a single atom, a group of atoms called a ***molecule***, or an ion. The three normal ***phases*** of matter are solid, liquid, and gas.

Solid The particles are held close together by strong forces of attraction. They vibrate, but about fixed central positions, so a solid keeps a fixed shape and volume.

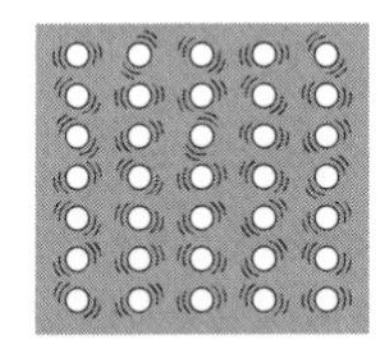

Liquid The particles are held close together. But the vibrations are strong enough to overcome the attractions, so the particles can change positions. A liquid has a fixed volume, but it can flow to fill any shape.

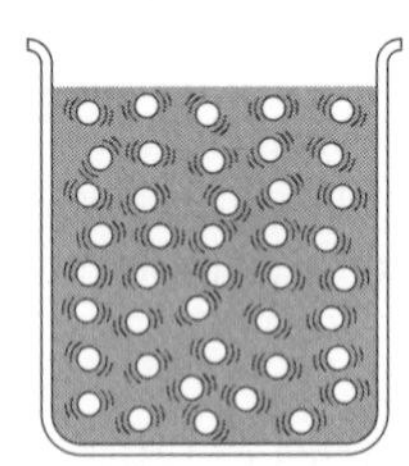

Gas The particles move at high speed, colliding with each other and with the walls of their container. They are too spread out and fast-moving to stick together, so a gas quickly fills any space available. Its pressure is due to the impact of its particles on the container walls.

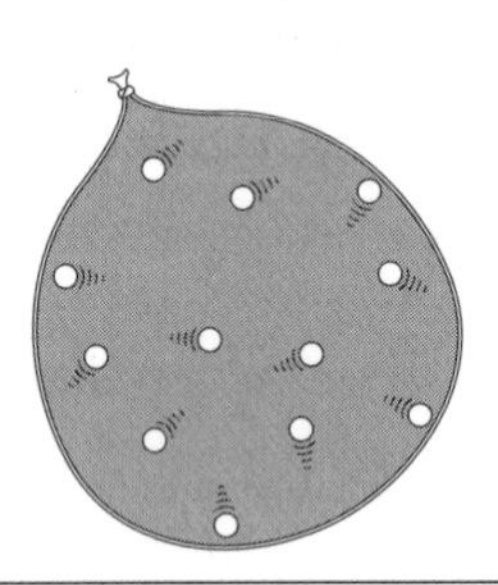

Temperature

The particles in, for example, a gas move at a range of speeds. However, the higher the temperature, the faster the particles move on average.

If two objects at the same temperature are in contact, there is no flow of heat between them. This is because the average kinetic energy of each particle due to its vibrating or speeding motion is the same in each object, so there is no overall transfer of energy from one object to the other.

Celsius scale On this scale, pure water freezes at 0 °C and boils at 100 °C (under standard atmospheric conditions).

Kelvin scale This has the same sized 'degree' as the Celsius scale, but its 'zero' is ***absolute zero*** (–273 °C), the temperature at which particles have the minimum possible kinetic energy. (The laws governing the behaviour of atoms do not permit zero energy).

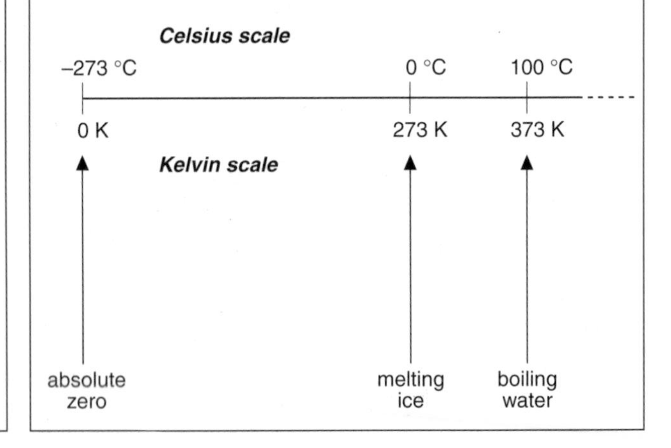

Linking heat and temperature

If, say, a block of copper absorbs heat, its internal energy increases and its temperature rises.

Copper has a ***specific heat capacity*** of 390 J kg^{-1} K^{-1}. This means that 390 J of energy are required to raise the temperature of 1 kg of copper by 1 K.

Specific heat capacities, in J kg^{-1} K^{-1}			
copper	390	aluminium	910
iron	470	ice	2100
glass	670	water (liquid)	4200

If a solid of mass m and specific heat capacity c is to increase its temperature by ΔT, then the heat input required is given by the following equation:

heat input = $mc\Delta T$

For example, to raise the temperature of 2 kg of copper by 10 K, the heat input required = $2 \times 390 \times 10 = 7800$ J.

Changing phase

The graph shows what happens when a very cold solid (ice) takes in heat at a steady rate. Melting and boiling are both examples of a change of ***phase***.

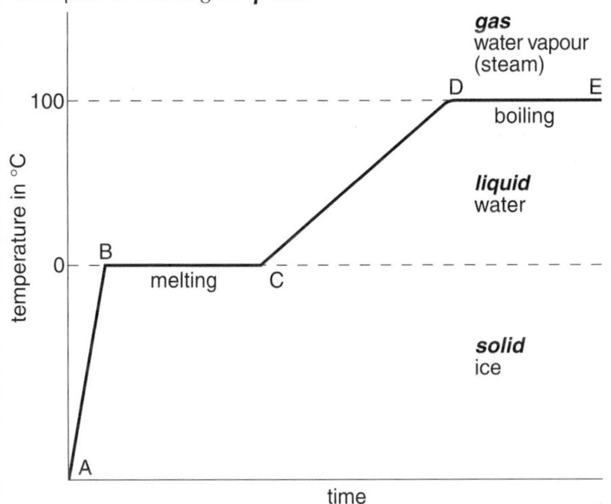

A to B The temperature rises until the ice starts to melt.

B to C Heat is absorbed, but with no rise in temperature. The energy input is being used to overcome the attractions between the particles as the solid changes into a liquid.

C to D The temperature rises until the water starts to boil.

D to E Heat is absorbed, but with no rise in temperature. The energy input is being used to separate the particles as the liquid changes into a gas (water vapour).

A liquid, such as water, starts to turn to gas well below its boiling point. This process is called ***evaporation***. It happens as faster particles escape from the surface.

Boiling is a rapid type of evaporation in which vapour bubbles, forming in the liquid, expand rapidly because their pressure is high enough to overcome atmospheric pressure.

The heat required to change a liquid into a gas (or a solid into a liquid) is called ***latent heat***. When water evaporates on the back of your hand, it takes the latent heat it needs from your hand. That is why there is a cooling effect.

Latent heat is released when a gas changes back into a liquid (or a liquid changes back into a solid).

Heat transfer

Heat can be transferred by ***conduction***, ***convection***, and ***radiation***, as well as by evaporation.

Conduction In all materials, fast-moving particles in one region can gradually pass on energy to neighbouring particles, and hence on to all the particles.

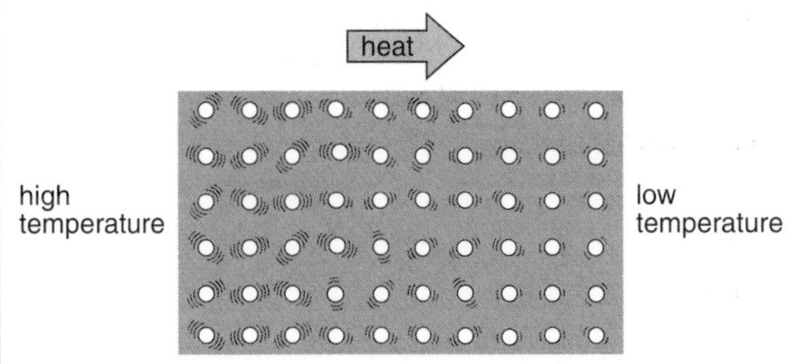

Metals are the best conductors of heat. This is because they have free electrons which can transfer energy rapidly from one part of the material to another. These same electrons also make metals good conductors of electricity.

Non-metal solids and liquids are normally poor conductors of heat because they do not have free electrons. Bad conductors are called ***insulators***. Gases are especially poor conductors: most insulating materials rely on tiny pockets of trapped air for their effect.

Convection Heat is carried by a circulating flow of particles in a liquid or gas.

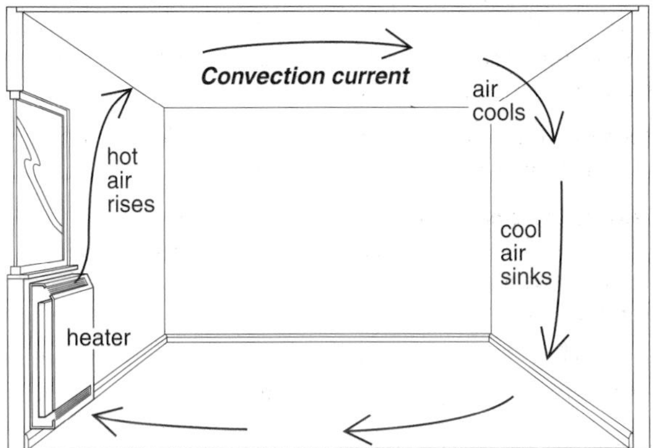

Most room heaters rely on convection. Hot air from the heater expands and floats upwards through the cooler air around it. Cooler air sinks to replace the hot air which has risen. In this way, a ***convection current*** is set up.

Radiation Hot objects radiate energy in the form of electromagnetic waves such as infrared (see A6). The higher the temperature, the more they emit. When this radiation is absorbed by other things, it produces a heating effect. So it is known as ***thermal radiation***.

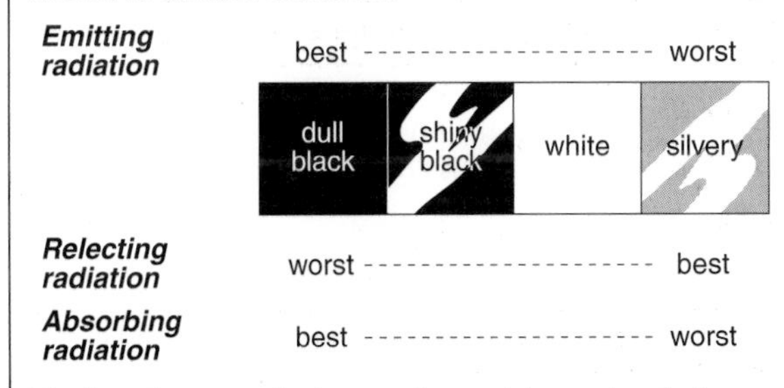

Black surfaces are the best emitters of thermal radiation and also the best absorbers. (They look black because they absorb light).

Shiny surfaces are poor emitters and also poor absorbers. They reflect most of the radiation that strikes them.

A4 Charges and circuits

Static electricity

If two materials are rubbed together, electrons may be transferred from one to another. As a result, one gains negative charge, while the other is left with an equal positive charge. If the materials are ***insulators*** (see right), the transferred charge does not readily flow away. It is sometimes called ***static electricity***.

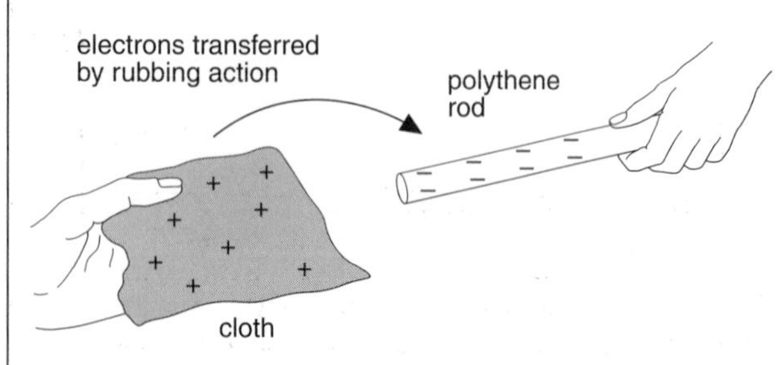

A charged object will attract an uncharged one. On the right, the charged rod has extra electrons. Being uncharged, the foil has equal amounts of – and + charge. The – charges are repelled by the rod and tend to move away, while the + charges are attracted. However, the force of attraction is greater because of the shorter distance.

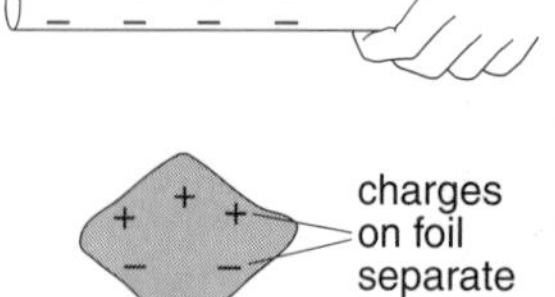

Charge which collects in one region because of the presence of charge on another object is called ***induced*** charge.

Current

+ –
cell
electron flow
conventional direction
A
ammeter
bulb

In the circuit above, chemical reactions in the cell push electrons out of the negative (–) terminal, round the circuit, to the positive (+) terminal. This flow of electrons is called a ***current***.

An arrow in the circuit indicates the direction from the + terminal round to the –. Called the ***conventional direction***, it is the *opposite* direction to the actual electron flow.

The SI unit of current is the ***ampere*** (**A**).

A current of 1 A is equivalent to a flow of 6×10^{18} electrons per second. However, the ampere is not defined in this way, but in terms of its magnetic effect (see B17).

Current may be measured using an ***ammeter*** as above.

Conductors and insulators

Current flows easily through metals and carbon. These materials are good ***conductors*** because they have free electrons which can drift between their atoms (see A3).

Most non-metals are ***insulators***. They do not conduct because all their electrons are tightly held to atoms and not easily moved. Although liquids and gases are usually insulators, they do conduct if they contain ions.

Semiconductors, such as silicon and germanium, are insulators when cold but conductors when warm.

Charge

Charge can be calculated using this equation:

charge = current × time

The SI unit of charge is the ***coulomb*** (**C**).

For example, if a current of 1 A flows for 1 s, the charge passing is 1 C. (This is how the coulomb is defined.) Similarly, if a current of 2 A flows for 3 s, the charge passing is 6 C.

Voltage (PD and EMF)

In the circuit below, several cells have been linked in a line to form a ***battery***. The ***potential difference* (PD)** across the battery terminals is 12 volts (V). This means that each coulomb (C) of charge will 'spend' 12 joules (J) of energy in moving round the circuit from one terminal to the other.

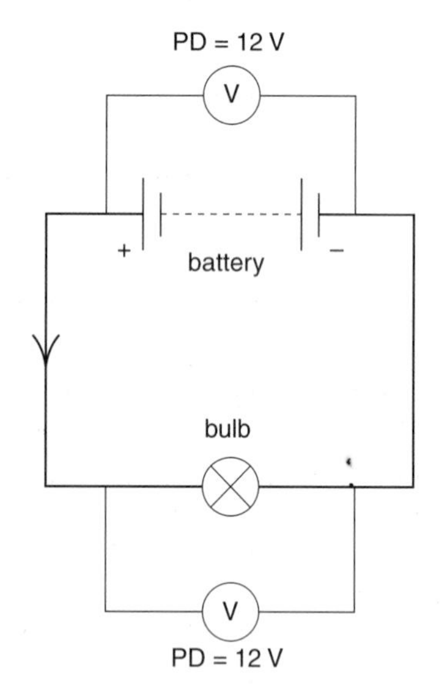

The PD across the bulb is also 12 V. This means that, for each coulomb pushed through it, 12 J of electrical energy is changed into other forms (heat and light energy).

PD may be measured using a ***voltmeter*** as shown above.

PD, energy, and charge are linked by this equation:

energy transformed = charge × PD

For example, if a charge of 2 C moves through a PD of 3 V, the energy transformed is 6 J.

The voltage produced by the chemical reactions inside a battery is called the ***electromotive force*** (**EMF**). When a battery is supplying current, some energy is wasted inside it, which reduces the PD across its terminals. For example, when a torch battery of EMF 3.0 V is supplying current, the PD across its terminals be might be only 2.5 V.

Ohm's law and resistance

If a conductor obeys ***Ohm's law***, then the current *I* through it is directly proportional to the PD *V* across it, provided the temperature is constant.

Metals obey Ohm's law. If a graph of *I* against *V* is plotted for a metal conductor at constant temperature, the result is as on the right. Expressed mathematically:

$$\frac{V}{I} = \text{constant}$$

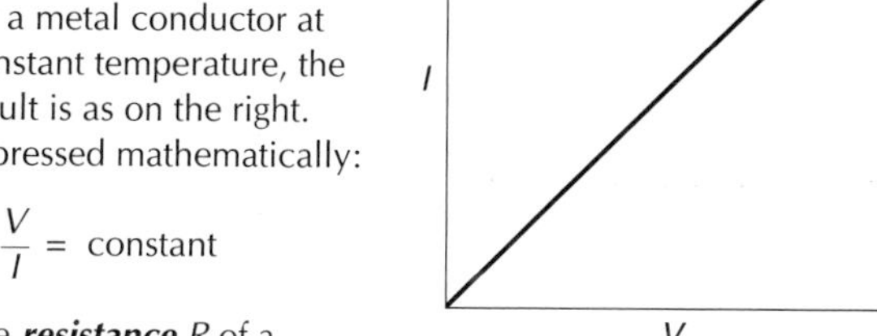

The ***resistance*** *R* of a conductor is calculated like this:

$$\text{resistance} = \frac{\text{PD}}{\text{current}} \quad \text{In symbols: } R = \frac{V}{I}$$

The SI unit of resistance is the ***ohm*** (Ω).

For example, if a PD of 1 V causes a current of 1 A, then the resistance is 1 Ω. (This is how the ohm is defined.)

Similarly, if a PD of 12 V causes a current of 4 A, then the resistance is 3 Ω.

The resistance of a metal conductor (such as a wire) depends on various factors:

- **Length** A long wire has more resistance than a short one.
- **Cross-sectional area** A thin wire has more resistance than a thick one.
- **Temperature** A hot wire has more resistance than a cold one.
- **Type of material** A nichrome wire has more resistance than a copper wire of the same dimensions.

Note:
- While the resistance of a metal *increases* with temperature, that of a semiconductor *decreases*.

Resistance components

Heating elements If a conductor (such as a wire) has resistance, then electrical energy is changed into heat when a current passes. This effect is used in heating elements.

Resistors These are components specially designed to provide resistance. In electronic circuits, they are needed so that other components are supplied with the correct current.

Variable resistors These have a control for varying the length of resistance material through which the current passes.

Thermistors These components have a resistance which changes considerably with temperature (e.g. high when cold, low when hot). They contain semiconducting materials.

Light-dependent resistors (LDRs) These have a high resistance in the dark but a low resistance in the light.

Diodes These have an extremely high resistance in one direction but a low resistance in the other. In effect, they allow current to flow in one direction only.

Symbols

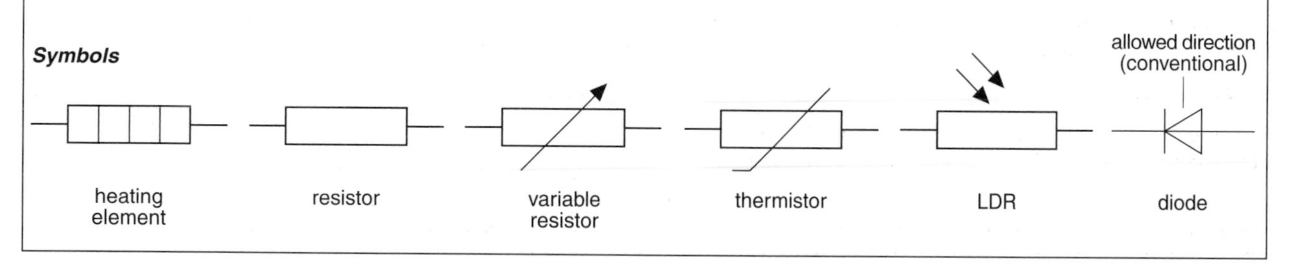

Circuit rules

Resistors in series The current through the battery and each resistor is the same. However, the voltage aross the battery is shared by the resistors.

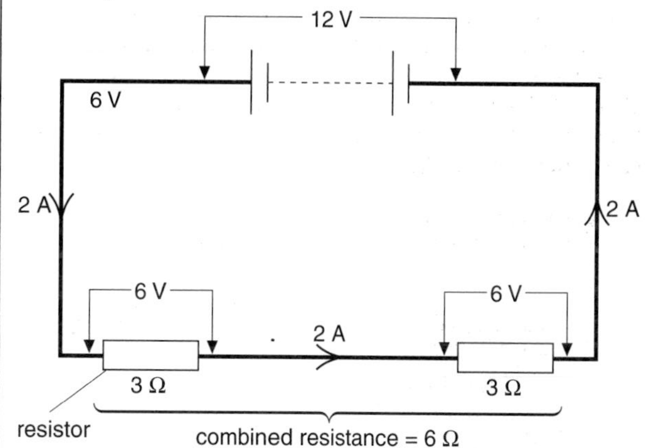

Resistors in parallel The voltage across the battery and each resistor is the same. However, the current from the battery is shared by the resistors.

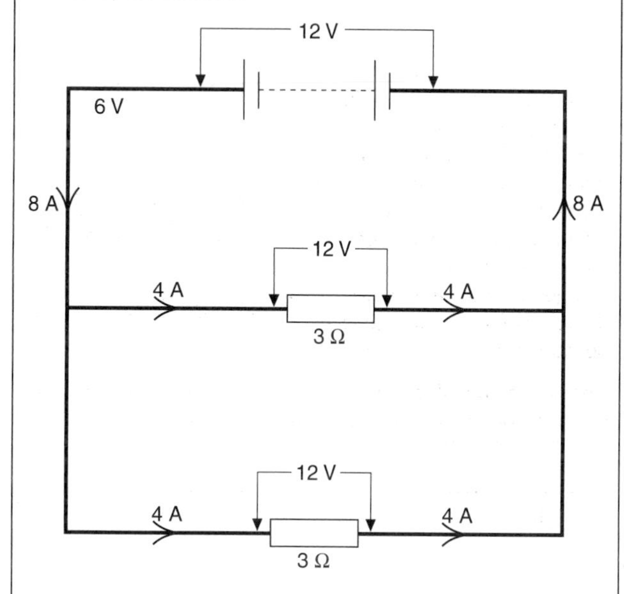

Power

Power *P* is calculated with this equation:

$$\text{power} = \text{PD} \times \text{current} \quad \text{In symbols: } P = VI$$

For example, if there is a PD of 12 V across a resistor and a current of 3 A through it, then the power = 12 × 3 = 36 W (watts). In other words, the resistor is changing 36 joules of electrical energy into heat every second.

Alternative forms of the power equation are:

$$P = I^2R \qquad P = \frac{V^2}{R}$$

A5 Magnets and currents

Magnets and fields

Strongly magnetic materials, such as iron and steel, are called ***ferromagnetic*** materials. They feel forces from other magnets and can be made into magnets.

The forces from a magnet seem to come from ***magnetic poles*** near its ends. In reality, every particle in a magnet acts like a tiny magnet. The two poles are the combined effect of all these tiny magnets lined up.

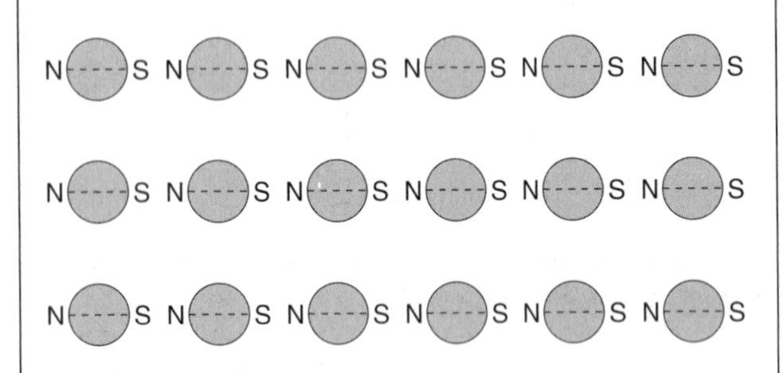

There are two types of pole: ***north*** (**N**) and ***south*** (**S**):
Unlike poles attract. Like poles repel.

The Earth is a weak magnet. As a result, a freely-suspended bar magnet turns until it ends are pointing roughly north-south – which is how the two types of pole got their names. However, the north end of the Earth is, magnetically, a south pole because it attracts the north pole of a magnet.

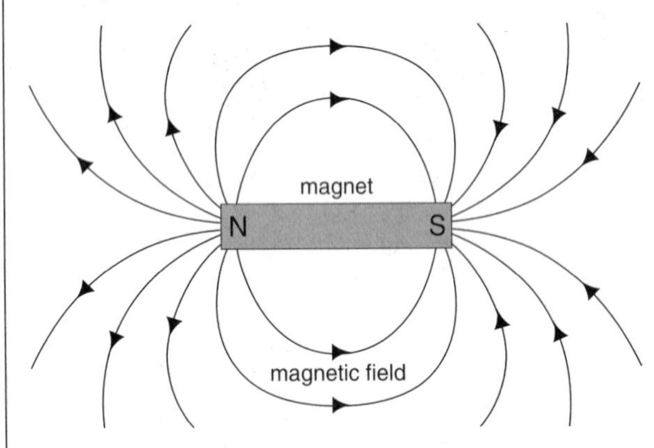

The region around a magnet where magnetic forces act is sometimes called a ***magnetic field***. However, see B17 for a more precise definition of a magnetic field. In diagrams, a magnetic field is represented by ***field lines***. The stronger the field, the closer the lines. The direction of the field is the direction in which a 'free' N pole would move (though in reality, magnetic poles always exist in pairs).

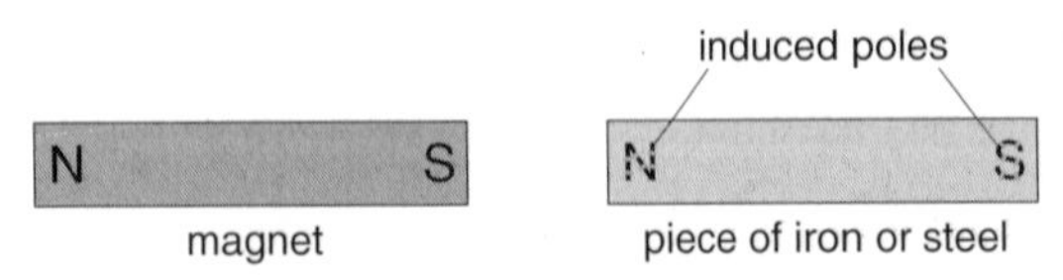

When a strongly magnetic material, such as iron or steel, is placed in a magnetic field, it becomes magnetized, as shown above. This is called ***induced magnetism***. A magnet attracts iron or steel because the direction of the induced magnetism means that two unlike poles are close together.

When a magnetic field is removed, iron quickly loses its magnetism, but steel becomes permanently magnetized.

Magnetic fields from currents

A current has a magnetic field around it. The greater the current, the stronger the field. The field round a current-carrying wire is shown on the right. The field direction is given by ***Maxwell's screw rule***. Imagine a screw moving in the conventional direction. The field turns the same way as the screw.

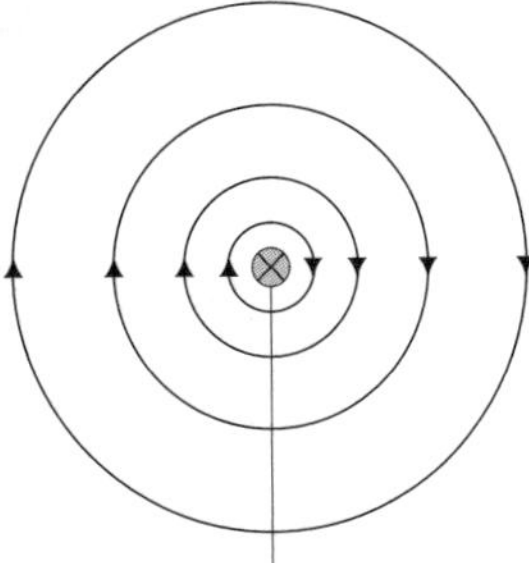
end view of wire: conventional current direction into paper

The field round a current-carrying coil (below) is similar to that round a bar magnet. The field direction can be worked out using either the screw rule or the ***right-hand grip rule***. Imagine gripping the coil with your right hand so that your fingers curl the same way as the conventional direction. Your thumb is then pointing to the N pole.

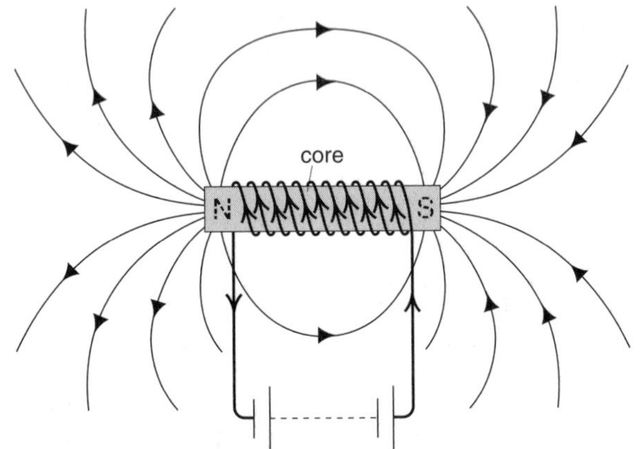

The field is very much stronger if the coil has an iron ***core***. Together, the coil and core form an ***electromagnet***. With an iron core, the field vanishes when the current is turned off. However, a steel core keeps its magnetism. Permanent magnets are made using this principle.

Orbiting electrons in atoms are tiny currents. They are the source of the fields from magnets.

Magnetic force on a current

There is a force on a current in a magnetic field. Its direction is given by ***Fleming's left-hand rule***:

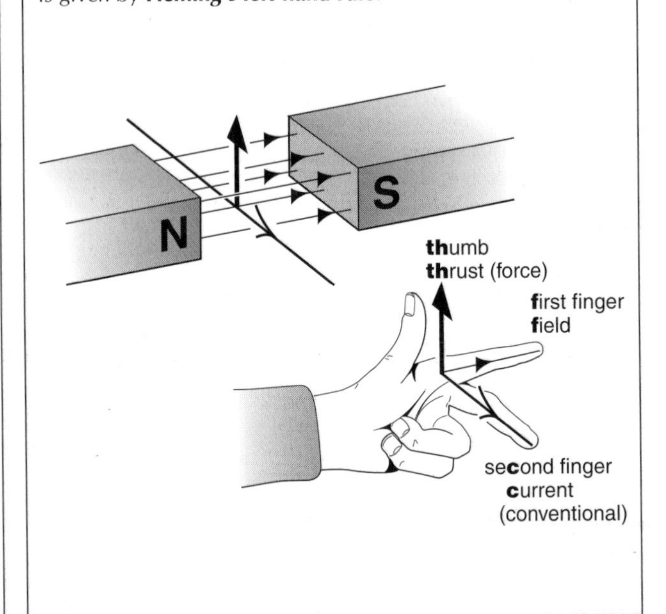

A simple electric motor

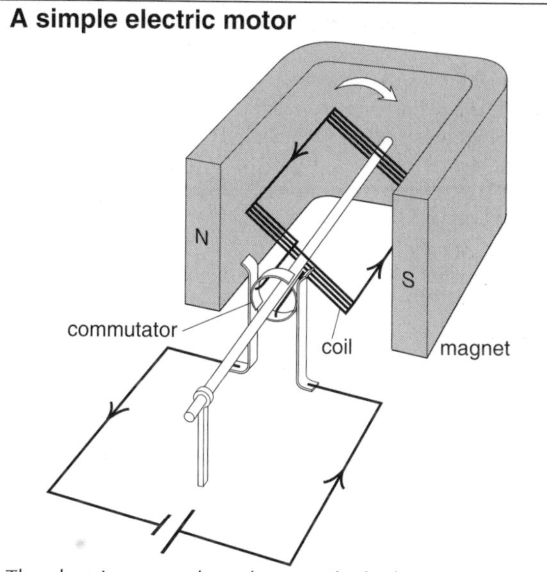

The electric motor above has a coil which can rotate in a magnetic field. When a current passes through the coil, the left side is pushed up, and the right side is pushed down, so there is a turning effect. A switching mechanism called a ***commutator*** keeps the left- and right-side current directions the same, whatever the position of the coil. So the turning effect is always the same way.

Generating AC

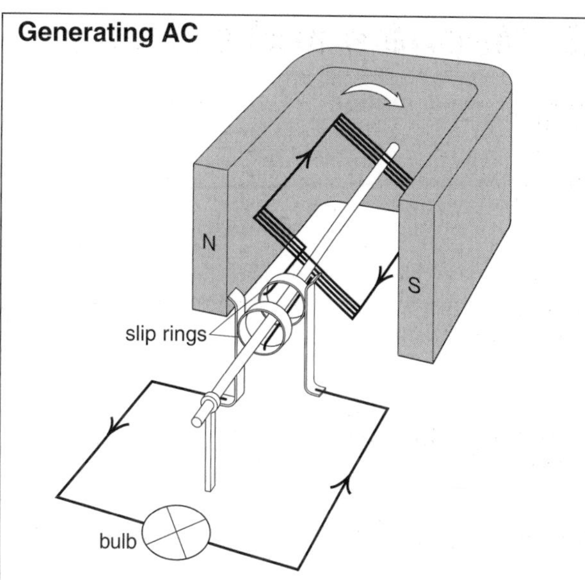

In the generator above, a coil is rotated in a magnetic field. This induces an EMF in the coil, so a current flows. The current keeps changing direction as the coil faces first one way and then the other: it is ***alternating current*** (**AC**). A generator which produces AC is called an ***alternator***.

'One way' current from a battery is ***direct current*** (**DC**).

Currents from magnetic fields

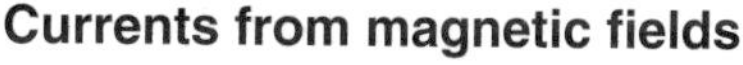
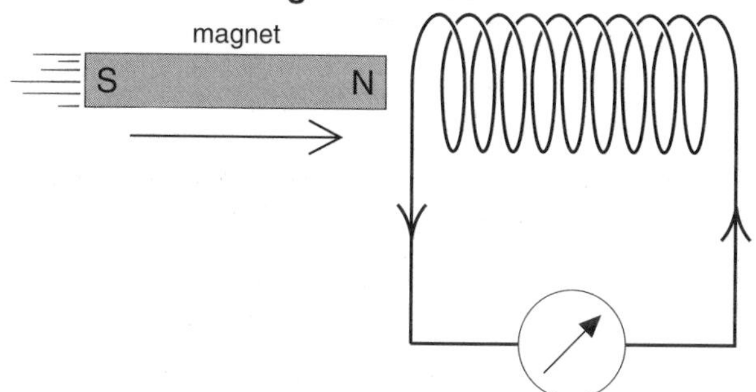

If one end of a bar magnet is moved into a coil, as above, an EMF (voltage) is generated in the coil. This effect is called ***electromagnetic induction***. The EMF makes a current flow in the circuit.

The induced EMF (and the current) is increased if:

- the magnet is moved faster,
- there are more turns on the coil,
- a magnet giving a stronger field is used.

If the magnet is moved out of the coil, the EMF is reversed.
If the magnet is stationary, the EMF is zero.

Varying a magnetic field can have the same effect as moving a magnet. Below, an EMF is induced in the right-hand coil whenever the electromagnet is switched on or off. The current flows one way at switch-on and the opposite way at switch-off.

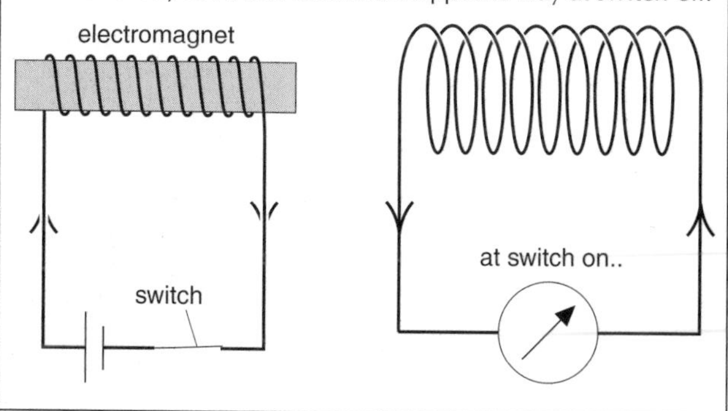

Transformers

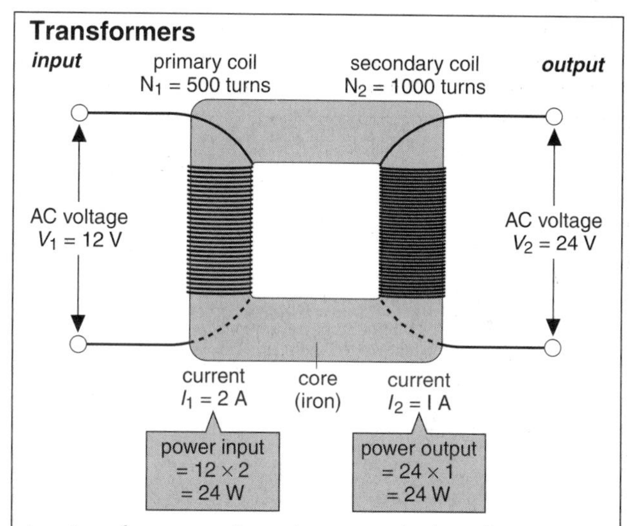

In a ***transformer***, an alternating current in the ***primary*** (input) coil creates a changing magnetic field in the core, which induces an alternating voltage in the ***secondary*** (output) coil. A ***step-up*** transformer, as above, increases the voltage. A ***step-down*** transfomer reduces it.

There is a link between the output and input voltages (V_2 and V_1) and the numbers of turns (N_2 and N_1) on the coils:

$$\frac{V_2}{V_1} = \frac{N_2}{N_1}$$

For the transformer in the diagram:

$$\frac{N_2}{N_1} = \frac{1000}{500} = 2 = \frac{24}{12} = \frac{V_2}{V_1}$$

If no power is wasted in the coils or core:

power output = power input

$$V_2 I_2 = V_1 I_1$$

This means that a transformer which *increases* voltage will *decrease* current, and vice versa.

A6 Waves and rays

Types of wave motion

Waves transfer energy from one place to another. Where ever there is wave motion, there must be:

- a source of oscillation,
- a material or field which can transmit oscillations.

Wave motion can be demonstrated using a 'slinky' spring, as shown below. The moving waves are called ***progressive waves***. There are two main types.

Transverse waves The oscillations are at right-angles to the direction of travel:

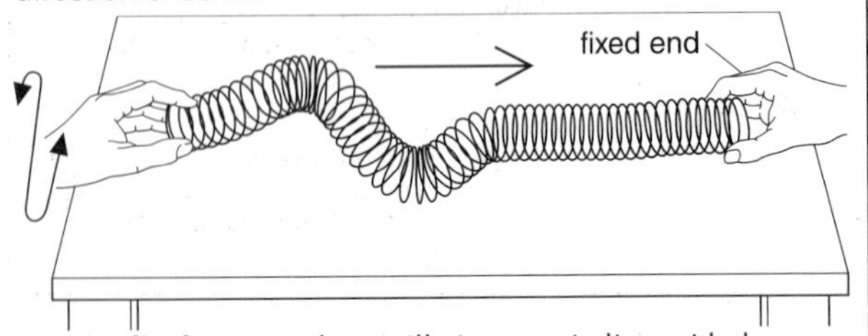

Longitudinal waves The oscillations are in line with the direction of travel, so that a compression ('squash') is followed by a rarefaction ('stretch'), and so on.

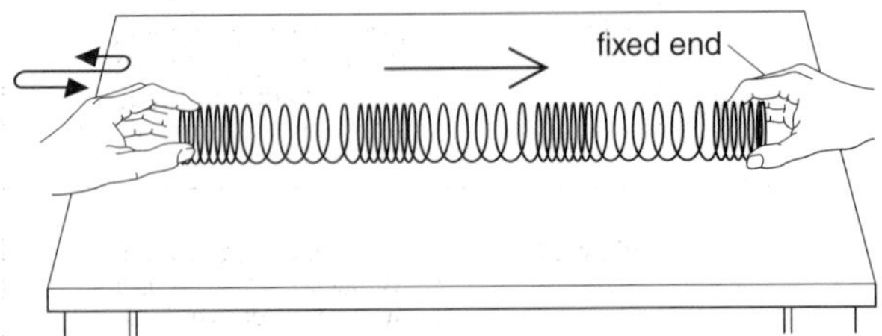

Wave features

The waves above are tiny ripples moving across the surface of some water.

Amplitude This is the magnitude (size) of the oscillation.

Frequency This is the number of waves emitted per second. The SI unit is the ***hertz*** (**Hz**). A frequency of, say, 5 Hz means that 5 waves are being emitted per second.

Wavelength In the example above this is the distance between one wave crest and the next.

Speed The speed, frequency, and wavelength of a wave are linked by this equation:

speed = frequency × wavelength

For example, if the frequency is 5 Hz and the wavelength is 2 m, then the wave speed is 10 m s^{-1}. You could predict this result without the equation. If there are 5 waves per second and each occupies a length of 2 m, then each wave will travel 2 m in $\frac{1}{5}$ s, or 10 m in a second.

Waves in a ripple tank

Wave effects can be investigated using a **ripple tank** in which ripples travel across the surface of shallow water.

Reflection Waves striking an obstacle are reflected. The angle of incidence is equal to the angle of reflection.

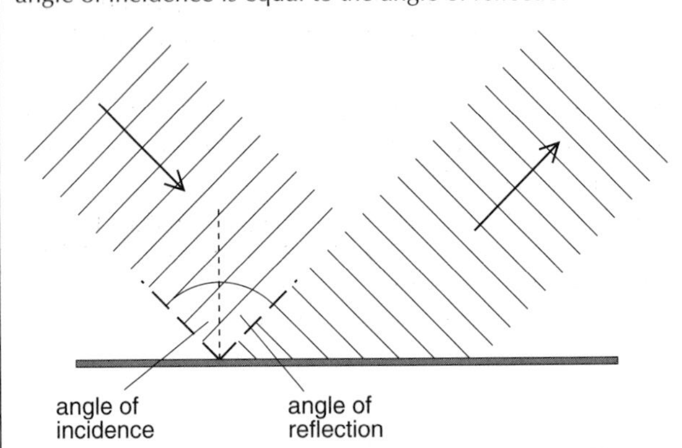

Refraction When waves are slowed down, they are ***refracted*** (bent), provided the angle of incidence is not zero. In a ripple tank, the waves can be slowed by using a flat piece of plastic to make the water shallower.

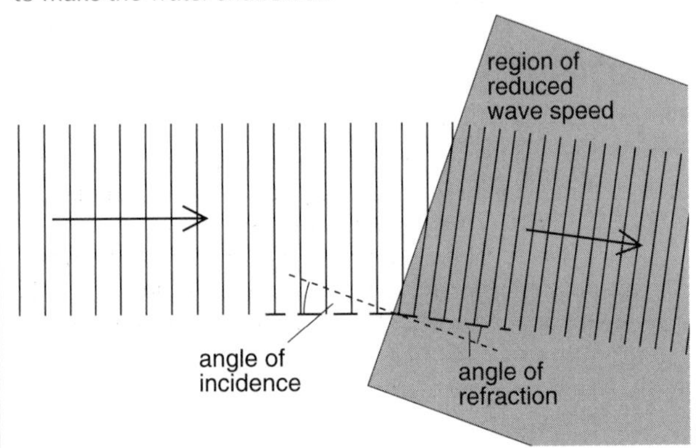

Diffraction Waves bend round the edges of a narrow gap. This is called ***diffraction***. It is significant if the gap size is about a wavelength. Wider gaps cause less diffraction.

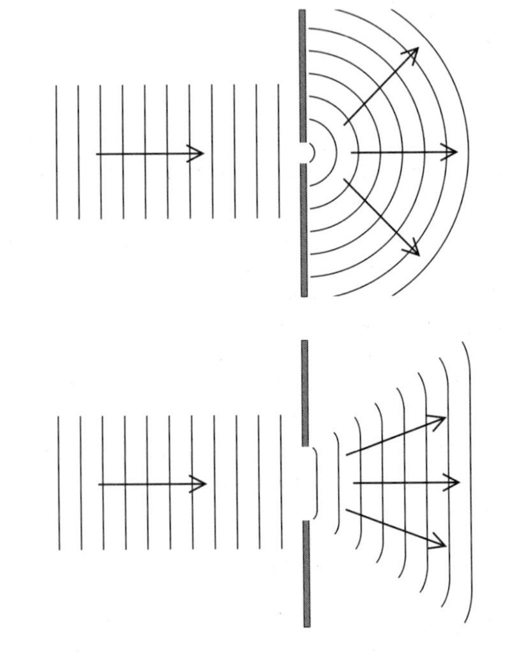

Interference If two identical sets of waves overlap, they may either reinforce or cancel each other, depending on whether they are in phase ('in step') or out of phase.

Light waves and rays

Light waves are transverse electric and magnetic field ripples. They can travel through empty space (a vacuum).

Light waves come from atoms. A burst of wave energy is given off whenever an electron loses energy by dropping to a lower orbit. Sometimes, this burst of wave energy acts like a particle, a **photon**.

The speed of light in empty space is 300 000 km s^{-1}. It is less in transparent materials such as air and water, which is why these materials refract light.

Our eyes experience different wavelengths as different colours. These range from red (0.000 7 mm) down to violet (0.000 4 mm). As light waves are so short, they are not noticeably diffracted by everyday objects.

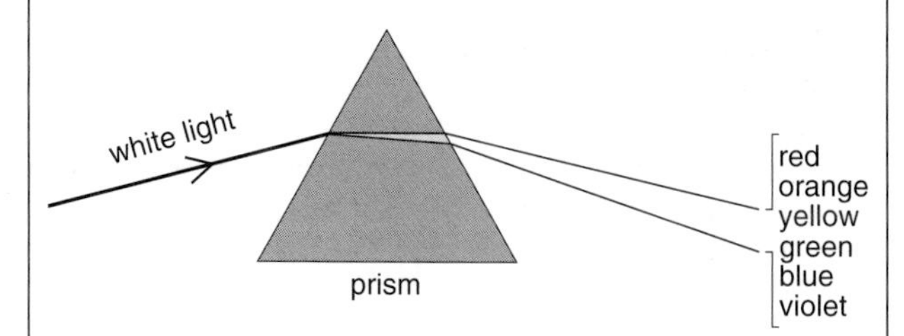

White light is not a single colour, but a mixture of all the colours of the rainbow. When white light enters a prism, the different wavelengths (i.e. colours) are slowed by different amounts, so they are refracted by different amounts. As a result, the white light splits into a range of colours called a ***spectrum***. The spreading effect is known as ***dispersion***. Violet light has the lowest speed in glass, so it is refracted most.

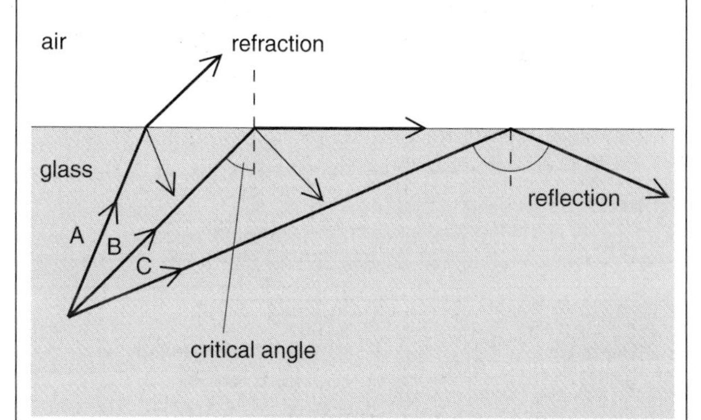

In diagrams, a ***ray*** is a line showing the direction in which light is travelling. In the diagram above:

- Ray A is mainly refracted when it passes from glass to air, although some light is also reflected.
- Ray B is also refracted, but only just. Beyond the ***critical angle***, no refraction can occur.
- Ray C strikes the surface at too great an angle for any refraction to occur. So all the light is reflected. This is called ***total internal reflection***.

In an optical fibre, light entering one end of the glass or plastic fibre is totally internally reflected until it comes out of the other.

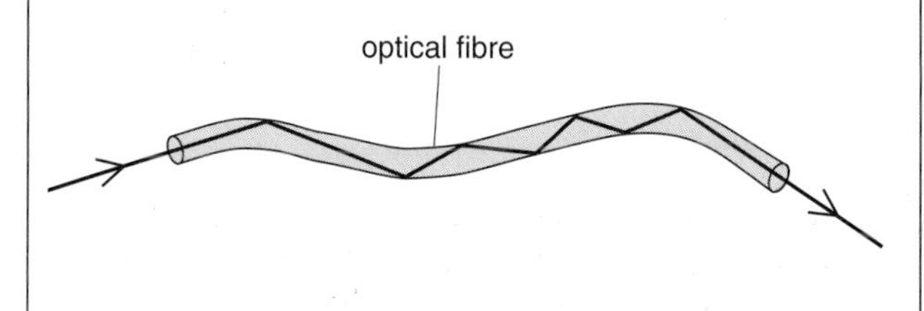

The electromagnetic spectrum

Light is one member of a whole family of transverse waves called the ***electromagnetic spectrum***. In empty space, these waves all travel at the same speed: 300 000 km s^{-1}.

Electromagnetic waves are emitted whenever electrons or other charged particles oscillate or lose energy. The greater the energy change, the lower the wavelength.

Wavelength in metres	Wave type	Typical sources, uses, and effects
10^{5}		
	radio waves: LW, MW, SW, VHF, UHF	From electrons oscillating in aerial. Used for communication.
3×10^{-2}		
	microwaves	From electrons oscillating in magnetron. Used for radar, communication, cooking.
10^{-3}		
	infrared	From hot objects. Used for heating.
7×10^{-7}		
	light	From very hot objects. Only form of radiation visible to human eye. Used for communication.
4×10^{-7}		
	ultraviolet	From very hot objects. Ionizes atoms. Causes fluorescence (makes some chemicals glow). Kills germs. Causes suntan.
10^{-9}		
	X-rays	From electrons stopped rapidly in X-ray tube. Causes ionization and fluorescence. Used for X-ray photography.
	gamma rays	From radioactive materials. Uses and effects as for X-rays.

Sound waves

Sound waves are longitudinal. When, say, a loudspeaker cone vibrates, it sends compressions and rarefactions through the air which the ear can detect.

Speed The speed of sound waves in dry air at room temperature is about 340 m s^{-1}. This rises if the air is warmer or damper. Sound travels faster through liquids than through gases, and faster still through solids.

Loudness The greater the amplitude of the sound waves, the louder the sound.

Wavelength This can vary from about 15 mm to 15 m, so sound waves will diffract round everyday objects.

Pitch The higher the frequency, the higher the pitch:

pitch: low — high

range of human hearing | ultrasound

frequency: 20 Hz — 20 000 Hz

B1 Units and dimensions

Physical quantity

Say a plank is 2 metres long. This measurement is called a ***physical quantity***. In this case, it is a length. It is made up of two parts:

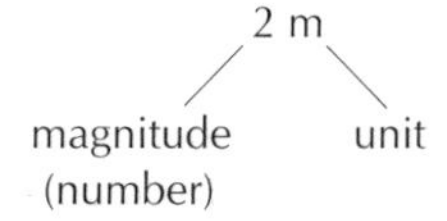

Note:

- '2 m' really means '2 × metre', just as, in algebra, $2y$ means '$2 \times y$'.

Physical quantity	Unit	
	Name	Symbol
length	metre	m
mass	kilogram	kg
time	second	s
current	ampere	A
temperature	kelvin	K
amount*	mole	mol

* In science, 'amount' is a measurement based on the number of particles (atoms, ions or molecules) present. One mole is 6.02×10^{23} particles, a number which gives a simple link with the total mass. For example, 1 mole (6.02×10^{23} atoms) of carbon-12 has a mass of 12 grams. 6.02×10^{23} is called the ***Avogadro constant***.

SI base units

Scientific measurements are made using SI units (standing for Système International d'Unités). The system starts with a series of ***base units***, the main ones being shown in the table above right. Other units are derived from these.

SI base units have been carefully defined so that they can be accurately reproduced using equipment available to national laboratories throughout the world.

SI derived units

There is no SI base unit for speed. However, speed is defined by an equation (see A1). If an object travels 12 m in 3 s:

$$\text{speed} = \frac{\text{distance travelled}}{\text{time taken}} = \frac{12\ \text{m}}{3\ \text{s}} = 4\,\frac{\text{m}}{\text{s}}$$

The units m and s have been included in the working above and treated like any other numbers or algebraic quantities. To save space, the final answer can be written as 4 m/s, or 4 m s^{-1}. (Remember, in maths, $1/x = x^{-1}$ etc.)

The unit m s^{-1} is an example of a ***derived SI unit***. It comes from a defining equation. There are other examples below. Some derived units are based on other derived units. And some derived units have special names. For example, 1 joule per second (J s^{-1}) is called 1 watt (W).

Prefixes

Prefixes can be added to SI base and derived units to make larger or smaller units.

Prefix	Symbol	Value	Prefix	Symbol	Value
pico	p	10^{-12}	kilo	k	10^{3}
nano	n	10^{-9}	mega	M	10^{6}
micro	μ	10^{-6}	giga	G	10^{9}
milli	m	10^{-3}	tera	T	10^{12}

For example:

1 mm = 10^{-3} m 1 km = 10^{3} m

Note:

- 1 gram (10^{-3} kg) is written '1 g' and not '1 mkg'.

Physical quantity	Defining equation (simplified)	Derived unit	Special symbol (and name)
speed	distance/time	m s^{-1}	–
acceleration	speed/time	m s^{-2}	–
force	mass × acceleration	kg m s^{-2}	N (newton)
work	force × distance	N m	J (joule)
power	work/time	J s^{-1}	W (watt)
pressure	force/area	N m^{-2}	Pa (pascal)
density	mass/volume	kg m^{-3}	–
charge	current × time	A s	C (coulomb)
voltage	energy/charge	J C^{-1}	V (volt)
resistance	voltage/current	V A^{-1}	Ω (ohm)

Dimensions

Here are three measurements:

length = 10 m area = 6 m^2 volume = 4 m^3

These three quantities have ***dimensions*** of length, length squared, and length cubed. Using the symbol L for length, these dimensions can be written:

[L] $[L^2]$ $[L^3]$

Starting with three basic dimensions – length [L], mass [M], and time [T] – it is possible to work out the dimensions of many other physical quantities from their defining equations. There are examples on the right and below.

Example 1

$$\text{speed} = \frac{\text{distance travelled}}{\text{time taken}} = \frac{[L]}{[T]} = [LT^{-1}]$$

So the dimensions of speed are $[LT^{-1}]$.

Example 2

$$\text{density} = \frac{\text{mass}}{\text{volume}} = \frac{[M]}{[L^3]} = [ML^{-3}]$$

So the dimensions of density are $[ML^{-3}]$.

Physical quantity	Defining equation (simplified)	Dimensions	
		from equation	reduced form
length	–	–	[L]
mass	–	–	[M]
time	–	–	[T]
speed	$\frac{\text{distance}}{\text{time}}$	$\frac{[L]}{[T]}$	$[LT^{-1}]$
acceleration	$\frac{\text{speed}}{\text{time}}$	$\frac{[LT^{-1}]}{[T]}$	$[LT^{-2}]$
force	mass × acceleration	$[M] \times [LT^{-2}]$	$[MLT^{-2}]$
work	force × distance	$[MLT^{-2}] \times [L]$	$[ML^2T^{-2}]$
power	$\frac{\text{work}}{\text{time}}$	$\frac{[ML^2T^{-2}]}{[T]}$	$[ML^2T^{-3}]$
pressure	$\frac{\text{force}}{\text{area}}$	$\frac{[MLT^{-2}]}{[L^{-2}]}$	$[ML^{-1}T^{-2}]$

Using dimensions to check equations

The two sides of an equation must always have the same dimensions. For example:

$$\begin{aligned} \text{work} &= \text{force} \times \text{distance moved} \\ [ML^2T^{-2}] &= [MLT^{-2}] \times [L] \\ &= [ML^2T^{-2}] \end{aligned}$$

An equation cannot be accurate if the dimensions on both sides do not match. It would be like claiming that '6 apples equals 6 oranges'.

Dimensions are a useful way of checking that an equation is reasonable.

Example *Check whether the equation PE = mgh is dimensionally correct.*

To do this, start by working out the dimensions of the right-hand side:

$$mgh = [M] \times [LT^{-2}] \times [L] = [ML^2T^{-2}]$$

These are the dimensions of work, and therefore of energy. So the equation is dimensionally correct.

Note:

- A dimensions check cannot tell you whether an equation is accurate. For example, both of the following are dimensionally correct, but only one is right:

  PE = mgh PE = $2mgh$

Dimensionless numbers

A pure number, such as 6, has no dimensions. Here are two consequences of this fact.

Dimensions and units of frequency The frequency of a vibrating source is defined as follows:

$$\text{frequency} = \frac{\text{number of vibrations}}{\text{time taken}}$$

As number is dimensionless, the dimensions of frequency are $[T^{-1}]$. The SI unit of frequency in the hertz (Hz):
1 Hz = 1 s^{-1}

Dimensions and units of angle
On the right, the angle θ in ***radians*** is defined like this:

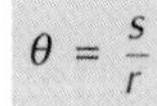

$$\theta = \frac{s}{r}$$

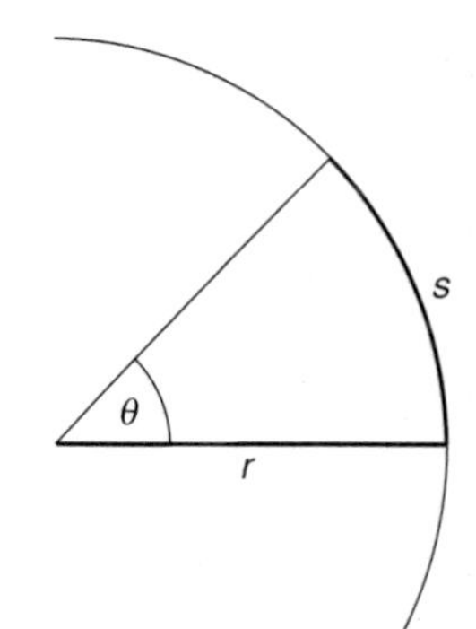

s/r has no dimensions because $[L] \times [L^{-1}] = 1$. However, when measuring an angle in radians, a unit is often included for clarity: 2 rad, for example.

B2 Measurements, uncertainties, and graphs

Scientific notation

The average distance from the Earth to the Sun is 150 000 000 km.

There are two problems with quoting a measurement in the above form:

- the inconvenience of writing so many noughts,
- uncertainty about which figures are important, (i.e. How approximate is the value? How many of the figures are significant?).

These problems are overcome if the distance is written in the form 1.50×10^8 km.

'1.50×10^8' tells you that there are three significant figures – 1, 5 and 0. The last of these is the least significant and, therefore, the most uncertain. The only function of the other zeros in 150 000 000 is to show how big the number is. If the distance were known less accurately, to two significant figures, then it would be written as 1.5×10^8 km.

Numbers written using powers of 10 are in ***scientific notation*** or ***standard form***. This is also used for small numbers. For example, 0.002 can be written as 2×10^{-3}.

Uncertainty

When making any measurement, there is always some ***uncertainty*** in the reading. As a result, the measured value may differ from the true value. In science, an uncertainty is sometimes called an ***error***. However, it is important to remember that it is *not* the same thing as a mistake.

In experiments, there are two types of uncertainty:

Systematic uncertainties These occur because of some inaccuracy in the measuring system or in how it is being used. For example, a timer might run slow, or the zero on an ammeter might not be set correctly.

There are techniques for eliminating some systematic uncertainties. However, this spread will concentrate on dealing with uncertainties of the random kind.

Random uncertainties These can occur because there is a limit to the sensitivity of the measuring instrument or to how accurately you can read it. For example, the following readings might be obtained if the same current was measured repeatedly using one ammeter:

2.4 2.5 2.4 2.6 2.5 2.6 2.6 2.5

Because of the uncertainty, there is variation in the last figure. To arrive at a single value for the current, you could find the mean of the above readings, and then include an estimation of the uncertainty:

current = 2.5 ± 0.1

(2.5 = mean; 0.1 = uncertainty)

Writing '2.5 ± 0.1' indicates that the value could lie anywhere between 2.4 and 2.6.

Note:

- On a calculator, the mean of the above readings works out at 2.5125. However, as each reading was made to only two significant figures, the mean should also be given to only two significant figures i.e. 2.5.
- Each of the above readings may also include a systematic uncertainty.

Uncertainty as a percentage

Sometimes, it is useful to give an uncertainty as a percentage. For example, in the current measurement above, the uncertainty (0.1) is 4% of the mean value (2.5), as the following calculation shows:

$$\text{percentage uncertainty} = \frac{0.1}{2.5} \times 100 = 4$$

So the current reading could be written as 2.5 ± 4%.

Combining uncertainties

Sums and differences Say you have to *add* two length readings, A and B, to find a total, C. If $A = 3.0 \pm 0.1$ and $B = 2.0 \pm 0.1$, then the minimum possible value of C is 4.8 and the maximum is 5.2. So $C = 5.0 \pm 0.2$.

Now say you have to subtract B from A. This time, the minimum possible value of C is 0.8 and the maximum is 1.2 . So $C = 1.0 \pm 0.2$, and the uncertainty is the same as before.

If $C = A + B$ or $C = A - B$, then:

uncertainty in C = uncertainty in A + uncertainty in B

The same principle applies when several quantities are added or subtracted: $C = A + B - F - G$, for example.

Products and quotients If $C = A \times B$ or $C = A/B$, then:

% uncertainty in C = % uncertainty in A + % uncertainty in B

For example, say you measure a current I, a voltage V, and calculate a resistance R using the equation $R = V/I$. If there is a 3% uncertainty in V and a 4% uncertainty in I, then there is a 7% uncertainty in your calculated value of R.

Note:

- The above equation is only an approximation – and a poor one for uncertainties greater than about 10%.
- To check that the equation works, try calculating the maximum and minimum values of C if, say, A is 100 ± 3 and B is 100 ± 4. You should find that $A \times B$ is 10 000 ± approximately 700 (i.e. 7%).
- The principle of adding % uncertainties can be applied to more complex equations: $C = A^2B/FG$, for example. As $A^2 = A \times A$, the % uncertainty in A^2 is twice that in A.

Calculated results

Say you have to calculate a resistance from the following readings:

voltage = 3.3 V (uncertainty ± 0.1 V, or ± 3%)
current = 2.5 A (uncertainty ± 0.1 A, or ± 4%)

Dividing the voltage by the current on a calculator gives a resistance of 1.32 Ω. However, as the combined uncertainty is ±7%, or ± 0.1 Ω, the calculated value of the resistance should be written as 1.3 Ω. As a general guideline, a calculated result should have no more significant figures than any of the measurements used in the calculation. (However, if the result is to be used in further calculations, it is best to leave any rounding up or down until the end.)

Choosing a graph

The general equation for a straight-line graph is:

$$y = mx + c$$

In this equation, m and c are ***constants***, as shown below. y and x are ***variables*** because they can take different values. x is the ***independent variable***. y is the ***dependent variable***: its value depends on the value of x.

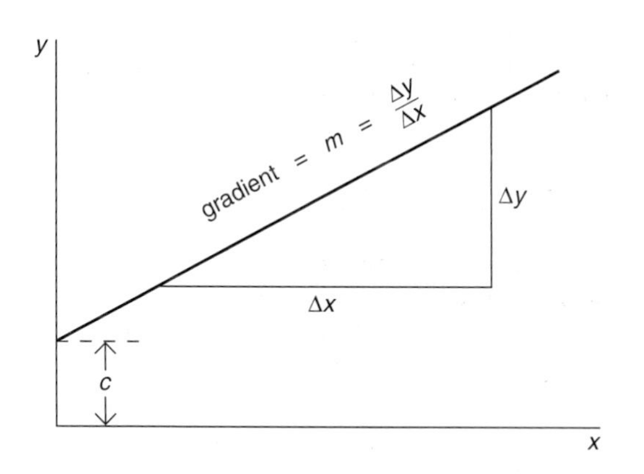

In experimental work, straight-line graphs are especially useful because the values of constants can be found from them. Here is an example.

Problem Theoretical analysis shows that the period T (time per swing) of a simple pendulum is linked to its length l, and the Earth's gravitational field strength g by the equation $T = 2\pi\sqrt{(l/g)}$. If, by experiment, you have corresponding values of l and T, what graph should you plot in order to work out a value for g from it?

Answer First, rearrange the equation so that it is in the form $y = mx + c$. Here is one way of doing this:

$$\underbrace{T^2}_{y} = \underbrace{\frac{4\pi^2}{g}}_{m}\,\underbrace{l}_{x} + \underbrace{0}_{c}$$

So, if you plot a graph of T^2 against l, the result should be a straight line through the origin (as $c = 0$). The gradient (m) is $4\pi^2/g$, from which a value of g can be calculated.

Showing uncertainties on graphs

In an experiment, a wire is kept at a constant temperature. You apply different voltages across the wire and measure the current through it each time. Then you use the readings to plot a graph of current against voltage.

The general direction of the points suggests that the graph is a straight line. However, before reaching this conclusion, you must be sure that the points' scatter is due to random uncertainty in the current readings. To check this, you could estimate the uncertainty and show this on the graph using short, vertical lines called uncertainty bars. The ends of each bar represent the likely maximum and minimum value for that reading. In the example below, the ***uncertainty bars*** show that, despite the points' scatter, it is reasonable to draw a straight line through the origin.

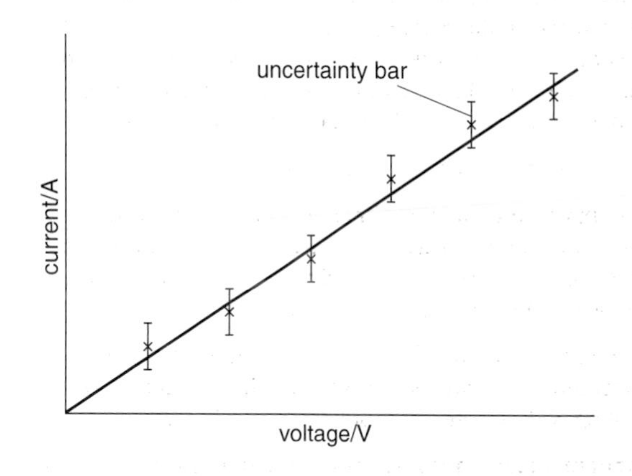

Labelling graph axes Strictly speaking, the scales on the graph's axes are pure, unitless numbers and not voltages or currents. Take a typical reading:

voltage = 10 V

This can be treated as an equation and rearranged to give:

voltage/V = 10

That is why the graph axes are labelled 'voltage/V' and 'current/A'. The values of these are pure numbers.

Reading a micrometer

The length of a small object can be measured using a micrometer screw gauge. You take the reading on the gauge like this.

gap being measured

fixed scale

scale on revolving barrel

0 5 mm

40 35 30 25

Read the highest scale division that can be seen: 5.5

Read the scale on the barrel, putting a decimal point in front: 0.32

Add: 5.82 mm

Reading a vernier

Some measuring instruments have a vernier scale on them for measuring small distances (or angles). You take the reading like this.

gap being measured

fixed scale

mm 0 10 20

0 5

sliding scale

Read highest scale division before ▲: 7

See where divisions coincide. Read this on sliding scale, putting a decimal point in front: 0.4

Add: 7.4 mm

B3 Analysing motion

Velocity-time graphs

The graphs which follow are for three examples of ***linear*** motion (motion in a straight line).

Graph A below shows how the velocity of a stone would change with time, if the stone were dropped near the Earth's surface and there were no air resistance to slow it.
The stone has a *uniform* (unchanging) acceleration a which is equal to the gradient of the graph.

$$a = \frac{\Delta v}{\Delta t}$$

In this case, the acceleration is g (9.81 m s^{-2}).

If air resistance is significant, then the graph is no longer a straight line (see B12).

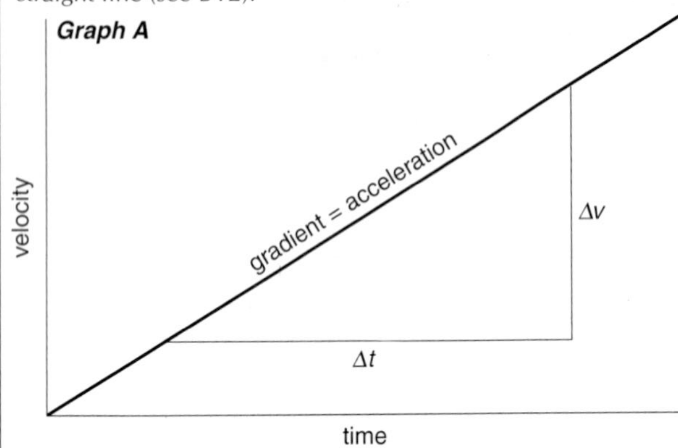

Graph B below is for a car travelling at a steady velocity of 30 m s^{-1}. In 2 s, the car travels a distance of 60 m. Numerically, this is equal to the area under the graph between the 0 and 2 s points. (Note: the area must be worked out using the scale numbers, not actual lengths.)

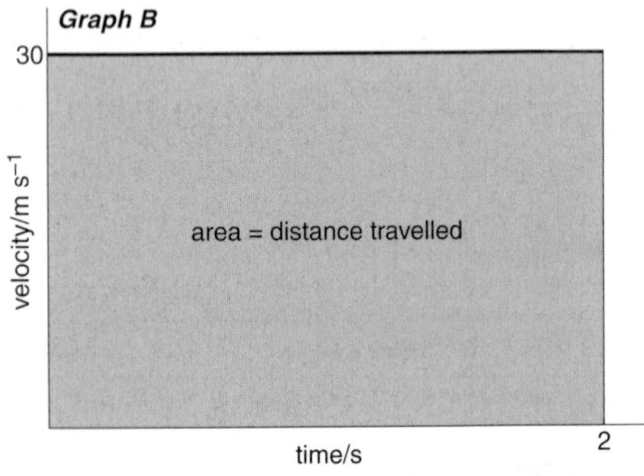

Graph C below is for a car with a changing velocity. However, the same principle applies as before: the area under the graph gives the distance travelled. (This is also true if the graph is not a straight line: see B12.)

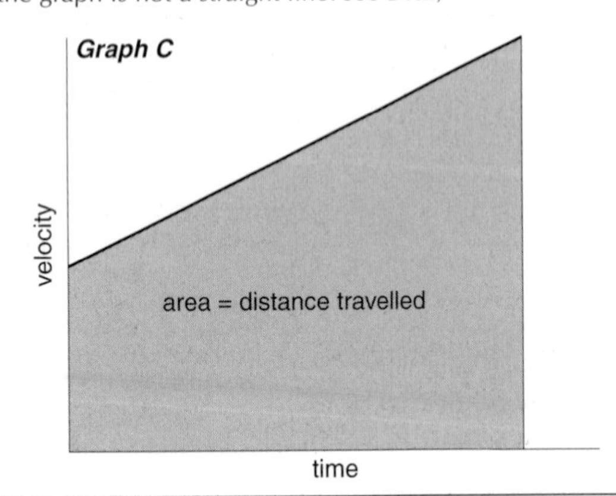

Equations of motion

The car below has uniform acceleration. In the following analysis, only motion between X and Y will be considered.

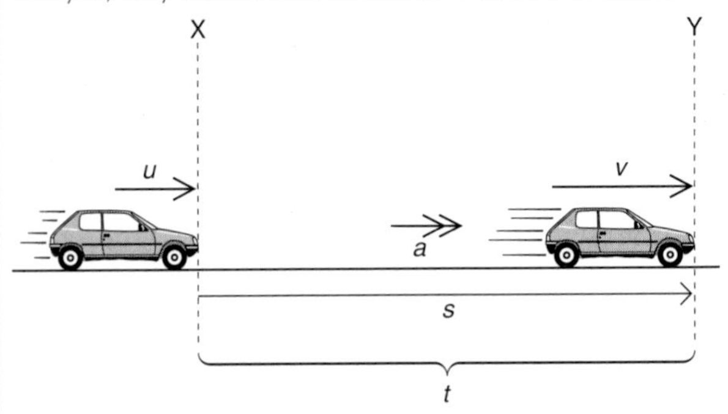

u = initial velocity (velocity on passing X)
v = final velocity (velocity on passing Y)
a = acceleration
s = displacement (in moving from X to Y)
t = time taken (to move from X to Y)

Here is a velocity-time graph for the car.

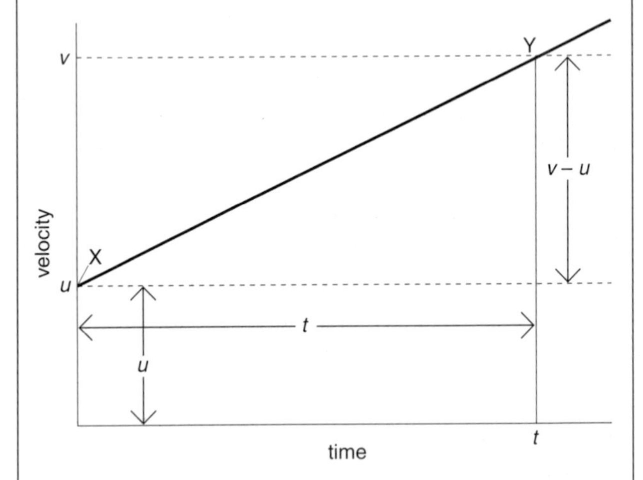

There are four equations (numbered 1–4 below) linking u, v, a, s, and t. They can be worked out as follows.

The acceleration is the gradient of the graph.
So $a = (v - u)/t$. This can be rearranged to give:

$$v = u + at \quad (1)$$

The distance travelled, s in this case, is the area under the graph. This is the area of one rectangle (height × base) plus the area of one triangle ($\frac{1}{2}$ × height × base). So it is $u \times t$ plus $\frac{1}{2} \times (v - u) \times t$. But $v - u = at$ from equation (1), so:

$$s = ut + \tfrac{1}{2}at^2 \quad (2)$$

As distance travelled = average velocity × time taken:

$$s = \tfrac{1}{2}(v + u)t \quad (3)$$

If equations (1) and (3) are combined so that t is eliminated:

$$v^2 = u^2 + 2as \quad (4)$$

Note:

- The equations are only valid for uniform acceleration.
- Each equation links a different combination of factors. You must decide which equation best suits the problem you are trying to solve.
- You must allow for vector directions. With horizontal motion, you might decide to call a vector to the right positive (+). With vertical motion, you might call a downward vector positive. So, for a stone thrown upwards at 30 m s^{-1}: $u = -30$ m s^{-1} and $g = +10$ m s^{-2}.

Motion problems

Here are examples of how the equations of motion can be used to solve problems. For simplicity, units will not be shown in some equations. It will be assumed that air resistance is negligible and that g is 10 m s^{-2}.

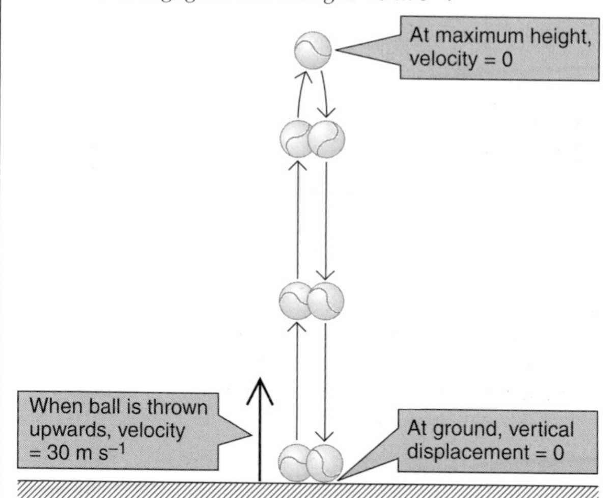

Example 1 *A ball is thrown upwards at 30 m s^{-1}. What time will it take to reach its highest point?*

The ball's motion only needs to be considered from when it is thrown to when it reaches its highest point. These are the 'initial' and 'final' states in any equation used.

When the ball is at it highest point, its velocity v will be zero. So, taking downward vectors as positive:

$u = -30$ m s^{-1} $\quad v = 0 \quad a = g = 10$ m s^{-2} $\quad t$ is to be found.

In this case, an equation linking u, v, a, and t is required. This is equation (1) on the opposite page:

$$v = u + at$$

So $0 = -30 + 10t$

Rearranged, this gives $t = 3.0$ s.

Example 2 *A ball is thrown upwards at 30 m s^{-1}. What is the maximum height reached?*

In this case:

$u = -30$ m s^{-1} $\quad v = 0 \quad a = g = 10$ m s^{-2} $\quad s$ is to be found.

This time, the equation required is (4) on the opposite page:

$$v^2 = u^2 + 2as$$

So $0 = (-30)^2 + (2 \times 10 \times s)$

This gives $s = -45$ m.

(Downwards is positive, so the negative value of s indicates an *upward* displacement.)

Example 3 *A ball is thrown upwards at 30 m s^{-1}. For what time is it in motion before it hits the ground?*

When the ball reaches the ground, it is back where it started, so its displacement s is zero. Therefore:

$u = -30$ m s^{-1} $\quad s = 0 \quad a = g = 10$ m s^{-2} $\quad t$ is to be found.

This time, the equation required is (2) on the opposite page:

$$s = ut + \tfrac{1}{2}at^2$$

So $0 = (-30t) + (\tfrac{1}{2} \times 10 \times t^2)$

This gives $t = 6$ s.

(There is also a solution $t = 0$, indicating that the ball's displacement is also zero at the instant it is thrown.)

Measuring g

By measuring the time t it takes an object to fall through a measured height h, a value of g can be found (assuming that air resistance is negligible).

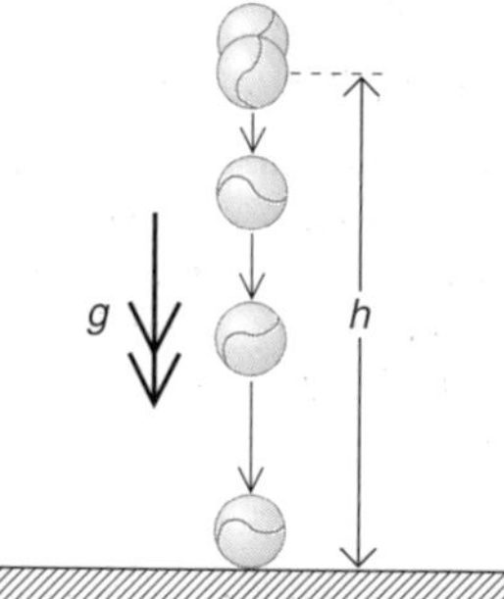

In the diagram on the right:

$u = 0 \quad a = g \quad s = h$

Applying equation (2) on the opposite page:

$$s = ut + \tfrac{1}{2}at^2$$

So $h = 0t + \tfrac{1}{2}gt^2$

This gives $g = \dfrac{2h}{t^2}$.

Downwards and sideways

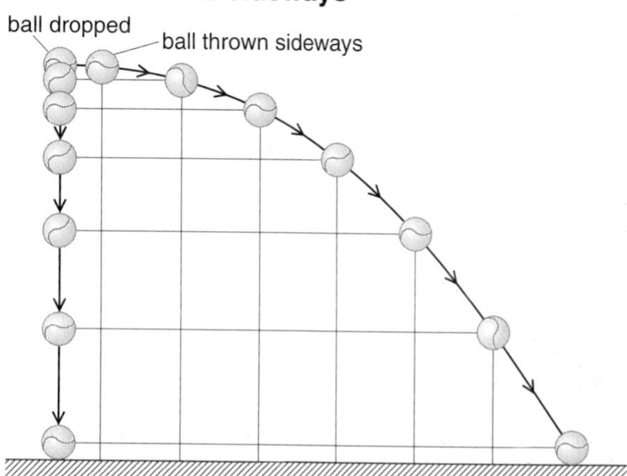

Above, one ball is dropped, while another is thrown sideways at the same time. There is no air resistance. The positions of the balls are shown at regular time intervals.

- Both balls hit the ground together. They have the same downward acceleration g.
- As it falls, the second ball moves sideways over the ground at a steady speed.

Results like this show that the vertical and horizontal motions are independent of each other.

Example *Below, a ball is thrown horizontally at 40 m s^{-1}. What horizontal distance does it travel before hitting the water? (Assume air resistance is negligible and g = 10 m s^{-2}).*

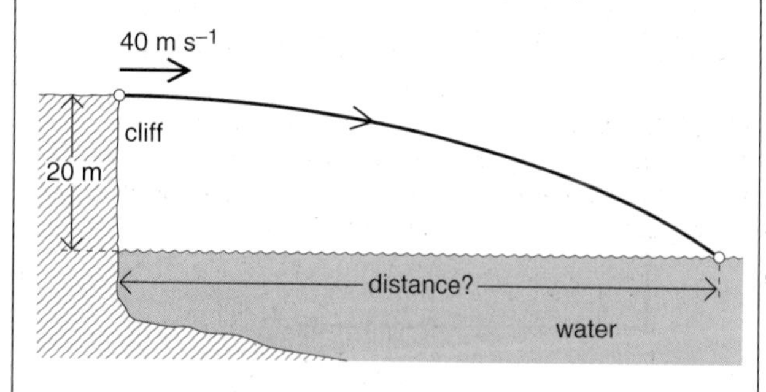

First, work out the time the ball would take to fall vertically to the sea. This can be done using the equation $s = ut + \frac{1}{2}at^2$, in which $u = 0$, $s = 20$ m, $a = -10$ m s^{-2}, and t is to be found. This gives $t = 2.0$ s.

Next, work out how far the ball will travel horizontally in this time (2 s) at a steady horizontal speed of 40 m s^{-1}.

As distance travelled = average speed × time, horizontal distance travelled = 40 × 2 = 80 m.

Find Vert t first

B4 Vectors

Vector arrows

Vectors are quantities which have both magnitude (size) and direction. Examples include displacement and force.

For problems in one dimension (e.g. vertical motion), vector direction can be indicated using + or –. But where two or three dimensions are involved, it is often more convenient to represent vectors by arrows, with the length and direction of the arrow representing the magnitude and direction of the vector. The arrowhead can either be drawn at the end of the line or somewhere else along it, as convenient. Here are two displacement vectors.

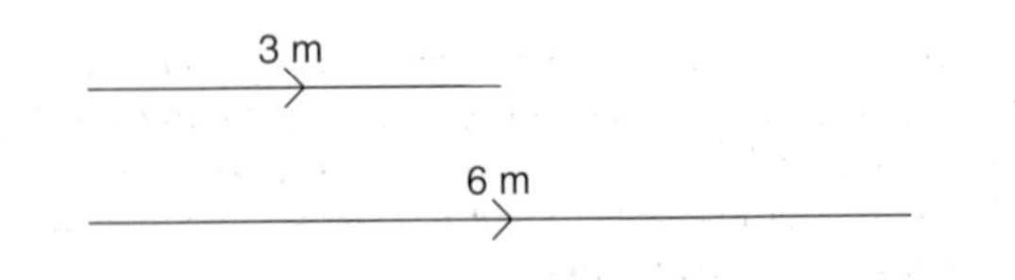

Adding vectors

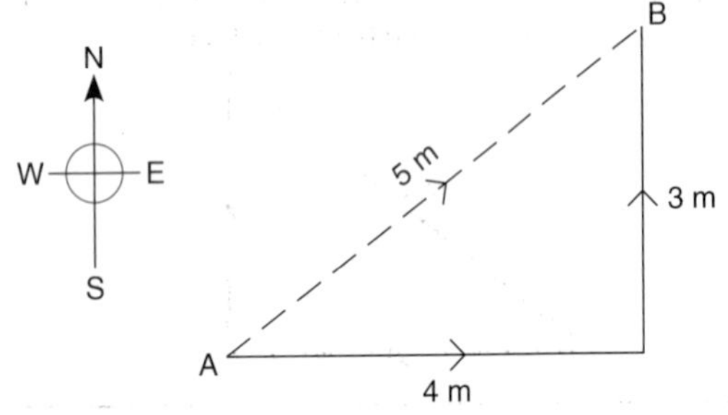

If someone starts at A, walks 4 m East and then 3 m North, they end up at B, as shown above. In this case, they are 5 m from where they started – a result which follows from Pythagoras' theorem. This is an example of vector addition. Two displacement vectors, of 3 m and 4 m, have been added to produce a ***resultant*** – a displacement vector of 5 m.

This principle works for any type of vector. Below, forces of 3 N and 4 N act at right-angles through the same point, O. The ***triangle of vectors*** gives their resultant. The vectors being added must be drawn head-to-tail. The resultant runs from the tail of the first arrow to the head of the second.

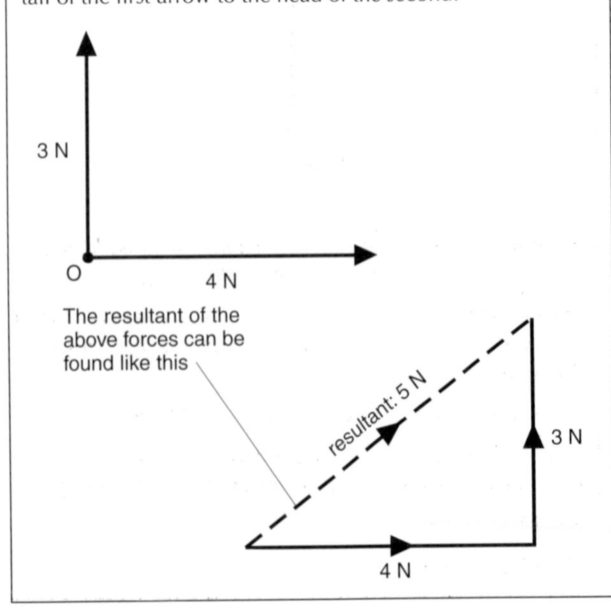

Parallelogram of vectors

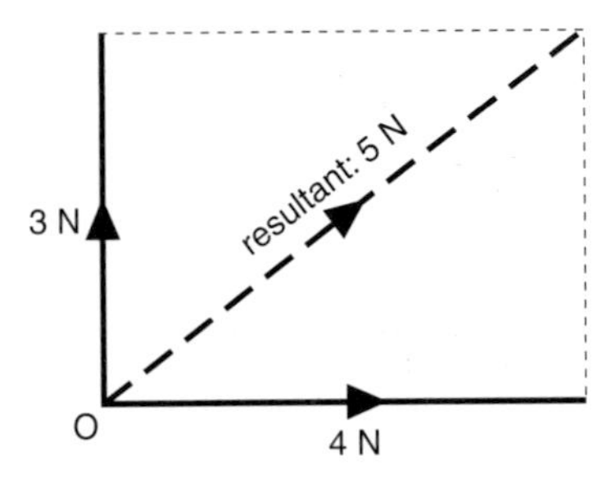

Above, you can see another way of finding the resultant of two forces, 3 N and 4 N, acting at right-angles through the same point. The vectors are drawn as two sides of a rectangle. The diagonal through O gives the magnitude and direction of the resultant. Note that the lines and angles in this diagram match those in the previous force triangle.

By drawing a parallelogram, the above method can also be used to add vectors which are not at right-angles. Here are two examples of a ***parallelogram of vectors***.

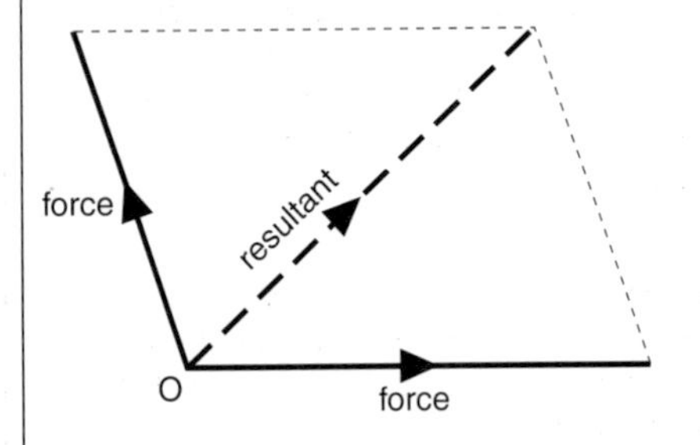

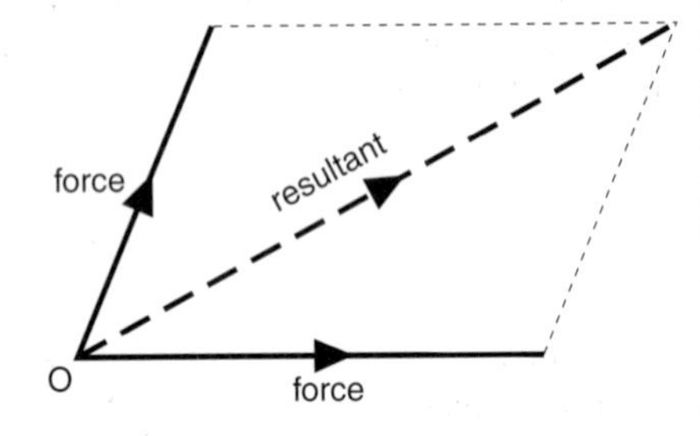

Note:

- The magnitude of the resultant depends on the relative directions of the vectors. For example, if forces of 3 N and 4 N are added, the resultant could be anything from 1 N (if the vectors are in opposite directions) to 7 N (if they are in the same direction).
- In the diagrams on this page, the resultant is always shown using a dashed arrow. This is to remind you that the resultant is a *replacement* for the other two vectors. There are *not* three vectors acting.

Multiplying vectors

When vectors are multiplied together, the product is not necessarily another vector. For example, work is the product of two vectors: force and displacement. But work is a scalar, not a vector. It has magnitude but no direction.

Methods of multiplying vectors have not been included in this book, other than for simple cases: for example, when force and displacement vectors are in the same direction.

Components

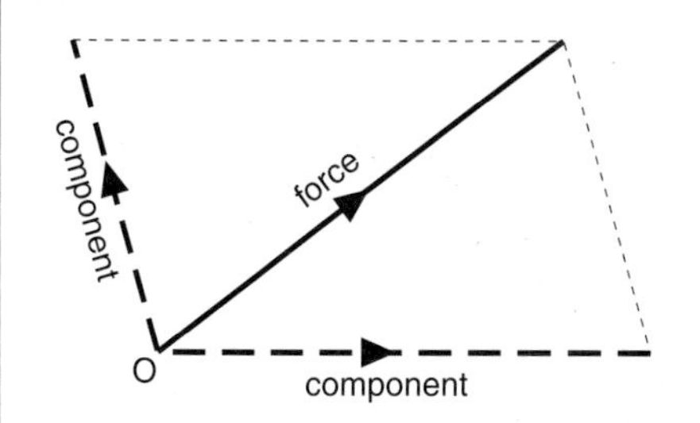

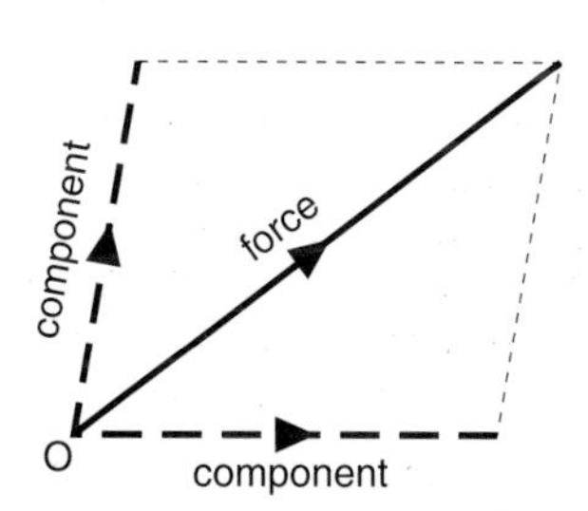

Two forces acting through a point can be replaced by a single force (the resultant) which has the same effect. Conversely, a single force can be replaced by two forces which have the same effect – a single force can be ***resolved*** into two ***components***. Two examples of the components of a force are shown above, though any number of other sets of components is possible.

Note:

- Any vector can be resolved into components.
- The components above are shown as dashed lines to remind you that they are a *replacement* for a single force. There are *not* three forces acting.

In working out the effects of a force (or other vector), the most useful components to consider are those at right-angles, as in the following example.

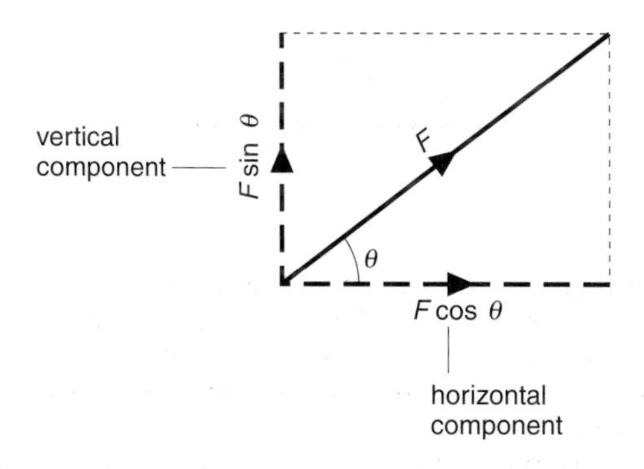

Below, you can see why the horizontal and vertical components have magnitudes of $F \cos \theta$ and $F \sin \theta$.

$$\cos \theta = \frac{F_x}{F}$$

So $F_x = F \cos \theta$

$$\sin \theta = \frac{F_y}{F}$$

So $F_y = F \sin \theta$

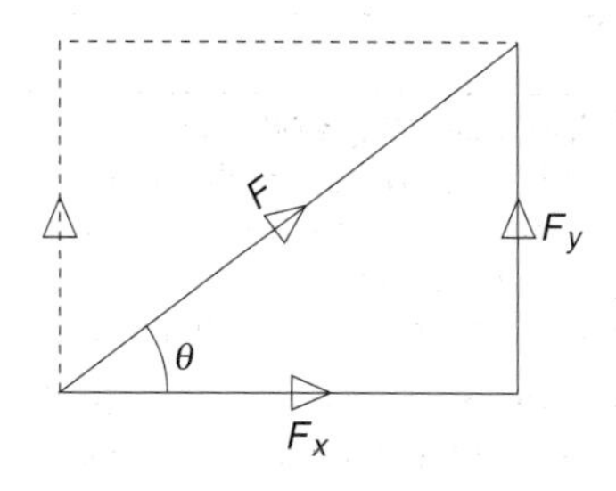

Equilibrium

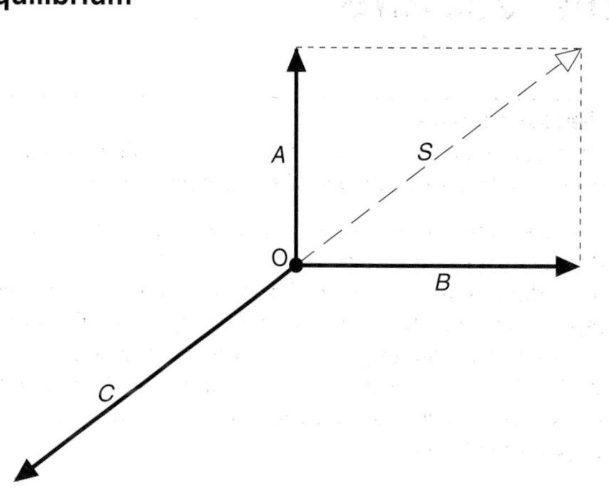

The particle O above has three forces acting on it – *A, B,* and *C*. Forces *A* and *B* can be replaced by a single force *S*. As force *C* is equal and opposite to *S*, the resultant of *A, B,* and *C*, is zero. This means that the three forces are in balance – the system is in ***equilibrium***.

If three forces are in equilibrium, they can be represented by the three sides of a triangle, as shown below. Note that the sides and angles match those in the previous force diagram. The forces can be drawn in any order, provided that the head of each arrow joins with the tail of another.

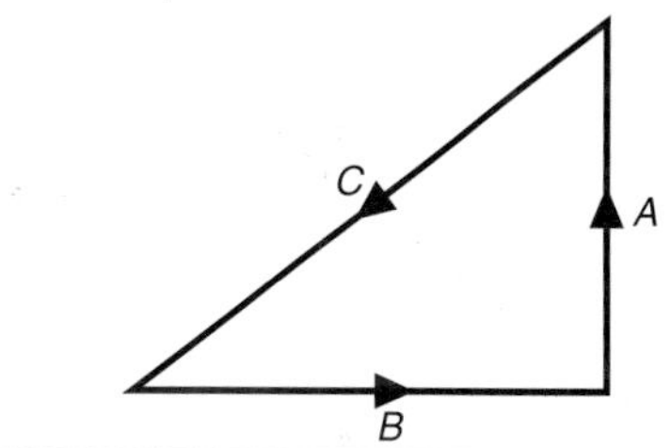

Resolving problem

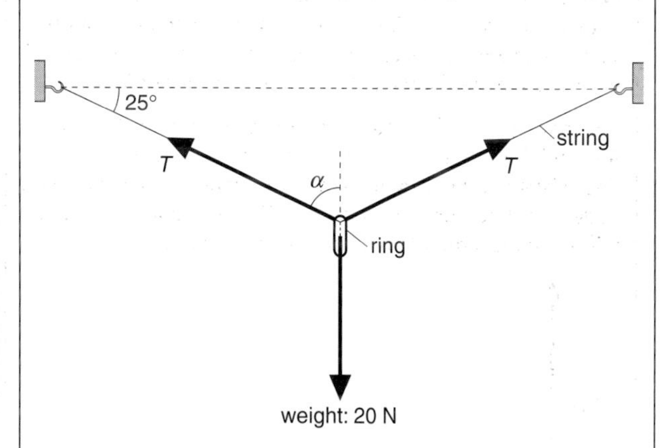

Example *Above, a ring is suspended from the middle of a piece of string. What is the tension in the string?*

Force *T* is the tension. It is present in both halves of the string. As angle α is 65°, this force has a component (upwards) of $T \cos 65°$. So:

total of upward components on ring = $2T \cos 65°$

As the system is in equilibrium, the total of upward components must equal the downward force on the ring.

So $2T \cos 65° = 20$

This gives $T = 24$ N

B5 Moments and equilibrium

Moment of a force

The turning effect of a force is called its ***moment***. Here are two examples.

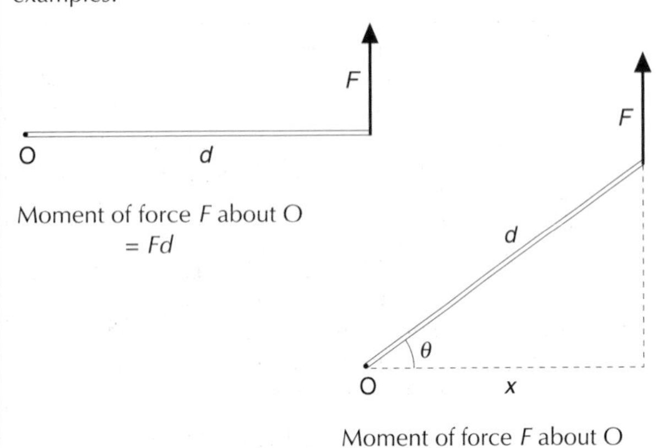

Moment of force F about O
$= Fd$

Moment of force F about O
$= Fx \;\; = Fd\cos\theta$

Note:

- In the diagram on the left, although O is shown as a point, it is really an *axis* going perpendicularly into the paper.
- Moments are measured in N m. However this is not the same unit as the N m, or J (joule), used for measuring energy.
- A moment can be *clockwise* or *anticlockwise*, depending on its *sense* (direction of turning). This can be indicated with a + or –. For example:

anticlockwise moment of 2 N m = +2 N m
clockwise moment of 2 N m = –2 N m

Principle of moments

The beam in the diagram on the right has weights on it. (The beam itself is of negligible weight.) The total weight is supported by an upward force R from the fulcrum.

The beam is in a state of balance. It is in equilibrium.

As the beam is not tipping to the left or right, the turning effects on it must balance. So, when moments are taken about O, as shown, the total clockwise moment must equal the total anticlockwise moment. (Note: R has zero moment about O because its distance from O is zero.)

As the beam is static, the upward force on it must equal the total downward force. So $R = 10 + 8 + 4 = 22$ N.

The beam is not turning about O. But it is not turning about any other axis either. So you would expect the moments about *any* axis to balance. This is exactly the case, as you can see in the next diagram. The beam and weights are the same as before, but this time, moments have been taken about point P instead of O. (Note: R does have a moment about P, so the value of R must be known before the calculation can be done.)

The examples shown on the right illustrate the ***principle of moments***, which can be stated as follows.

> If an object is in equilibrium, the sum of the clockwise moment about any axis is equal to the sum of the anticlockwise moments.

Here is another way of stating the principle. In it, moments are regarded as + or –, and the ***resultant moment*** is the algebraic sum of all the moments:

> If a rigid object is in equilibrium, the resultant moment about any axis is zero.

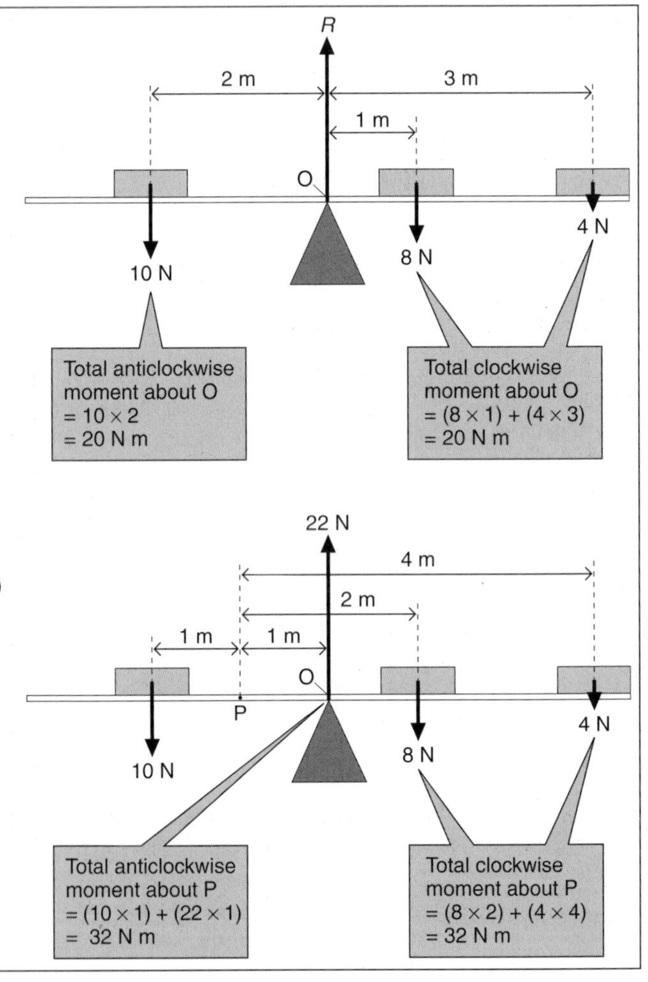

Centre of gravity

All the particles in an object have weight. The weight of the whole object is the resultant of all these tiny, downward gravitational forces. It appears to act through a single point called the ***centre of gravity***.

In the case of a rectangular beam with an even weight distribution, the centre of gravity is in the middle. Unless negligible, the weight must be included when analysing the forces and moments acting on the beam.

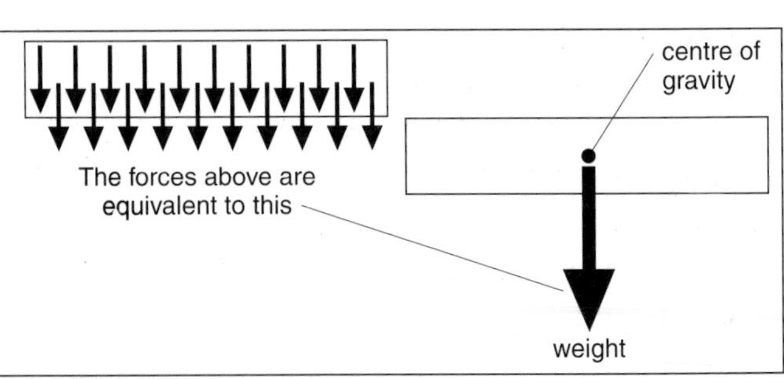

Conditions for equilibrium

There are two types of motion: ***translational*** (from one place to another) and ***rotational*** (turning). If a static, rigid object is in equilibrium, then:

- the forces on it must balance, otherwise they would cause translational motion,
- the moments must balance, otherwise they would cause rotational motion.

The balanced beam on the opposite page is a simple system in which the forces are all in the same plane. A ***coplanar*** system like this is in equilibrium if:

- the vertical components of all the forces balance,
- the horizontal components of all the forces balance,
- the moments about any axis balance.

To check for equilibrium, components can be taken in any two directions. However, vertical and horizontal components are often the simplest to consider. The balanced beam is especially simple because there are no horizontal forces.

Equilibrium problem

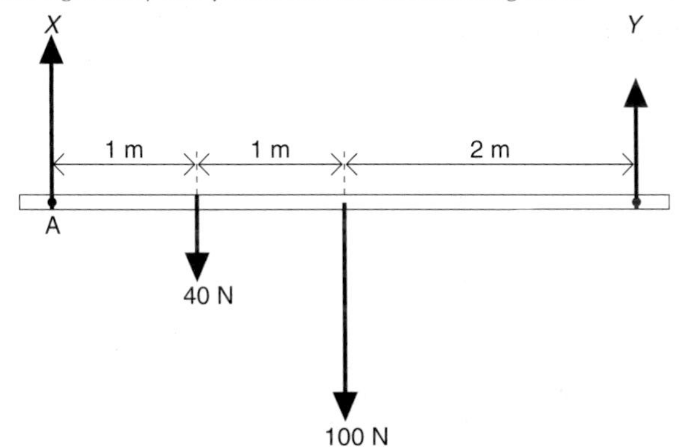

Example *A plank with a bucket on it is supported by two trestles. What force does each trestle exert on the plank?*

The first stage is to draw a ***free-body diagram*** showing just the rigid body (the plank) and the forces acting on it:

X   *Y*

1 m   1 m   2 m

A

40 N

100 N

The body is in equilibrium, so the moments must balance, and the forces also. *X* and *Y* are the unknown forces.

Taking moments about A:

total clockwise moment = total anticlockwise moment

$$(40 \times 1) + (100 \times 2) = (Y \times 4)$$

This gives $Y = 60$ N.

Note the advantage of taking moments about A: *X* has a zero moment, so it does not feature in the equation.

Comparing the vertical forces:

total upward force = total downward force

$$Y + X = 40 + 100$$

As *Y* is 60 N, this gives $X = 80$ N.

Couples and torque

A pair of equal but opposite forces, as below, is called a ***couple***. It has a turning effect, but no resultant force.

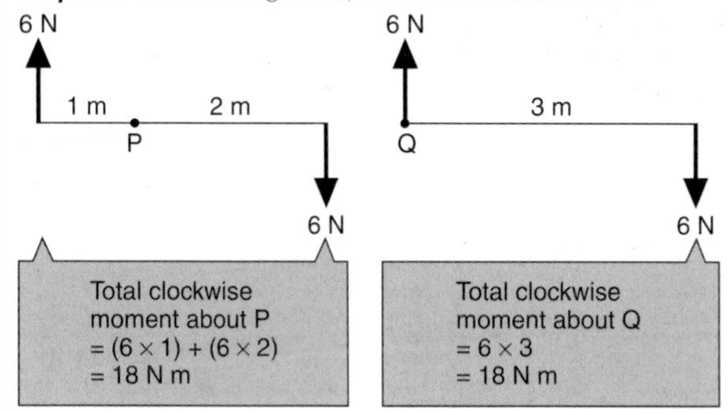

To find the total moment of a couple, you could choose any axis, work out the two moments and add them up. Whichever axis you choose, the answer is the same, so the simplest way of calculating the total moment is like this:

moment of couple = one force × perpendicular distance between forces

Note:

- The total moment of a couple is called a ***torque***.
- Strictly speaking, a couple is any system of forces which has a turning effect only i.e. one which produces rotational motion without translational (linear) motion.

Stability

For a static object, there are three types of equilibrium, as shown below. Whether the equilibrium is ***stable***, ***unstable***, or ***neutral*** depends on the couple formed by the weight and the reaction when the object is displaced.

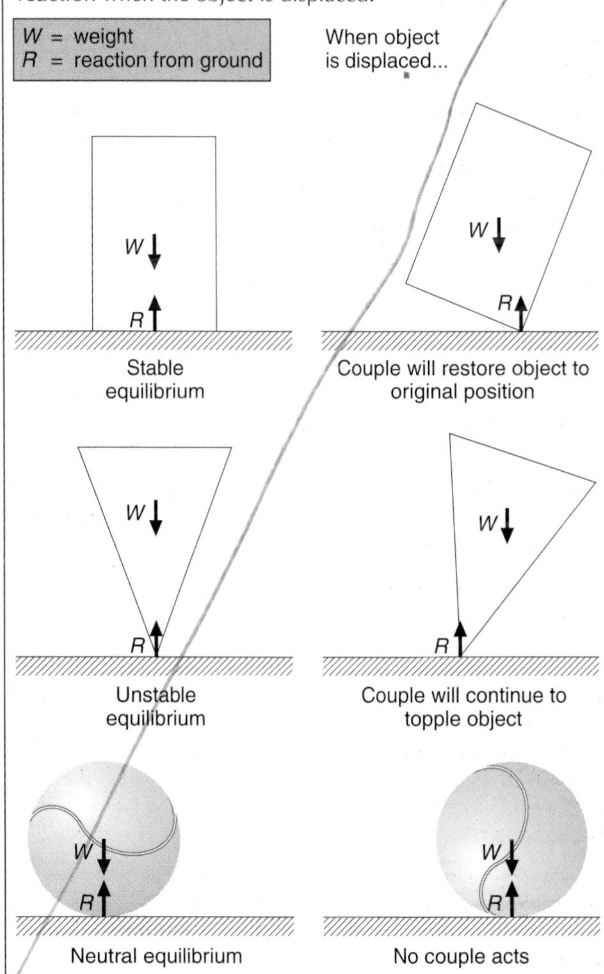

B6 Motion and momentum

Newton's first law

The equation $F = ma$ implies that, if the resultant force on something is zero, then its acceleration is also zero. This idea is summed up by ***Newton's first law of motion***:

> If there is no resultant force acting:
> - a stationary object will stay at rest,
> - a moving object will maintain a constant velocity (a steady speed in a straight line).

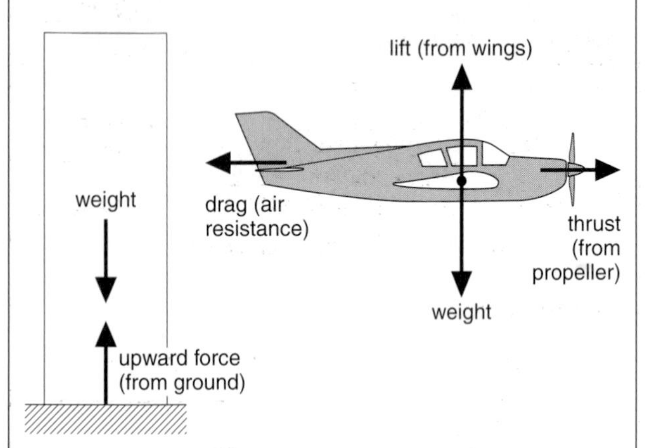

From Newton's first law, it follows that if an object is at rest or moving at constant velocity, then the forces on it must be balanced, as in the examples above.

The more mass an object has, the more it resists any change in motion (because more force is needed for any given acceleration). Newton called this resistance to change in motion ***inertia***.

Momentum and Newton's second law

The product of an object's mass m and velocity v is called its ***momentum***:

> momentum = mv

Momentum is measured in kg m s^{-1}. It is a vector.

According to ***Newton's second law of motion***:

> The rate of change of momentum of an object is proportional to the resultant force acting.

This can be written in the following form:

$$\text{resultant force} \propto \frac{\text{change in momentum}}{\text{time taken}}$$

With the unit of force defined in a suitable way (as in SI), the above proportion can be changed into an equation:

$$F = \frac{mv - mu}{t} \qquad (1)$$

initial velocity: u

final velocity: v

m

F

Linked equations

Equation (1) can be rewritten $F = \dfrac{m(v - u)}{t}$

But acceleration $a = \dfrac{(v - u)}{t}$. So $F = ma$ (2)

Equations (1) and (2) are therefore different versions of the same principle.

Note:

- In arriving at the equation $F = ma$ above, the mass m is assumed to be constant. But according to Einstein (see C18), mass increases with velocity (though insignificantly for velocities much below that of light). This means that $F = ma$ is really only an approximation, though an acceptable one for most practical purposes.
- When using equations (1) and (2), remember that F is the resultant force acting. For example, on the right, the resultant force is $26 - 20 = 6$ N upwards. The upward acceleration a can be worked out as follows:

$$a = \frac{F}{m} = \frac{6}{2} = 3 \text{ m s}^{-2}$$

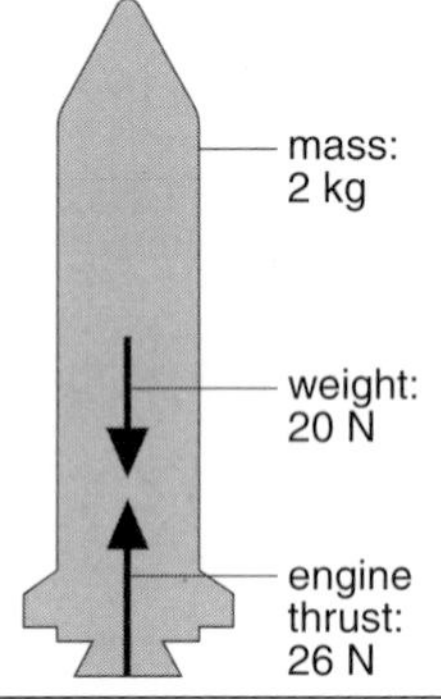

Impulse

Equation (1) can also be rewritten $Ft = mv - mu$

In words force × time = change in momentum

The quantity 'force × time' is called an ***impulse***.

A given impulse always produces the same change in momentum, irrespective of the mass. For example, if a resultant force of 6 N acts for 2 s, the impulse delivered is $6 \times 2 = 12$ N s.

This will produce a momentum change of 12 kg m s^{-1}

So a 4 kg mass will gain 3 m s^{-1} of velocity

or a 2 kg mass will gain 6 m s^{-1} of velocity, and so on.

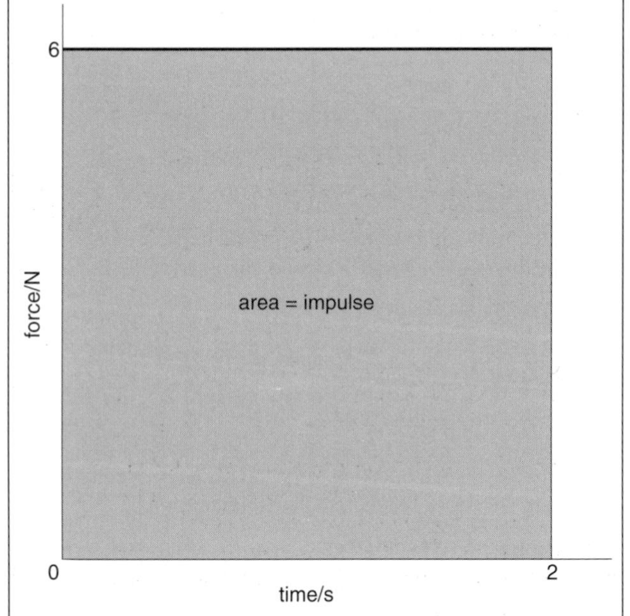

The graph above is for a uniform force of 6 N. In 2 s, the impulse delivered is 12 N s. Numerically, this is equal to the area of the graph between the 0 and 2 s points.

Newton's third law

A single force cannot exist by itself. Forces are always pushes or pulls between *two* objects, so they always occur in pairs. One force acts on one object; its equal but opposite partner acts on the other. This idea is summed up by ***Newton's third law of motion***:

> If A is exerting a force on B, then B is exerting an equal but opposite force on A.

The law is sometimes expressed as follows.

> To every action, there is an equal but opposite reaction.

Examples of action-reaction pairs are given below.

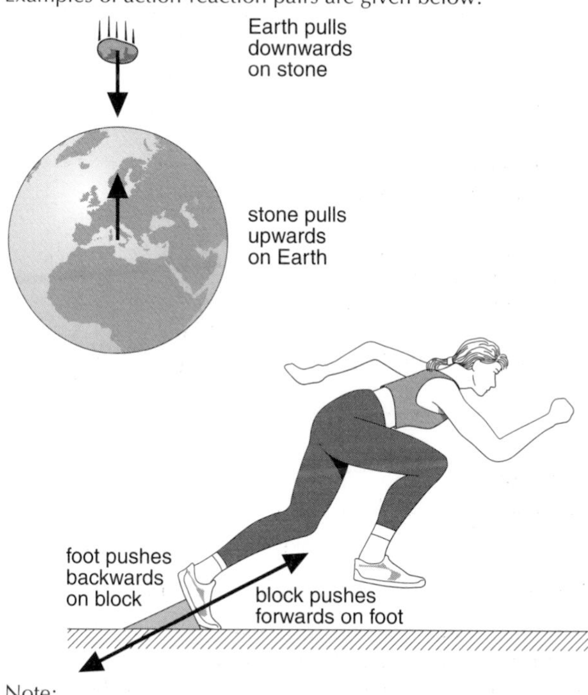

Note:
- It does not matter which force you call the action and which the reaction. One cannot exist without the other.
- The action and reaction do not cancel each other out because they are acting on *different* objects.

Momentum problem

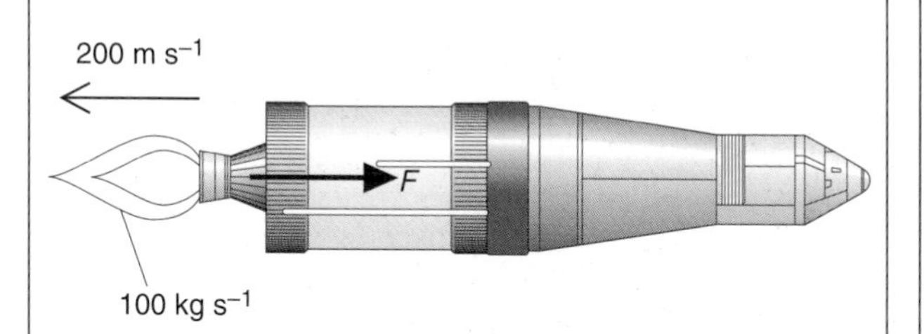

Example *A rocket engine ejects 100 kg of exhaust gas per second at a velocity (relative to the rocket) of 200 m s⁻¹. What is the forward thrust (force) on the rocket?*

By Newton's third law, the forward force on the rocket is equal to the backward force pushing out the exhaust gas. By Newton's second law, this force F is equal to the momentum gained per second by the gas, so it can be calculated using equation (1) with the following values:

$m = 100$ kg $\quad t = 1$ s $\quad u = 0 \quad v = 200$ m s^{-1}

So $F = \dfrac{mv - mu}{t} = \dfrac{(100 \times 200) - (100 \times 0)}{1} = 20\,000$ N

Conservation of momentum

Trolleys A and B below are initially at rest. When a spring between them is released, they are pushed apart.

By Newton's third law, the force exerted by A on B is equal (but opposite) to the force exerted by B on A. These equal forces also act for the same time, so they deliver equal (but opposite) impulses. As a result, A gains the same momentum to the left as B gains to the right.

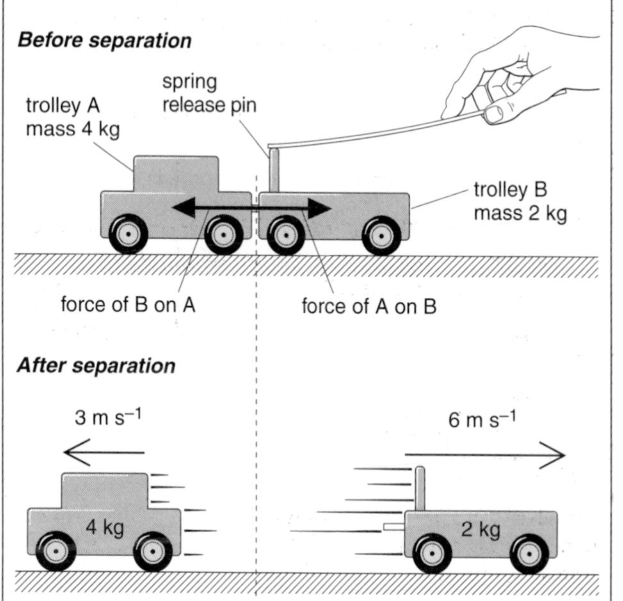

Momentum is a vector, so its direction can be indicated using + or –. If vectors to the right are taken as +:

Before the trolleys separate
total momentum = 0

After the trolleys separate
momentum of A = 4 × (–3) = –12 kg m s^{-1}
momentum of B = 2 × (+6) = +12 kg m s^{-1}
so total momentum = 0 kg m s^{-1}

Together, trolleys A and B make up a ***system***. The total momentum of this system is the same (zero) before the trolleys push on each other as it is afterwards. This illustrates the ***law of conservation of momentum***.

> When the objects in a system interact, their total momentum remains constant, provided that there is no external force on the system.

Below, the separating trolleys are shown with velocities of v_1 and v_2 instead of actual values. In cases like this, it is always best to choose the same direction as positive for all vectors. It does not matter that A is really moving to the left. If A's velocity is 3 m s^{-1} to the left, then $v_1 = -3$ m s^{-1}.

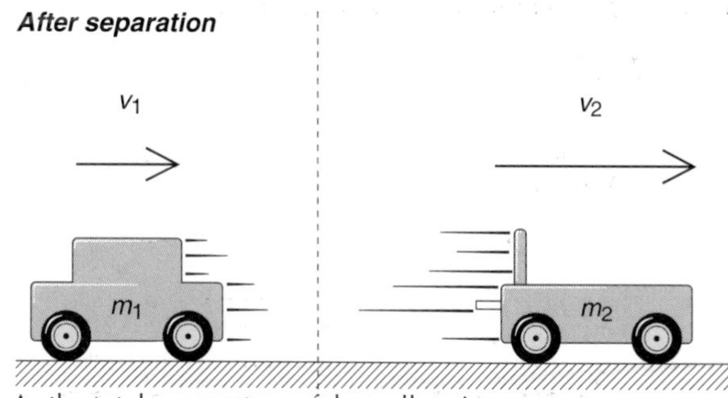

As the total momentum of the trolleys is zero:

$m_1 v_1 + m_2 v_2 = 0$

So, if v_2 is positive, v_1 must be negative.

B7 Work, energy, and momentum

Work

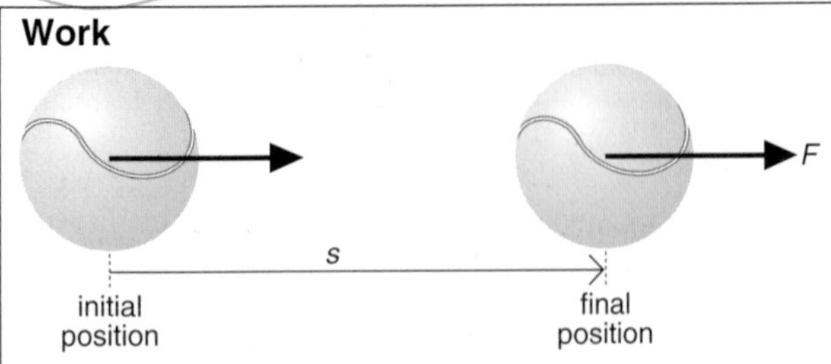

Above, F is the resultant force on an object. If W is the work done when the force has caused a displacement s, then:

$$W = Fs$$

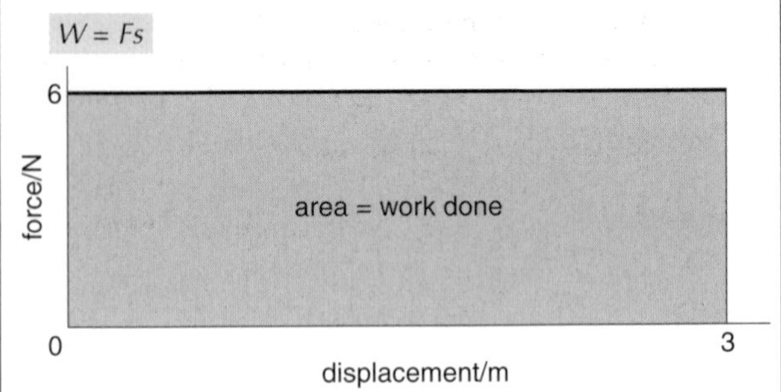

The graph above is for a uniform force of 6 N. When the displacement is 3 m, the work done is 18 J. Numerically, this is equal to the area under the graph between the 0 and 3 m points. (The same principle applies for a changing force: see B12.)

Using a ramp Below, a load is raised, first by lifting it vertically, and then by pulling it up a frictionless ramp. The force needed in each case is shown, but not the balancing force. (F_1 must balance the weight, so $F_1 = mg$.)

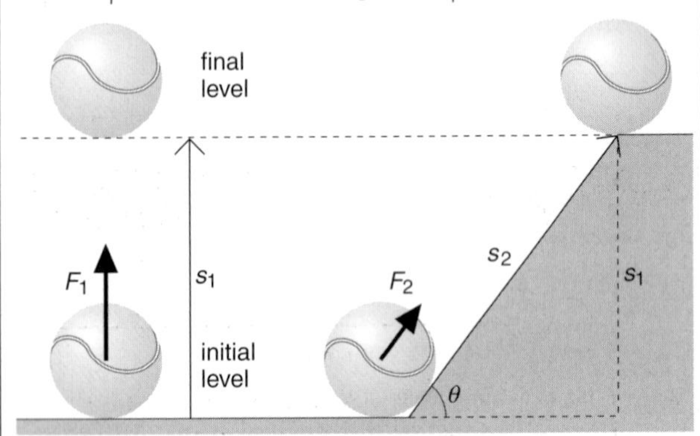

The gain in potential energy is the same in both cases. So, by the law of conservation of energy, the work done must also be the same. Therefore:

$$F_2 s_2 = F_1 s_1 \qquad (1)$$

As $s_2 > s_1$, it follows that $F_2 < F_1$. So, by using the ramp, the displacement is increased, but the force needed to raise the load is reduced. The ramp is a simple form of machine.

Equation (1) leads to two further results:

As $s_1 = s_2 \sin\theta$, $\quad F_2 = F_1 \sin\theta$

As $F_1 = mg$, $\quad F_2 = mg \sin\theta$

You can also get the last result by finding the component of mg down the ramp. F_2 is the force needed to balance it.

The frictionless ramp wastes no energy. But this is not true of most machines. Where there is friction, the work done *by* a machine is less than the work done *on* it.

Finding an equation for kinetic energy (KE)

Below, an object of mass m is accelerated from velocity u to v by a resultant force F. While gaining this velocity, its displacement is s and its acceleration is a.

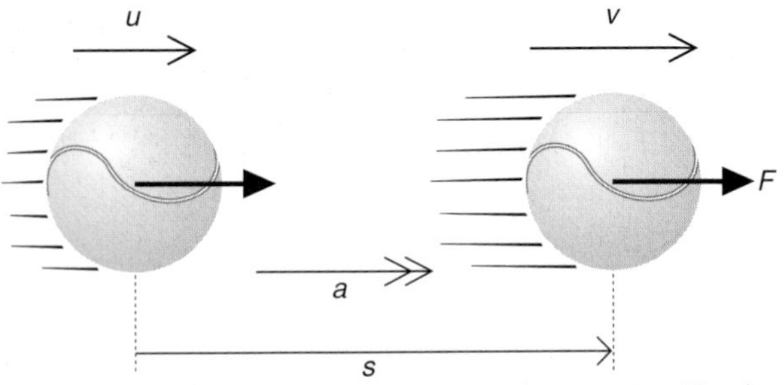

From the law of conservation of energy, the KE gained by the object is equal to the work done on it, Fs.

From equation (4) in B3: $v^2 - u^2 = 2as$.

$\therefore \quad as = \frac{1}{2}v^2 - \frac{1}{2}u^2$

So $\quad mas = \frac{1}{2}mv^2 - \frac{1}{2}mu^2$

But $\quad mas = Fs \quad$ (because $F = ma$)

So $\quad Fs = \frac{1}{2}mv^2 - \frac{1}{2}mu^2$.

As Fs is the work done, the right-hand side of the equation represents the KE gained. So, when the object's velocity is v, its KE $= \frac{1}{2}mv^2$.

Collisions

Whenever objects collide, their total momentum is conserved, provided that there is no external force acting.

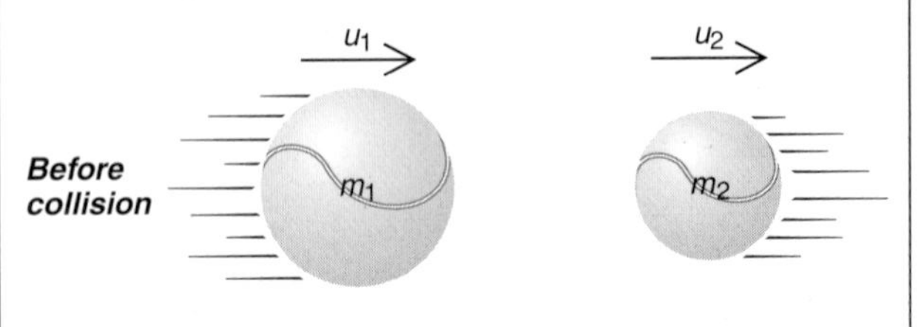

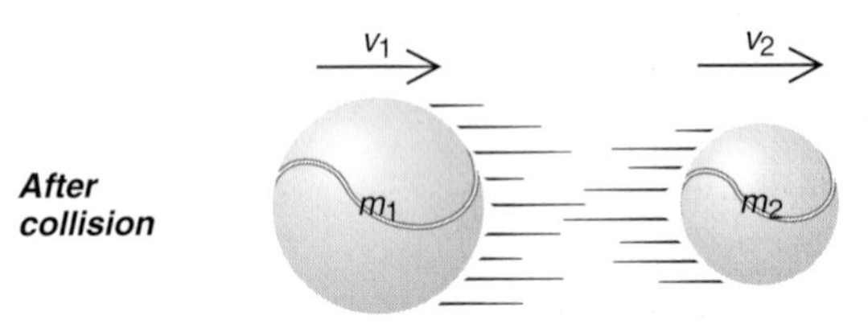

Above, two balls collide and then separate. All vectors have been defined as positive to the right. As the total momentum is the same before and after:

$$m_1 u_1 + m_2 u_2 = m_1 v_1 + m_2 v_2$$

Elastic collision An elastic collision is one in which the total kinetic energy of the colliding objects remains constant. In other words, no energy is converted into heat (or other forms). If the above collision is elastic:

$$\tfrac{1}{2}m_1 u_1^2 + \tfrac{1}{2}m_2 u_2^2 = \tfrac{1}{2}m_1 v_1^2 + \tfrac{1}{2}m_2 v_2^2$$

One consequence of the above is that the speed of separation of A and B is the same after the collision as before:

$$u_1 - u_2 = -(v_1 - v_2)$$

Inelastic collision In an inelastic collision, kinetic energy is converted into heat. The total amount of *energy* is conserved, but the total amount of *kinetic energy* is not.

Collision problems

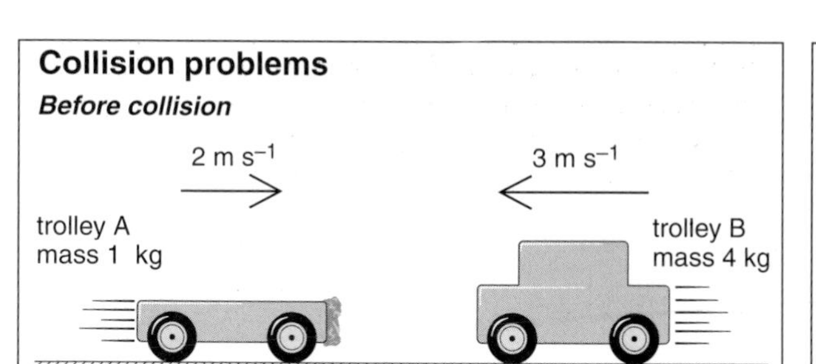

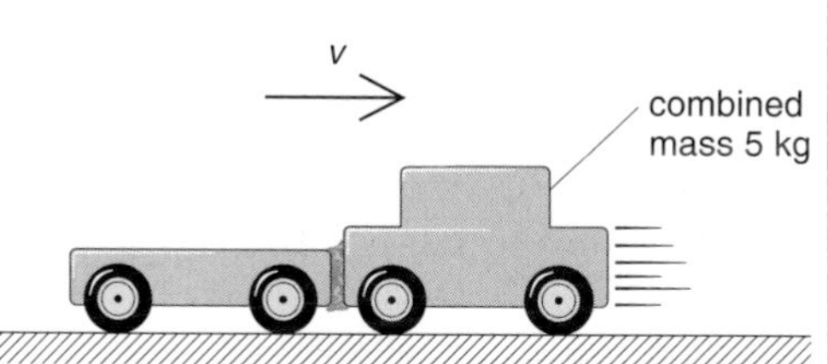

Example 1 The trolleys above collide and stick together. What is their velocity after the collision? (Assume no friction.)

All vectors to the right will be taken as positive.
The unknown velocity is v (to the right).

Momentum = mass × velocity

Before the collision

momentum of A = 1 × 2 = 2 kg m s^{-1}

momentum of B = 4 × (−3) = −12 kg m s^{-1}

∴ total momentum = −10 kg m s^{-1} (2)

After the collision

A and B have a combined mass of 5 kg, and a combined velocity of v. So total momentum = 5 × v.

As the total momentum is the same before and after:

$5v = -10$ which gives $v = -2$ m s^{-1}

So the trolleys have a velocity of 2 m s^{-1} to the *left*.

Example 2 When the trolleys collide, how much of their total kinetic energy is lost (converted into other forms)?

$\text{KE} = \frac{1}{2}mv^2$

Before the collision

KE of A = $\frac{1}{2} \times 1 \times 2^2$ = 2 J

KE of B = $\frac{1}{2} \times 4 \times (-3)^2$ = 18 J

∴ total KE = 20 J (3)

After the collision

total KE = $\frac{1}{2} \times 5 \times (-2)^2$ = 10 J

Comparing the total KEs before and after, 10 J of KE is lost.

Example 3 If the collision had been elastic, what would the velocities of the trolleys have been after separation?

Let v_1 be the final velocity A, and v_2 be the final velocity of B (both defined as positive to the right).

As both total momentum and total KE are conserved:

total momentum after collision = −10 kg m s^{-1} (from 2)
total KE after collision = 20 J (from 3)

So $(1 \times v_1) + (4 \times v_2) = -10$

And $(\frac{1}{2} \times 1 \times v_1^2) + (\frac{1}{2} \times 4 \times v_2^2) = 20$

Solving these equations for v_1 and v_2 gives:

$v_1 = -6$ m s^{-1} and $v_2 = -1$ m s^{-1}

Note:

- There is an alternative solution which gives the velocities before the collision: 2 m s^{-1} and −3 m s^{-1}.

Recoiling particles

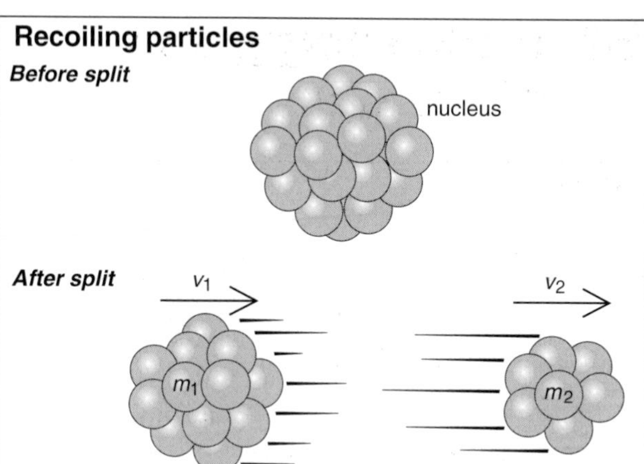

Above, an atomic nucleus splits into two smaller particles with a loss of nuclear energy (see also B34). The particles share the energy released (as kinetic energy) and shoot apart. All vectors have been defined as positive to the right.

As the total momentum is conserved, $m_1v_1 + m_2v_2 = 0$ (4)

Also KE of A = $\frac{1}{2}m_1v_1^2$ (5)

and KE of B = $\frac{1}{2}m_2v_2^2$ (6)

From (4), (5), and (6), the following can be obtained:

$$\frac{\text{KE of A}}{\text{KE of B}} = \frac{m_2}{m_1}$$

This means, for example, that if A has 9 times the mass of B, then B will shoot out with 9 times the KE of A. In other words, it will have 90% of the available energy. The energy is only shared equally if A and B have the same mass.

Power and velocity

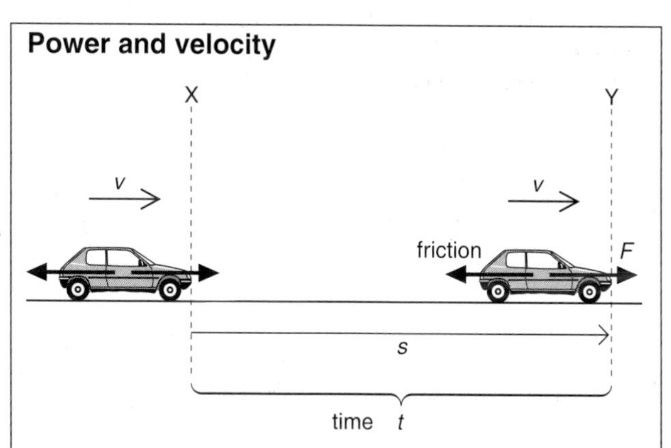

Above, the car's engine provides (via the driven wheels) a forward force F which balances the total frictional force (mainly air resistance) on the car. As a result, the car maintains a steady velocity v. The displacement of the car is s in time t. P is the power being delivered to the wheels.

In moving from X to Y, work done (by F) = Fs.

$$\text{power} = P = \frac{\text{work done}}{\text{time taken}} = \frac{Fs}{t}$$

But $v = \frac{s}{t}$ so $P = Fv$

i.e. power delivered = force × velocity

For example, if a force of 200 N is needed to maintain a steady velocity of 5 m s^{-1} against frictional forces:

power delivered = 200 × 5 = 1000 W

All of this power is wasted as heat in overcoming friction. Without friction, no forward force would be needed to maintain a steady velocity, so no work would be done.

B8 Circular motion

Angular displacement

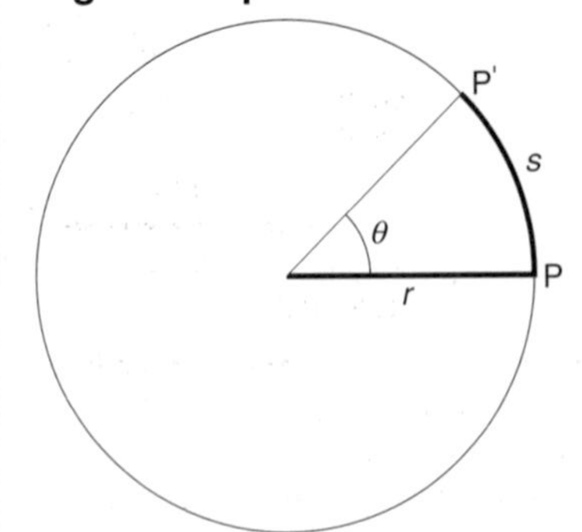

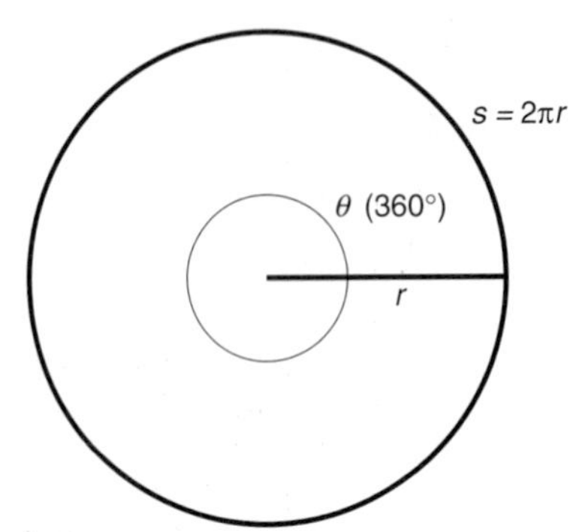

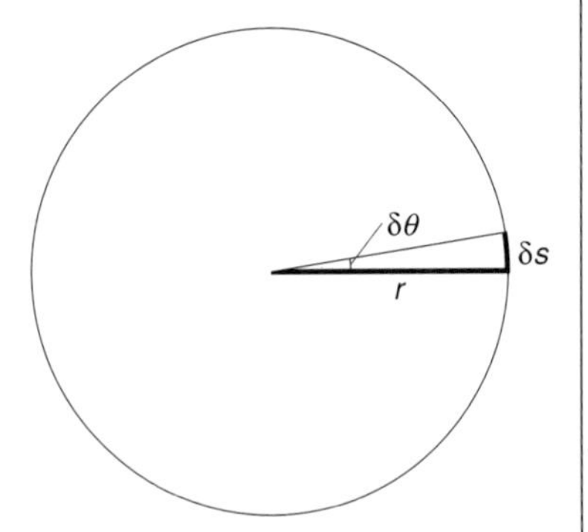

If point P moves to P′, then the angle θ is called the ***angular displacement***. It is measured in ***radians*** (see also B1):

$$\theta = \frac{s}{r}$$

If s is the full circumference of the circle:

$$\theta = \frac{2\pi r}{r} = 2\pi$$

So $\quad 2\pi$ radians = 360°

$$\therefore\ 1 \text{ radian} = \frac{360}{2\pi} = 57.3°$$

Above, $\delta\theta$ is a very small angle. ($\delta\theta$ counts as one symbol.) δs is so small that it can either be the arc of a circle or the side of a triangle. So:

$$\sin \delta\theta = \frac{s}{r} = \delta\theta$$

i.e. for *small* angles $\sin \delta\theta = \delta\theta$.

Rate of rotation

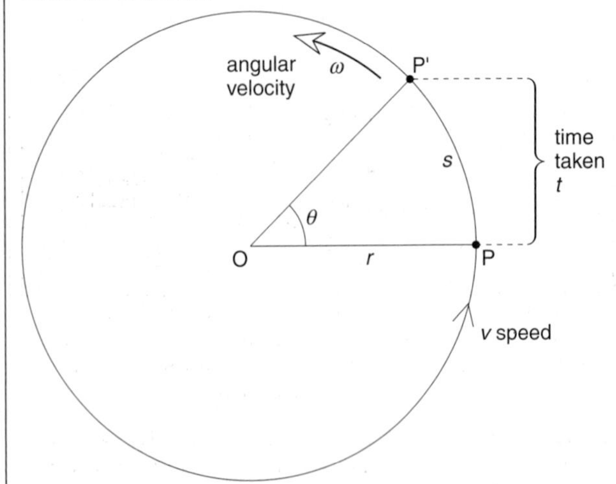

P is a point on a wheel which is turning at a steady rate. In time t, it moves to P′. The rate of rotation can be measured either as an ***angular velocity*** or as a ***frequency***.

Angular velocity ω

$$\text{angular velocity} = \frac{\text{angular displacement}}{\text{time taken}}$$

In symbols $\quad \omega = \dfrac{\theta}{t}$

For example, if a wheel turns through 10 radians in 2 sec, then $\omega = 5$ rad s^{-1}.

Frequency f

$$\text{frequency} = \frac{\text{number of rotations}}{\text{time taken}}$$

Frequency is measured in hertz (Hz). For example, if a wheel completes 12 rotations in 4 seconds, then $f = 3$ Hz.

Period T This is time taken for one rotation. If a wheel makes 3 complete rotations per second ($f = 3$ Hz), then the time taken for one rotation is $\frac{1}{3}$ second. So:

$$T = \frac{1}{f}$$

Linking v, ω, and r

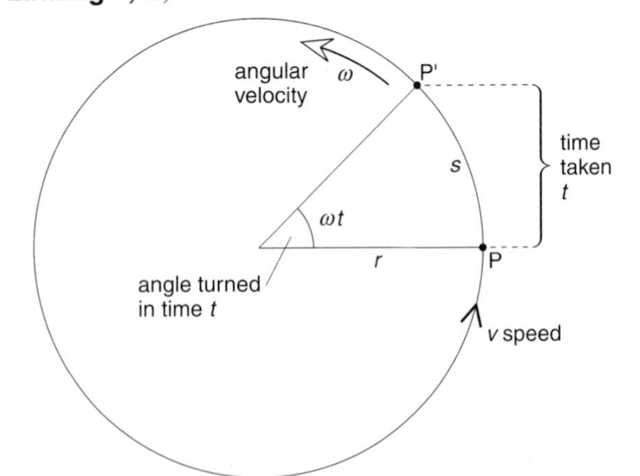

Above, a particle is moving in circle with a steady speed v. (It is not a steady velocity because the direction of the velocity vector is changing.) The particle moves a distance s in time t, so:

$$v = \frac{s}{t}$$

As the angular velocity is ω, the angle turned in time t is ωt (from the equation on the left). But $\omega t = s/r$. So $s = \omega t r$. Substituting this in the above equation gives:

$$v = \omega r$$

Linking ω, f, and T As there are 2π radians in one full rotation (360°):

$$\omega = 2\pi f$$

For example, a wheel turning at 3 rotations per second ($f = 3$ Hz) has an angular velocity of 6π radians per second.

As $T = 1/f$, it follows from the previous equation that:

$$T = \frac{2\pi}{\omega}$$

Centripetal acceleration

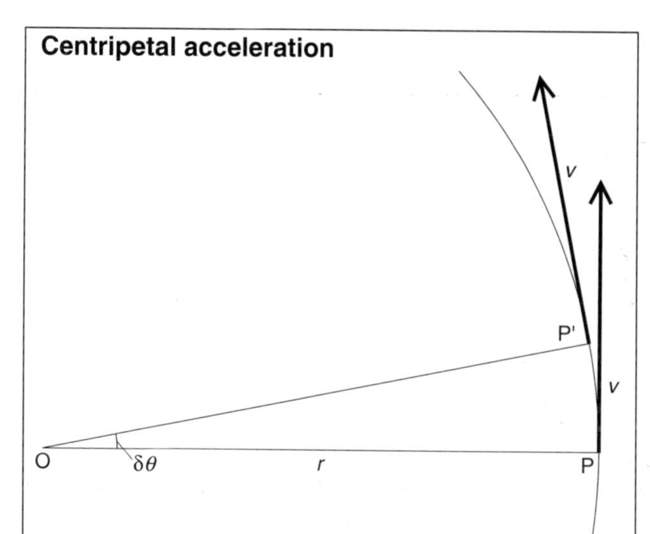

Above, a particle is moving in a circle with a steady speed v. The diagram shows how the velocity vector changes direction as the particle moves from P to P′ in time δt.

Below, the velocity vectors from the previous diagram have been used in a triangle of vectors (see B4).

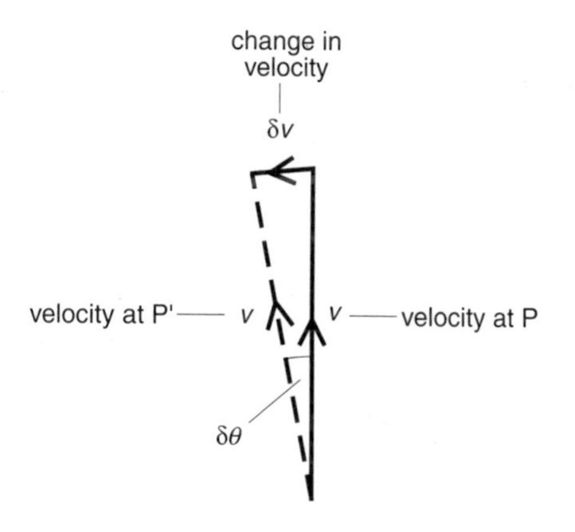

The δv vector represents the *change* in velocity because it is the velocity vector which must be *added* to the velocity at P to produce the new velocity (the resultant) at P′. Note that the change in velocity is towards O. In other words, the particle has an *acceleration* towards the centre of the circle. This is called ***centripetal acceleration***.

If a is the centripetal acceleration $\qquad a = \dfrac{\delta v}{\delta t}$

But, from the triangle above $\delta\theta = \dfrac{\delta v}{v}$. So $\delta v = v\delta\theta$

Substituting this in the previous equation $\qquad a = \dfrac{v\delta\theta}{\delta t}$

But $\delta\theta = \omega\delta t$. So $\qquad a = v\omega$

Using $v = \omega r$, two more versions of the above equation can be obtained. So:

$$a = v\omega \qquad a = \frac{v^2}{r} \qquad a = \omega^2 r$$

For example, if a particle is moving at a steady speed of 3 m s^{-1} in a circle of radius 2 m, its centripetal acceleration a is found using the middle equation: $a = 3^2/2 = 4.5$ m s^{-2}.

Note:

- When something accelerates, its velocity changes. As velocity is a vector, this can mean a change in *speed* or *direction* (or both). Centripetal acceleration is produced by a change in direction, not speed.

Centripetal force

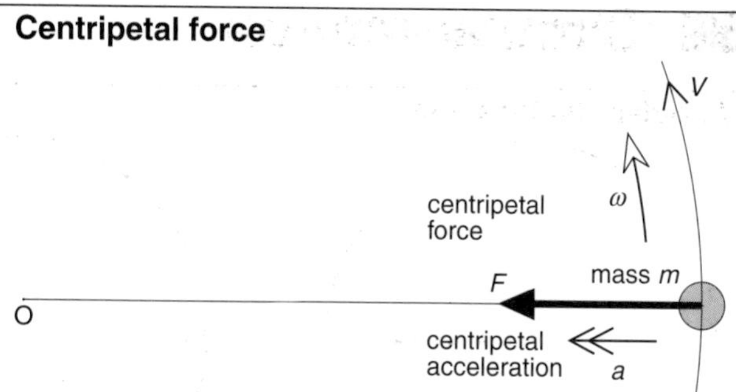

To produce centripetal acceleration, a ***centripetal force*** is needed. It must act towards the centre of the circle. The centripetal force F, mass m, and centripetal acceleration a, are linked by the equation $F = ma$. So, using the equations for a in the previous column:

$$F = mv\omega \qquad F = \frac{mv^2}{r} \qquad F = m\omega^2 r$$

Note:

- centripetal force is *not* produced by circular motion. It is the force *needed* for circular motion. Without it, the object would travel in a straight line.

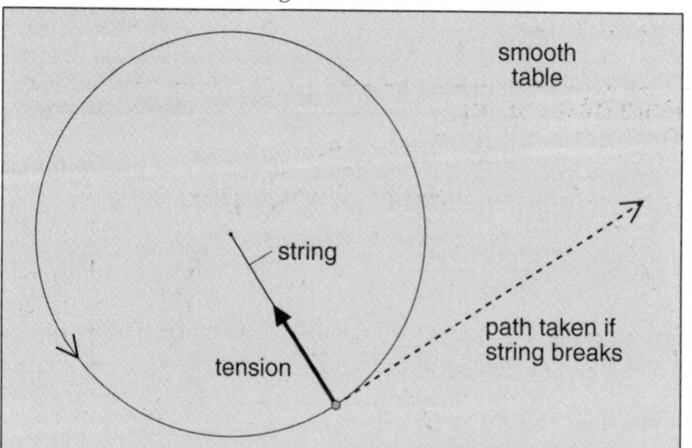

Above, a mass moves in a circle on a smooth table. The tension in the string provides the centripetal force needed. There is no outward 'centrifugal force' on the mass. If the string breaks, the mass travels along a tangent.

Angle of bank An aircraft must bank to turn. This is so that the lift L (from the wings) and the weight mg can produce a resultant to provide the centripetal force F where:

$$F = \frac{mv^2}{r}$$

In the triangle of vectors (below right):

$$L\cos\theta = mg \quad \text{and} \quad L\sin\theta = \frac{mv^2}{r}$$

Dividing the second equation by the first gives $\tan\theta = v^2/r$ where θ is the angle of bank required for the turn.

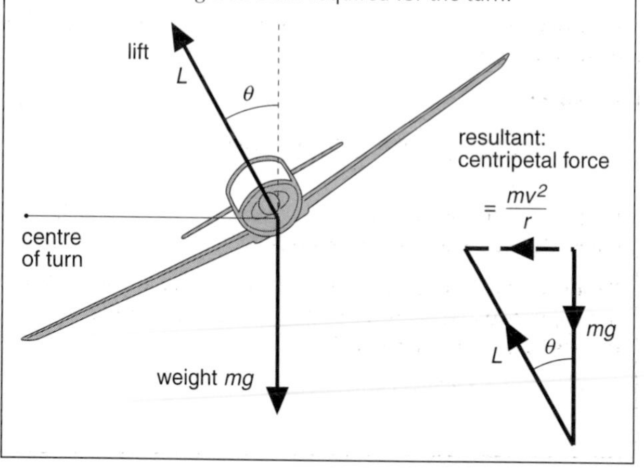

B9 Gravitation

Gravitational force

All masses attract each other with a ***gravitational force***. If point masses m_1 and m_2, are a distance r apart, and F is the force on each, then according to ***Newton's law of gravitation***:

$$F \propto \frac{m_1 m_2}{r^2}$$

With a suitable constant, the above proportion can be turned into an equation:

$$F = \frac{G m_1 m_2}{r^2}$$

G is called the ***gravitational constant***. It is found by experiment using large laboratory masses and an extremely sensitive force-measuring system. In SI units, the value of G is 6.67×10^{-11} N m^2 kg^{-2}.

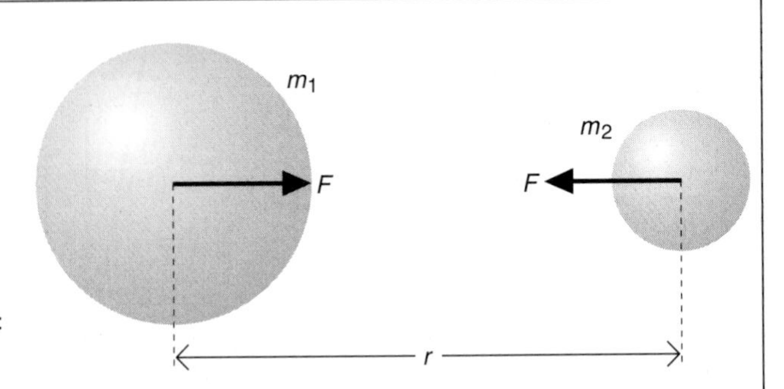

The equation on the left is also valid for spherical masses of uniform density, with centres r apart, as above.

Note:
- Newton's law of gravitation is an example of an ***inverse square law***. If the distance r doubles, the force F drops to one quarter, and so on.
- Gravitational forces are always forces of *attraction*.
- Gravitational forces are extremely weak, unless at least one of the objects is of planetary mass or more.

Gravitational field

If a mass feels a gravitational force, then it is in a ***gravitational field***. The ***gravitational field strength*** g is defined like this:

$$g = \frac{\text{gravitational force}}{\text{mass}}$$

In symbols $g = \frac{F}{m}$

For example, if a mass of 2 kg feels a gravitational force of 10 N, then g is 5 N kg^{-1}.

Note:
- Gravitational field strength is a vector.
- g is a variable and can have different values. The symbol g above does not imply the particular value of 9.81 N kg^{-1} near the Earth's surface.
- The force acting on a mass in a gravitational field can be found by rearranging the equation above: $F = mg$.

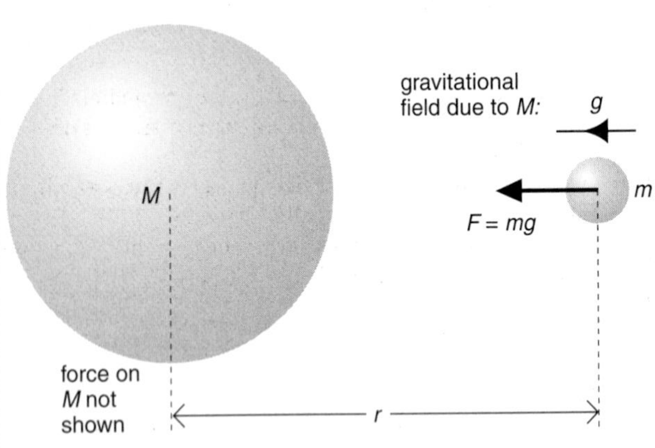

Above, mass M produces a gravitational field which acts on mass m.

As $F = \frac{GMm}{r^2}$ and $F = mg$

it follows that

$$g = \frac{GM}{r^2}$$

It is equally true to say that m produces a gravitational field which acts on M. Either way, mass × gravitational field strength gives a force of the same magnitude, GMm/r^2.

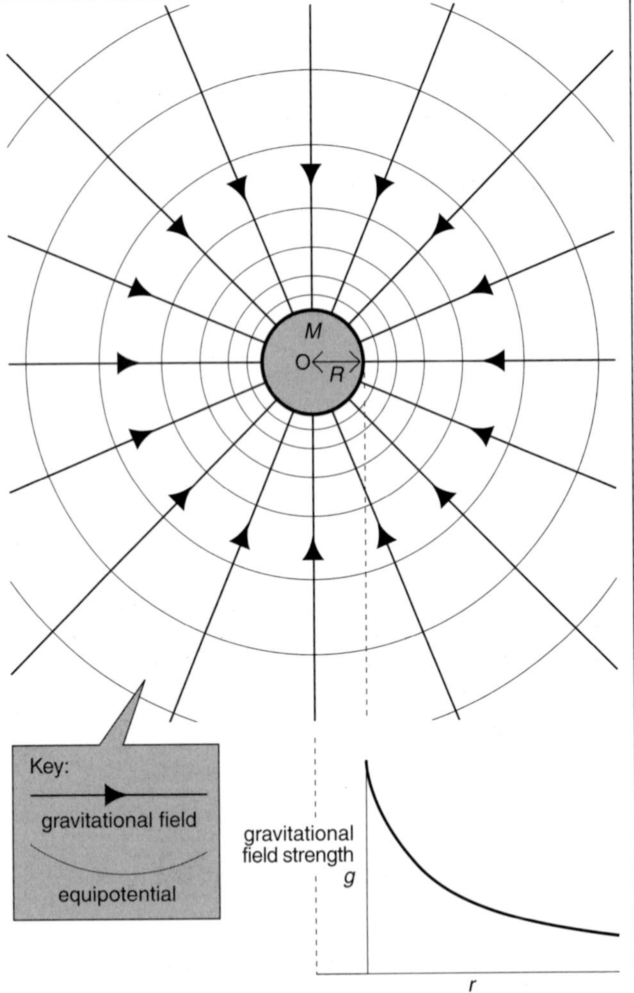

Note:
The gravitational field around a spherical mass is shown above. It is called a ***radial*** field because of its shape.

- Inside the mass, the equation on the left does not apply. g falls to zero at the centre.
- Equipotential lines are explained on the next page.

The Earth's gravitational field strength

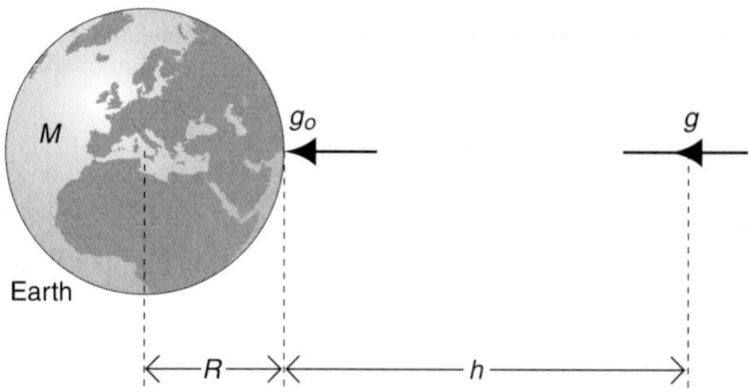

At the surface If M is the Earth's mass, R is its radius, and g_o is the gravitational field strength at its surface, then:

$$g_o = \frac{GM}{R^2} \quad (1)$$

Note:
- g_o is 9.81 N kg^{-1}. It is more commonly known as g (without the $_o$). Here however, the $_o$ has been added to distinguish it from other possible values of g.
- Using measured values of g_o, R, and G in the above equation, the Earth's mass M can be calculated. With R known, the Earth's average density can also be found.

Above the surface In this case, $g = GM/r^2$. From this and equation (1), the following result is obtained:

$$g = \frac{g_o R^2}{r^2}$$

So as the distance from the Earth increases, g decreases.

Gravitational potential

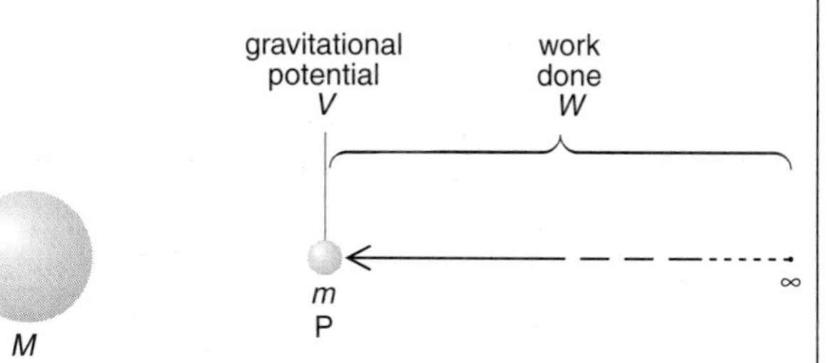

Work must be done to move a mass against a gravitational field. Above, mass M causes a gravitational field. Mass m has been moved through this field, from an infinite distance (where the gravitational force is zero), to point P.

The ***gravitational potential*** V (at point P) is defined as follows:

$$V = \frac{W}{m} \quad (2)$$

where W is the work done in moving a mass m from infinity (∞) to point P.

Note:
- Like energy, gravitational potential is a scalar.
- At infinity, the gravitational potential is *zero*.
- Elsewhere, the gravitational potential is *negative*. This is because gravity is a force of attraction. Work is done *by* the mass as it is pulled from ∞ to P, so *negative* work is done *on* it. For example, if 1000 J of work are done by a 2 kg mass when it moves from ∞ to P, then −1000 J of work are done on it. So $V = -1000/2 = -500$ J kg^{-1}.

Linking potential and field strength

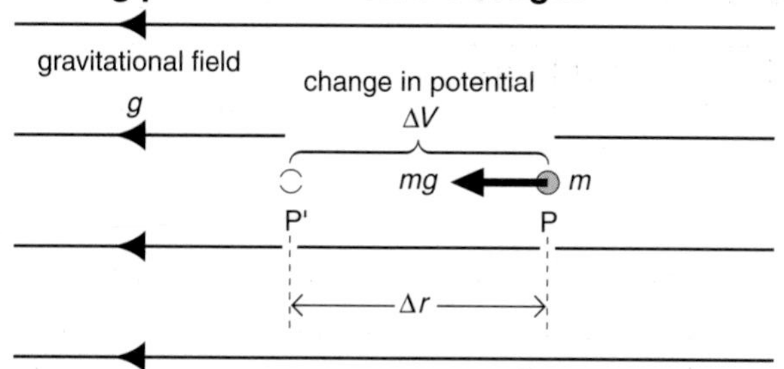

Above, work ΔW is done on a small mass m in moving it from P to P′ in a uniform gravitational field g. So, from (2):

$$\Delta W = m\Delta V \quad (3)$$

This equation gives the work done *on* the mass.

So work done *by* mass $= -m\Delta V$

But work done *by* mass = force × distance moved $= mg\Delta r$

So $mg\Delta r = -m\Delta V$

Therefore $g = -\dfrac{\Delta V}{\Delta r}$

In calculus notation, there is a more general version of this equation which also applies to non-uniform fields:

$$g = -\frac{dV}{dr}$$

Note:
- In the above equations, the minus sign indicates that g is in the direction of decreasing potential.

Gravitational potential in a radial field

A radial field is shown on page 34. Provided r is not less than the radius of the sphere:

$$g = \frac{GM}{r^2}$$

Also, $g = -\dfrac{dV}{dr}$

Combining these, and using calculus, gives $V = -\dfrac{GM}{r}$

Note:
- $V \propto 1/r$. So if the distance r doubles, the gravitational potential V halves, and so on. (Inside the mass, this does not apply.)
- In the diagram on the opposite page, each ***equipotential line*** is a line joining points of equal potential.
- In the case of the Earth, the gravitational potential V_o at the surface is $-GM/R$, where R is the radius.

  As $g_o = \dfrac{GM}{R^2}$

  it follows that $V_o = -g_o R$.

Escape speed

This is the speed, v_{esc}, at which an object must leave a planet's surface to completely escape its gravitational field (i.e. be 'thrown' to infinity). For this, the object must be given enough KE to do the work necessary to move it from the surface (where $V_o = -g_o R$) to infinity (where $V = 0$).
The required gain in potential is $g_o R$. So, from (3), the amount of work to be done is $mg_o R$. Therefore:

$$\tfrac{1}{2} m v_{esc}^2 = mg_o R \qquad \therefore \; v_{esc} = \sqrt{2g_o R}$$

The escape speed from the Earth is 11.2×10^3 m s^{-1}.

B10 Circular orbits and rotation

An orbit equation

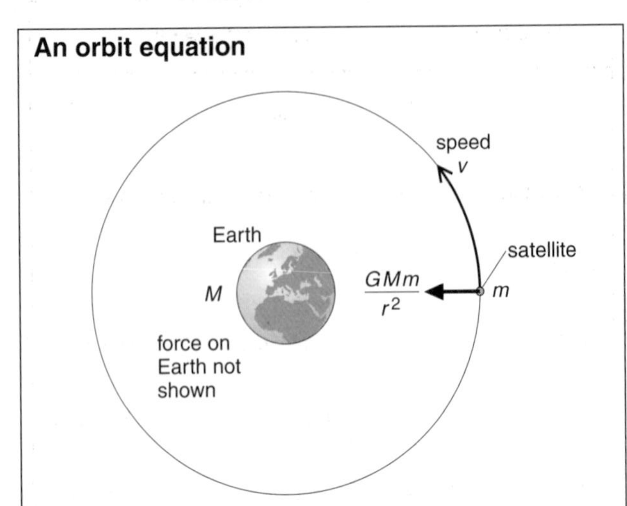

Above, a satellite is in a circular orbit around the Earth. The gravitational force on the satellite provides the centripetal force needed for the circular motion. So:

$$\frac{GMm}{r^2} = \frac{mv^2}{r} \qquad (1)$$

Note:

- The equation can be used to find the speed v needed for an orbit of any given radius r.
- As m cancels from each side of the equation, the speed needed does not depend on the mass of the satellite.

A value for *GM* To use the above equation, you do not need to know the Earth's mass M. Instead, a value for GM can be found using equation (1) in B9. Rearranged, this gives:

$$GM = g_o R^2 \qquad (2)$$

where R is the Earth's radius (12.8×10^9 m), and g_o is the gravitational field strength at its surface (9.81 N kg^{-1}).

Period of orbit

The period T is the time taken for one orbit.
Equation (1) can be rewritten using a different version of the equation for centripetal force:

$$\frac{GMm}{r^2} = mr\omega^2 \qquad (3)$$

Cancelling m, then substituting $\omega = 2\pi/T$ (see B8) and rearranging, gives the following link between T and r:

$$\frac{T^2}{r^3} = \frac{4\pi^2}{GM} \qquad (4)$$

As $4\pi^2/GM$ is a constant, T^2/r^3 has the same value for all satellites. So as r increases, the period gets longer.

Weightlessness

An astronaut in a satellite is in a state of free fall. Her acceleration towards the Earth is exactly the same as that of the satellite, so the floor of the satellite exerts no forces on her. As a result, she experiences exactly the same sensation of weightlessness as she would in zero gravity. However, she is not really weightless. A few hundred kilometres above the Earth, the gravitational force on her is almost as strong as it is down on the surface.

Geostationary orbit

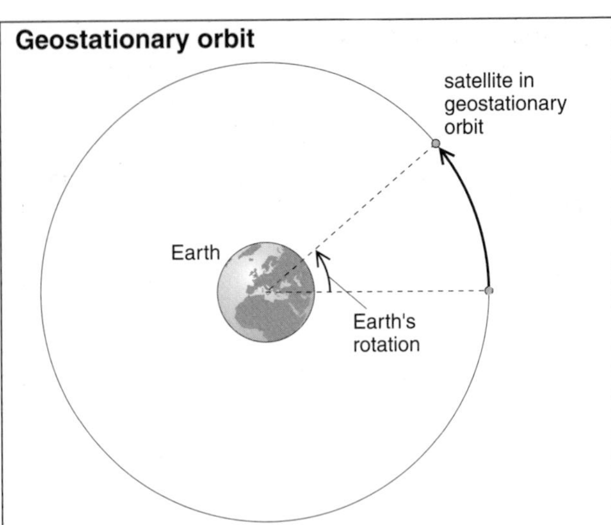

If a satellite is in a ***geostationary orbit***, then viewed from Earth, it appears to be in a fixed position in the sky. This is because the period of its orbit exactly matches the period of the Earth's rotation (24 hours). Communications satellites are normally in geostationary orbits.

Equation (3) can be used to calculate the value of r needed for a geostationary orbit. ω is found using $\omega = 2\pi/T$, with $T = 24 \times 3600$ s. GM is found using equation (2). r works out at 4.23×10^7 m.

Sun, planets, and moons

	Distance from Sun/ $\times 10^7$ km	Period of orbit/ days
Mars	22.8	687.0
Earth	15.0	365.3
Venus	10.8	224.7
Mercury	5.8	88.0
Sun		

Planets are natural satellites of the Sun. Most are in approximately circular orbits, so equation (4) also applies to them (except that M in the equation now becomes the mass of the Sun).

So (period of planet)$^2 \propto$ (distance from Sun)^3

This is called ***Kepler's third law***.

T^2/r^3 has the same value for all the planets around the Sun. If this value is known from astronomical data, equation (4) can be used to calculate the mass of the Sun (M).

Moons are natural satellites of planets. So the above method can also be used to find the mass of a planet.

Equivalent quantities

Motion can be *translational* (e.g. linear) or *rotational*. Quantities used in measuring linear motion all have their rotational equivalents, as shown below.

Linear quantity	Symbol	Rotational quantity	Symbol
displacement	s	angular displacement	θ
velocity	v	angular velocity	ω
acceleration	a	angular acceleration	α
force	F	torque	T
mass	m	moment of inertia	I

Note:
- In physics, the symbol T may stand for torque, period or tension. Above, it represents torque.
- Moment of inertia is the property of a body which resists angular acceleration. It is explained below.
- The equivalent quantities above do not have the same units.

Equivalent equations

The equations used when dealing with linear motion all have their equivalents in rotational motion, as shown below.

Linear equation		Rotational quantity	
velocity	$v = \frac{\theta}{t}$	angular velocity	$\omega = \frac{\theta}{t}$
acceleration	$a = \frac{v}{t}$	angular acceleration	$\alpha = \frac{\omega}{t}$
force	$F = ma$	torque	$T = I\alpha$
work done	$W = Fs$	work done	$W = T\theta$
KE	$E = \frac{1}{2}mv^2$	KE	$E = \frac{1}{2}I\omega^2$
power	$P = Fv$	power	$P = T\omega$
momentum	$p = mv$	angular momentum	$L = I\omega$

Note:
- The equations above are in simplified, non-calculus form. They assume uniform changes, and uniform forces and torques.
- Any rotational equation can be found by taking the linear equation and replacing the symbols with their rotational equivalents.
- Whether the motion is linear or rotational, work and energy are measured in joules. (Similarly power is measured in watts.)

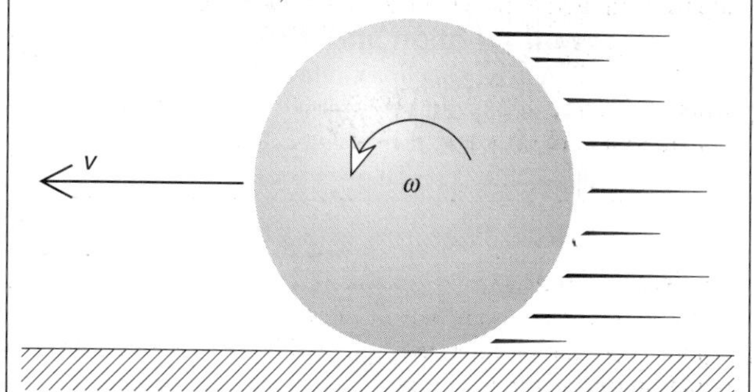

The rolling ball above has both linear *and* rotational motion. In this case:

$$\text{total KE} = \frac{1}{2}mv^2 + \frac{1}{2}I\omega^2$$

Moment of inertia

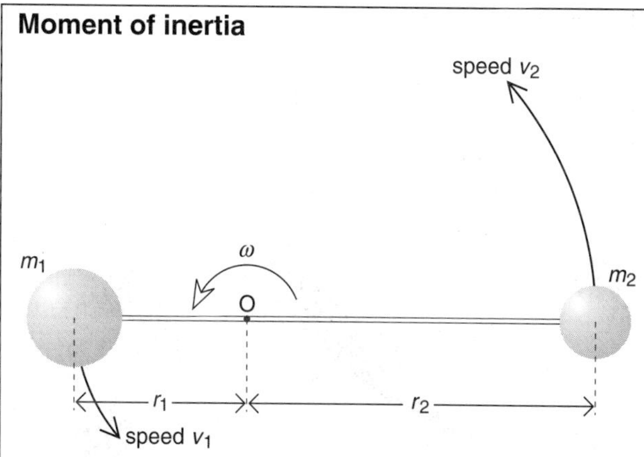

The dumb-bell above is rotating about an axis through its centre of mass O. (The bar of the dumb-bell has no mass.) All parts of the dumb-bell have the same angular velocity ω. The rotational KE of the system is the sum of the linear KEs of the two masses. So:

$$\text{rotational KE} = \frac{1}{2}m_1v_1^2 + \frac{1}{2}m_2v_2^2$$

But $v_1 = \omega r_1$ and $v_2 = \omega r_2$. So the above equation can be rewritten:

$$\text{rotational KE} = \frac{1}{2}(m_1r_1^2 + m_2r_2^2)\omega^2$$

Comparing this with the equation for rotational KE in the right-hand table at the top of the page shows that:

$$\text{moment of inertia } I = m_1r_1^2 + m_2r_2^2$$

This principle applies to all objects – for example, the one on the right. The moment of inertia is the sum of the mr^2 terms for all the particles in an object. Expressed mathematically:

$$\text{moment of inertia } I = \Sigma(mr^2)$$

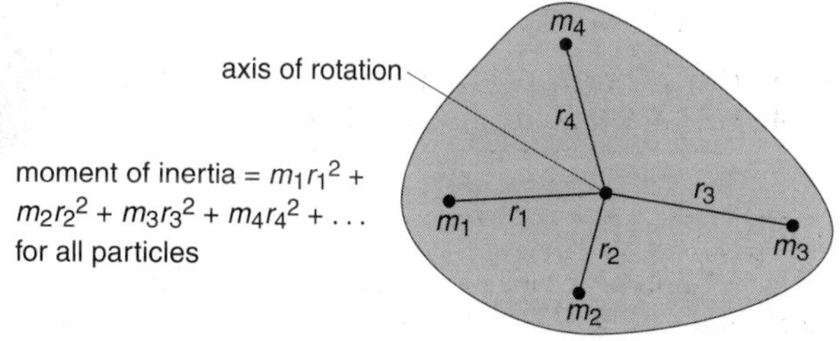

moment of inertia $= m_1r_1^2 + m_2r_2^2 + m_3r_3^2 + m_4r_4^2 + \ldots$ for all particles

Note:
- An object's moment of inertia depends on which axis it is being rotated about. The more spread out the mass, the higher the moment of inertia.
- From this, it follows that objects with the same mass can have different moments of inertia.

B11 Cycles, oscillations, and SHM

Periodic motion

This is motion in continually repeating ***cycles***. Here are two examples:

Circular motion Particle A moving at a steady speed in a circle (see the bottom diagram below).

T is the ***period*** (the time for one cycle).
f is the ***frequency*** (the number of cycles per second).
ω is the ***angular velocity*** (measured in rad s^{-1}).

T, f, and ω are linked by the equations on the right.

Oscillatory motion A swinging pendulum (see the diagram below). r is the ***amplitude***.

T, f, and ω are also used when describing oscillatory motion, although ω has no direct physical meaning. They are linked by the same equations as for circular motion:

$T = \frac{1}{f}$ $\qquad \omega = 2\pi f$ $\qquad T = \frac{2\pi}{\omega}$ (see B8)

Defining simple harmonic motion

One commonly-occurring type of oscillatory motion is called ***simple harmonic motion*** **(SHM)**.

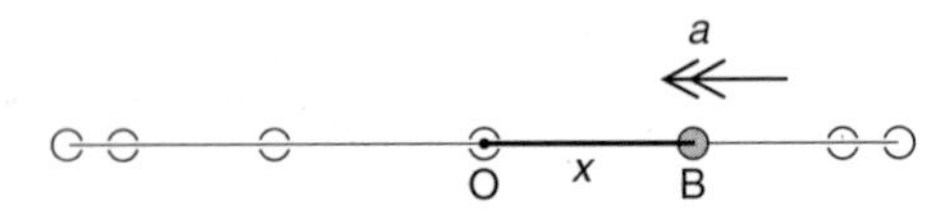

If particle B (above) oscillates about O with SHM, its acceleration is proportional to its displacement from O, and directed towards O.

If x is the displacement, and a is the acceleration (in the x direction), then this can be expressed mathematically:

$$a = -\text{(positive constant)}\ x \qquad (1)$$

The minus sign indicates that a is always in the opposite direction to x.

Linking circular motion and SHM

Below, particle A is moving in a circle with a steady angular velocity ω. Particle B is oscillating about O along the horizontal axis so that it is always vertically above or beneath A. The amplitude of the oscillation is equal to the radius of the circle, r.

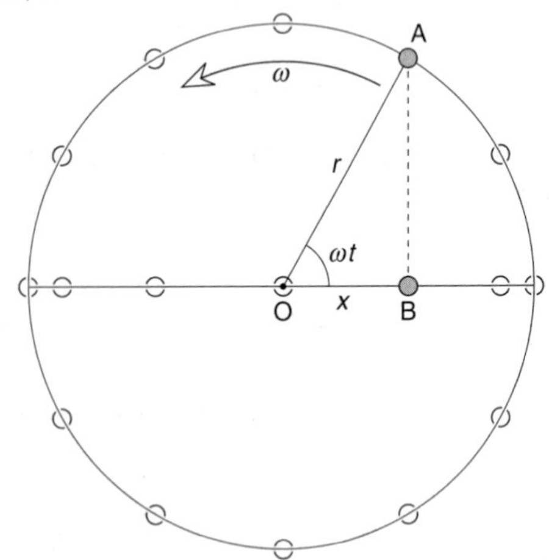

For particle B: $\quad x = r\cos\omega t \qquad (2)$

Using calculus, B's velocity v and acceleration a can be found from the above equation. These are the results:

$$v = -r\omega\sin\omega t \qquad (3)$$

$$a = -r\omega^2\cos\omega t \qquad (4)$$

From equations (4) and (2), it follows that:

$$a = -\omega^2 x \qquad (5)$$

Note:

- Equation (5) on the left has the same form as equation (1). So particle B is moving with SHM.
- The constant in equation (1) is equal to ω^2.
- Using calculus notation, the equation for SHM can be written in the following form:

$$\frac{d^2x}{dt^2} = -\omega^2 x$$

SHM and the simple pendulum

Provided its swings are small, and air resistance is neglible, a simple pendulum moves with SHM. The following analysis shows why.

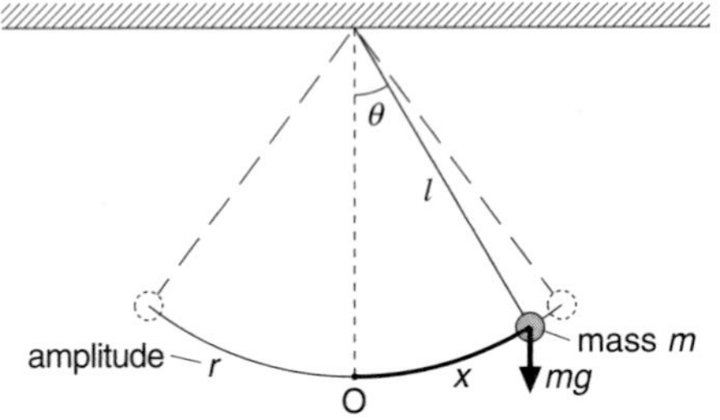

The mass m (above) has been displaced by x. It is being pulled towards O by a component of its weight:

$$\text{force (towards O)} = mg\sin\theta$$

But for very small angles $\quad \sin\theta = \frac{x}{l}$ (see B8)

So $\quad \text{force (towards O)} = \frac{mgx}{l}$

But $\quad \text{force} = \text{mass} \times \text{acceleration}$

So $\quad \text{acceleration (towards O)} = \frac{gx}{l}$

So acceleration (in x direction) $a = \frac{-gx}{l}$

Comparing this with equation (5) shows that the motion is SHM and that:

$$\frac{g}{l} = \omega^2$$

As $T = \frac{2\pi}{\omega}$

$$T = 2\pi\sqrt{\frac{l}{g}}$$

Note:

- T does not depend on the amplitude (for smaller swings, the period stays the same). This is true for *all* SHM.

Maxima and minima

A pendulum swings with SHM. The graphs on the right show how certain quantities vary during one cycle.

Maximum values of velocity and acceleration can be worked out from equations (3) and (4). $\cos \omega t$ and $\sin \omega t$ each have a maximum value of 1 so:

maximum velocity = $r\omega$
maximum acceleration = $r\omega^2$

As the pendulum swings downwards, it loses potential energy (PE) and gains kinetic energy (KE). If there is no air resistance, the total PE + KE is constant, and equal to the maximum KE. So:

$$\text{total PE + KE} = \tfrac{1}{2} m v_{max}^2$$

But $v_{max} = r\omega$. So:

$$\text{total PE + KE} = \tfrac{1}{2} m r^2 \omega^2$$

Note that the total PE + KE is proportional to the *square* of the amplitude (r^2).

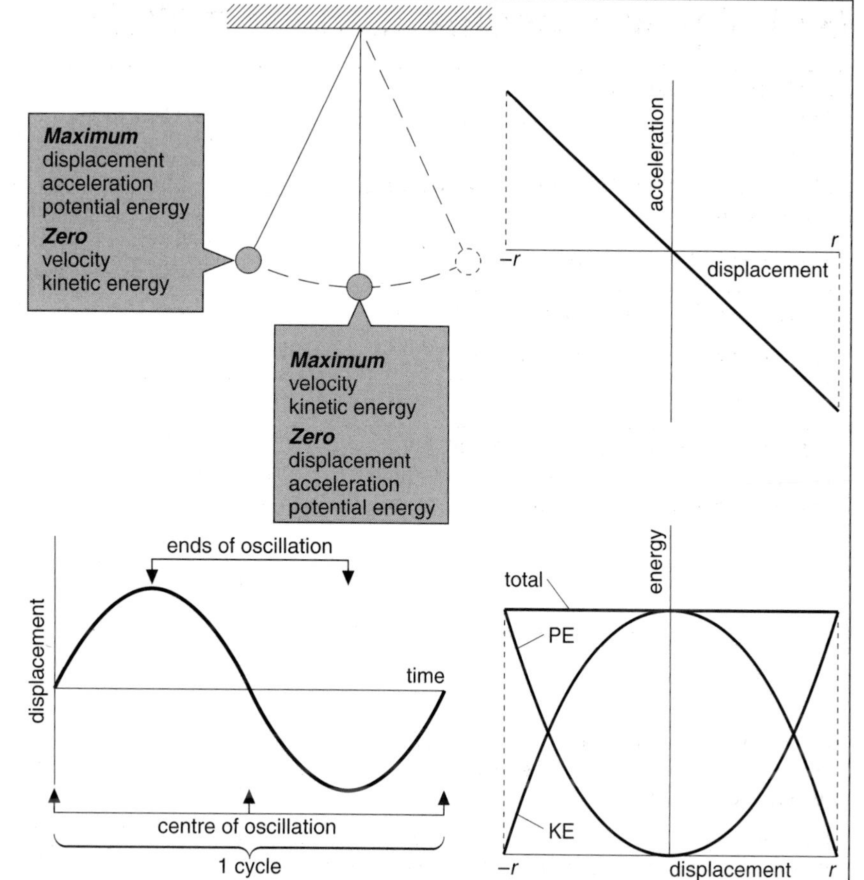

SHM and a mass on a spring

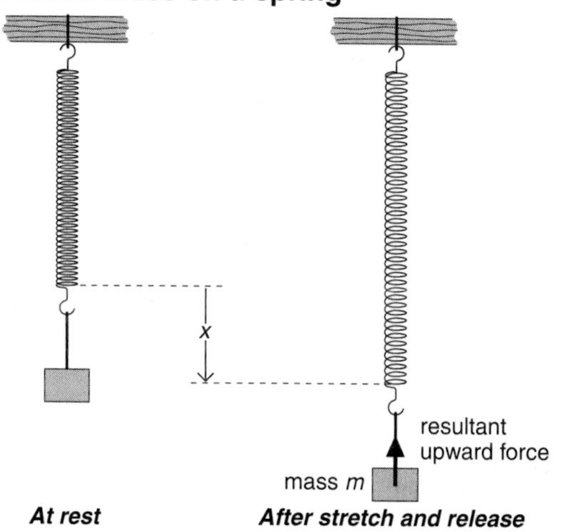

Above, a mass hangs from a spring. When pulled down and released, the mass makes small, vertical oscillations. The analysis on the right shows that, because the spring obeys Hooke's law (see B25), its motion must be SHM.

According to Hooke's law, the force F from a spring and its length increase x are in proportion. Expressed mathematically, $F = kx$, where k is the ***spring constant***. So, if the mass m is pulled down by x and then released:

resultant upward force on mass = kx

But force = mass × acceleration

So acceleration (upwards) = $\dfrac{kx}{m}$

So acceleration (in x direction) $a = -\dfrac{kx}{m}$

Comparing this with equation (5) shows that the motion is SHM, and that:

$$\frac{k}{m} = \omega^2$$

As $T = \dfrac{2\pi}{\omega}$ $\quad T = 2\pi\sqrt{\dfrac{m}{k}}$

In any oscillating system to which Hooke's law applies, the motion is SHM.

Forced vibrations and resonance

Sometimes, an external source of vibration may force something to oscillate at a frequency other than its natural frequency. Examples include:

- engine vibrations making bus windows oscillate,
- the spinning drum causing vibrations in a washing machine.

If the incoming frequency matches the natural frequency of the system, then the amplitude of the oscillations reaches a maximum. This effect is called ***resonance***.

Damping

A pendulum does not go on swinging for ever. Energy is gradually lost (because of air resistance) and the oscillations die away. This effect is called ***damping***.

In road vehicles, dampers (wrongly called 'shock absorbers') are fitted to the suspension springs so that unwanted oscillations die away quickly.

Some systems have so much damping that no real oscillations occur. The minimum damping needed for this is called ***critical damping*** (see next unit, B12).

B12 More motion graphs

In this unit, all motion is assumed to be in a straight line.

Displacement-time graphs

Uniform velocity The graph below describes the motion of a car moving with uniform velocity. The displacement and time have been taken as zero when the car passes a marker post. The gradient of the graph is equal to the velocity v:

$$v = \frac{\Delta s}{\Delta t}$$

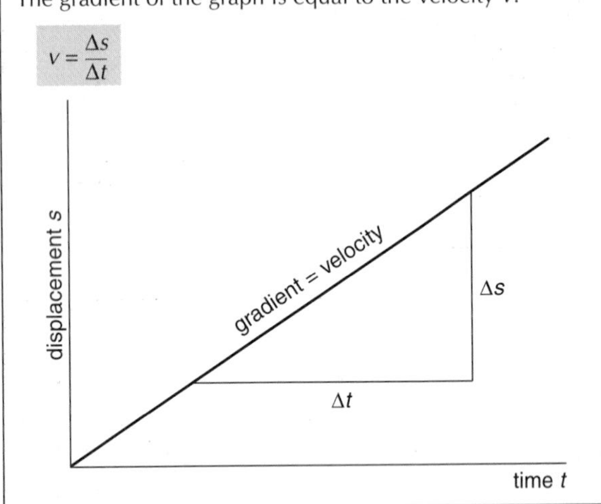

Changing velocity The gradient of this graph is increasing with time, so the velocity is increasing. The velocity v at any instant is equal to the gradient of the *tangent* at that instant.

In calculus notation $v = \frac{ds}{dt}$

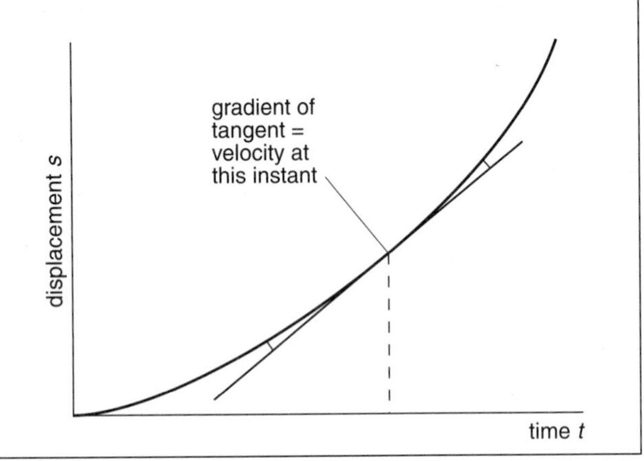

Velocity-time graphs

Uniform acceleration The graph below describes the motion of a car gaining velocity at a steady rate. The time has been taken as zero when the car is stationary. The gradient of the graph is equal to the acceleration.

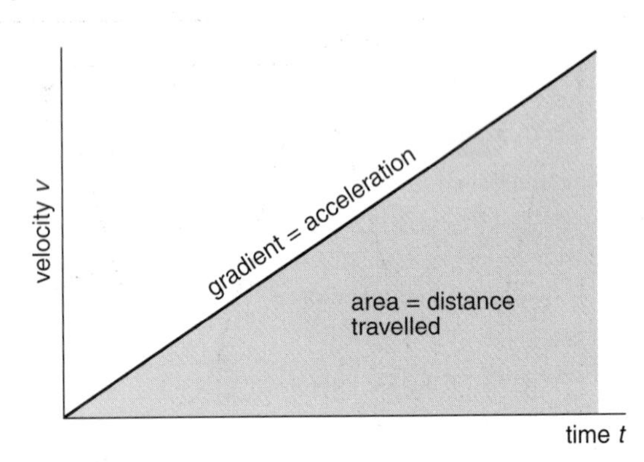

Changing acceleration The acceleration a at any instant is equal to the gradient of the *tangent* at that instant.

In calculus notation $a = \frac{dv}{dt}$

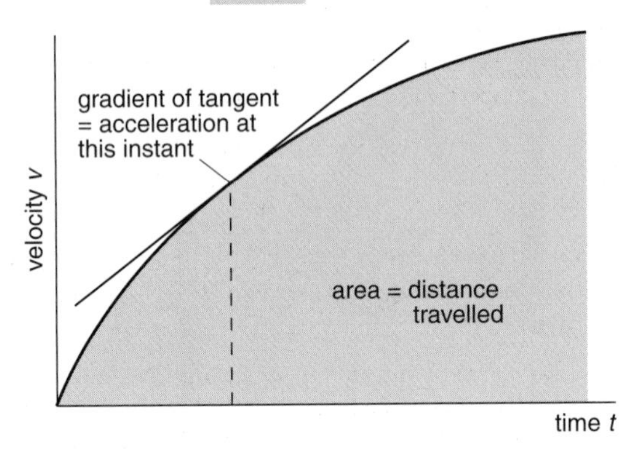

Upwards and downwards

A ball bounces upwards from the ground. The graph on the right shows how the velocity of the ball changes from when it leaves the ground until it hits the ground again. Downward velocity has been taken as positive. Air resistance is assumed to be negligible.

Initially, the ball is travelling upwards, so it has negative downward velocity. This passes through zero at the ball's highest point and then becomes positive.

The gradient of the graph is constant, and equal to g.

Note:

- The ball has downward acceleration g, even when it is travelling upwards. (Algebraically, losing upward velocity is the same as gaining downward velocity.)
- The ball has downward acceleration g, even when its velocity is zero (at its highest point).

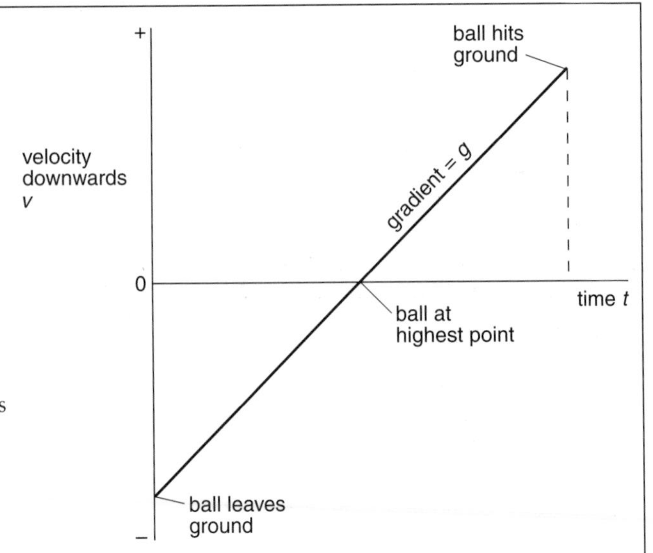

Terminal velocity

Air resistance on a falling object can be significant. As the velocity increases, the air resistance increases, until it eventually balances the weight. The resultant force is then zero, so there is no further gain in velocity. The object has reached its ***terminal velocity***.

air resistance

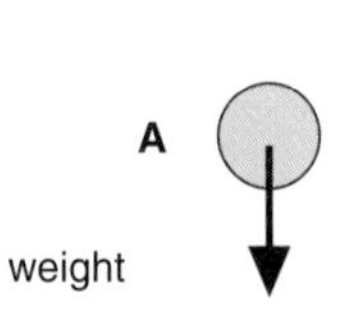

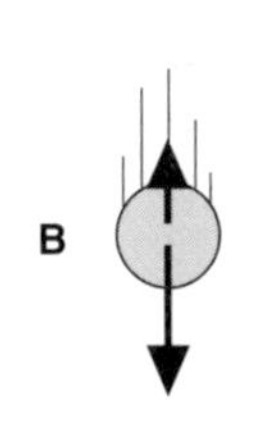

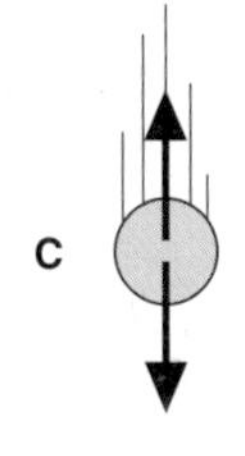

weight

velocity : 0 – – – – – – – – – – – – – – – – – terminal
acceleration : g – – – – – – – – – – – – – – – – – 0

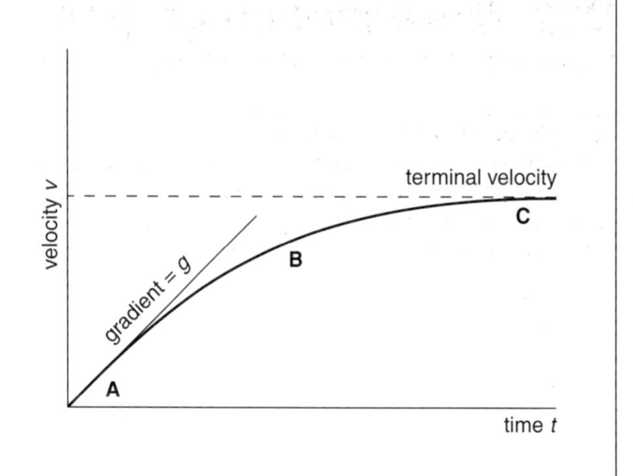

Force, impulse, and work

The area under a force-time graph is equal to the impulse delivered by the force.

The area under a force-displacement graph is equal to the work done by the force.

The graphs on the right are for a non-uniform force: for example, the force used to stretch a spring.

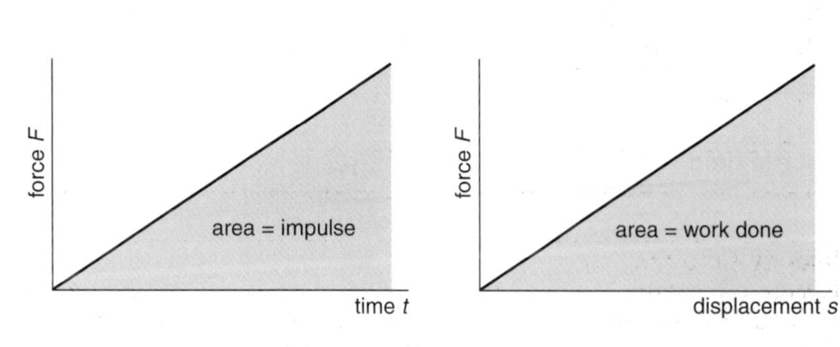

SHM

The graphs on the right are for an object moving with SHM: for example, a pendulum making small swings.

At the ends of each swing, the velocity is zero. The displacement and acceleration have their peak values, but when one is positive, the other is negative, and vice versa.

At the centre of each swing, the velocity has its peak positive or negative value, but the displacement and acceleration are both zero.

Damped oscillations The graphs below are for damped oscillations. The oscillating systems are losing energy to some external material such as the surrounding air or liquid. Where there is ***critical damping***, the time it takes for the displacement to settle to zero is a minimum.

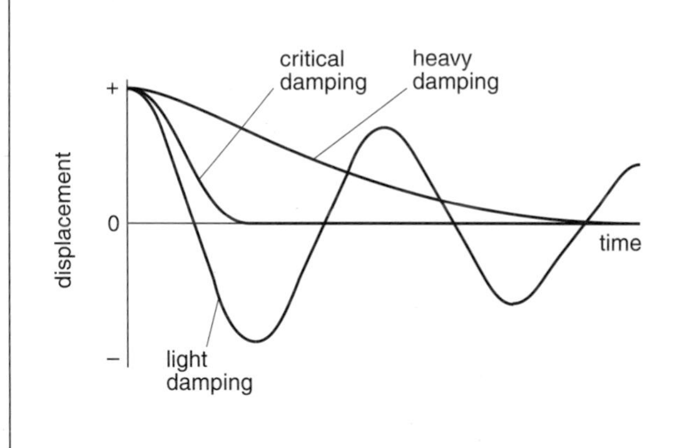

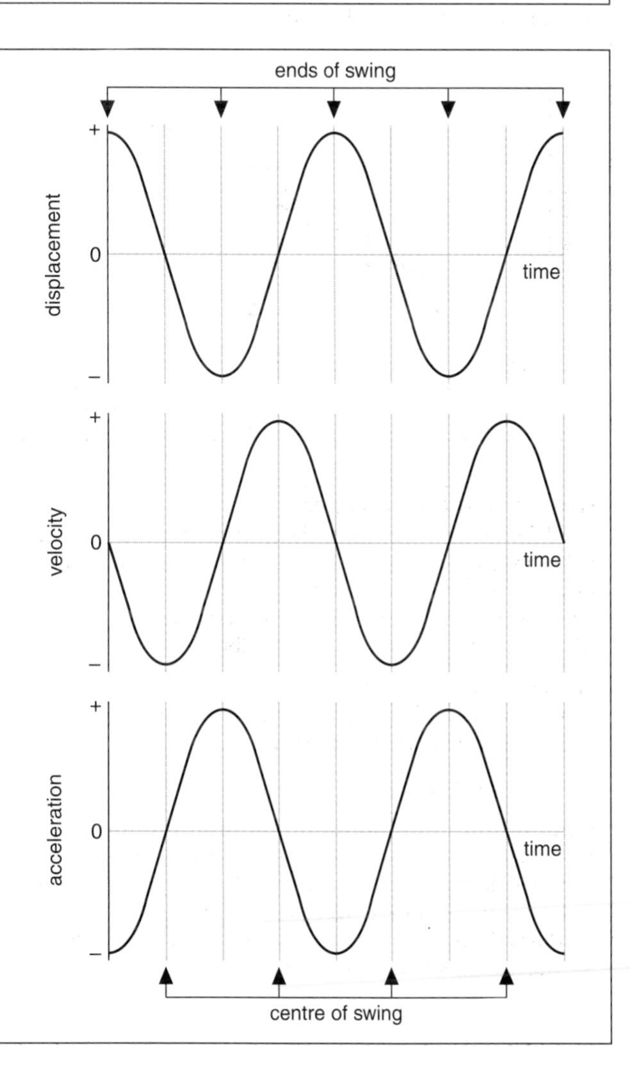

B13 Electric charges and fields

Electric force

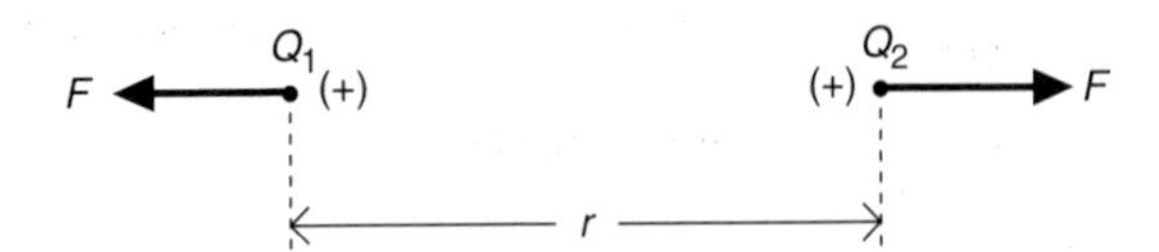

Charges attract or repel each other with an ***electric force***. If point charges Q_1 and Q_2, are a distance r apart, and F is the force on each, then according to ***Coulomb's law***:

$$F \propto \frac{Q_1 Q_2}{r^2}$$

This is an example of an ***inverse square law***. If r doubles, the force F drops to one quarter, and so on.

With a suitable constant, the above proportion can be turned into an equation:

$$F = \frac{kQ_1 Q_2}{r^2}$$

The unit of charge for Q_1 and Q_2 is the coulomb (C).

The value of k is found by experiment. It depends on the ***medium*** (material) between the charges. For a vacuum, k is 8.99×10^{-9} N m^2 C^{-2}, and is effectively the same for air.

In practice, it is more convenient to use another constant, ε_o, and rewrite the equation on the left in the following form:

In a vacuum $$F = \frac{Q_1 Q_2}{4\pi\varepsilon_o r^2}$$

ε_o is called the ***permittivity of free space***. Its value is 8.85×10^{-12} C^2 N^{-1} m^{-2}.

Note:
- Although '4π' complicates the above equation, it simplifies others derived from it.
- In the above equation, if, say, Q_1 and Q_2 are *like* charges (e.g. – and –), then F is *positive*. So a positive F is a force of *repulsion*. Similarly, it follows that a negative F is a force of *attraction*.

Electric field

If a charge feels an electric force, then it is in an ***electric field***. If a charge q feels a force F, then the ***electric field strength*** E is defined like this:

$$E = \frac{\text{electric force}}{\text{charge}} \qquad \text{In symbols} \quad E = \frac{F}{q} \qquad (1)$$

For example, if a charge of 2 C feels an electric force of 10 N, then E is 5 N C^{-1}.

Note:
- Electric field strength is a vector. Its direction is that of the force on a positive (+) charge.

The force acting on a charge in an electric field can be found by rearranging the equation above:

$$F = qE$$

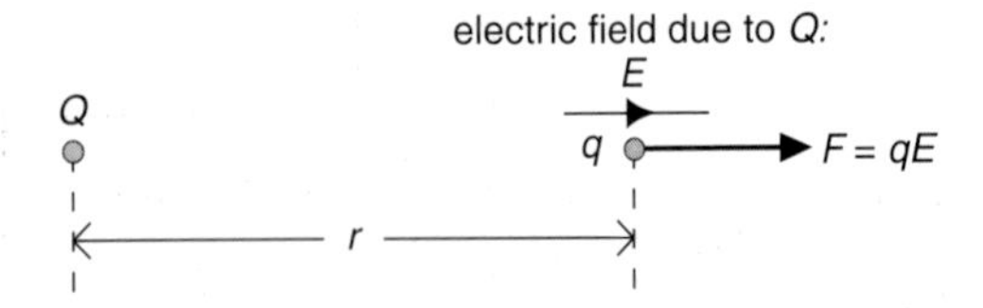

Above, charge Q produces an electric field which acts on a small charge q. As $F = qE$

$$\text{and} \quad F = \frac{Qq}{4\pi\varepsilon_o r^2} \quad \text{it follows that} \quad E = \frac{Q}{4\pi\varepsilon_o r^2} \qquad (2)$$

The electric field round a charged, spherical conductor is shown on the right. It is a ***radial*** field.

Note:
- The charge is on the surface of the conductor.
- Outside the conductor, the electric field is the same as if all the charge were concentrated at the centre, and the above equation applies.
- Inside the conductor, there is no electric field. The reason for this is given on the opposite page.
- The equipotential lines in the diagram on the right are explained on the opposite page.

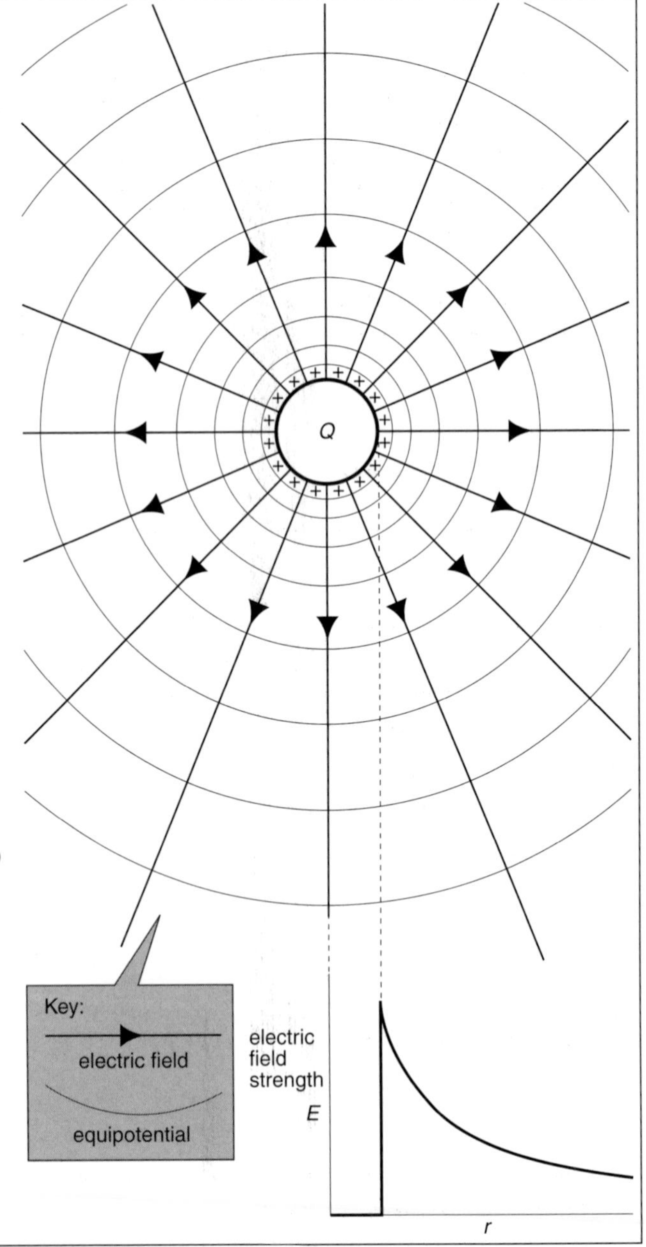

Electric potential

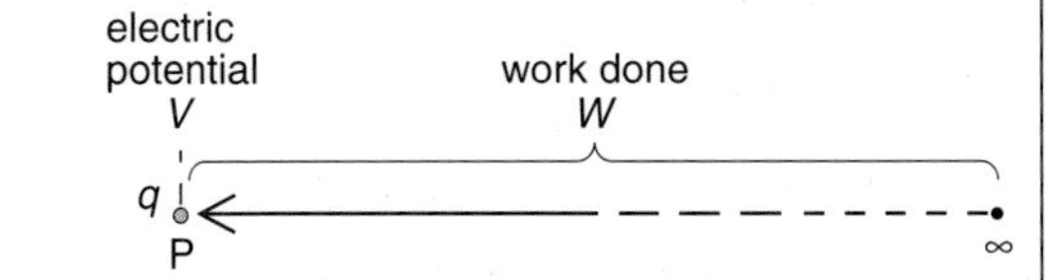

Above, charge Q causes an electric field. A small charge q has been moved through this field, from an infinite distance (where the electric force is zero), to point P.

The ***electric potential*** V (at point P) is defined as follows:

$$V = \frac{W}{q} \quad (3)$$

where W is the work done in moving a charge q from infinity (∞) to point P.

The SI unit of electric potential is the ***volt*** (V). For example, if 1000 J of work is done in moving a charge of +2 C from ∞ to P, then the potential at P = 1000/2 = 500 V.

Note:

- Electric potential is a scalar.
- At infinity, the electric potential is *zero.*
- Elsewhere, the electric potential due to *positive* charge is *positive.* Similarly, the electric potential due to a *negative* charge is *negative.*
- Equation (3) can also be used to find the work done in moving a charge q between two points. In this case, V is the ***potential difference*** **(PD)** between the points.

Electric potential in a radial field

A radial field is shown on page 42. Provided r is not less than the radius of the sphere:

$$E = \frac{Q}{4\pi\varepsilon_o r^2} \qquad \text{Also, } E = -\frac{dV}{dr}$$ (see bottom panel)

Combining these, and using calculus gives:

$$V = \frac{Q}{4\pi\varepsilon_o r}$$ (This also applies to a point charge.)

Note:

- In the diagram on the opposite page, each ***equipotential line*** is a line joining points of equal potential.
- Inside the charged conductor, all points are at the same potential, so the potential gradient (see bottom panel) is zero. From this it follows that E is also zero, so there is no electric field inside the conductor.

Comparing electric and gravitational fields

For particles of similar size, electric forces are very much stronger than gravitational ones. For example, electric forces hold atoms together to form solids.

Electric and gravitational fields have similar features. That is why the equations is this unit have a similar form to those in B9. However, comparing equivalent equations, a minus sign may be present in one but absent from the other. This arises because of the differing force directions.

Gravity is always a force of attraction. Mass is always positive and it produces a gravitational field which is directed *towards* it.

Electric charges may attract or repel. However, if a charge is positive, then it produces an electric field which is directed *away* from it.

Linking potential and field strength

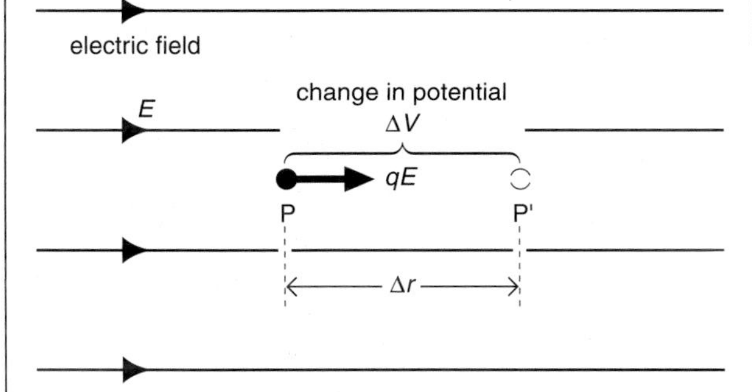

Above, work ΔW is done on a small charge q in moving it from P to P' in a uniform electric field E. So, from (3):

$$\Delta W = q\Delta V \quad (3)$$

This equation gives the work done *on* the charge.

So work done *by* charge = $-q\Delta V$

But work done by charge = force × distance moved = $qE\Delta r$

So $qE\Delta r = -q\Delta V$

Therefore $$E = -\frac{\Delta V}{\Delta r} \quad (4)$$

In calculus notation, there is a more general version of this equation which also applies to non-uniform fields:

$$E = -\frac{dV}{dr}$$

Note:

- In the above equations, the minus sign indicates that E is in the direction of *decreasing* potential.

The metal plates on the right have a small test charge q between them. The charge feels a force F. So, from equation (1):

$$E = \frac{F}{q}$$

There is a potential difference V between the plates. From the graph on the right, and equation (4), the potential gradient is $-V/d$. So:

$$E = \frac{V}{d} \quad (5)$$

The constant potential gradient means that the electric field is uniform.

The above equations show different aspects of electric field strength. If, say, E is 10 N C^{-1}, you can think of this either as a force of 10 N per coulomb or a potential drop of 10 V per metre. (E can be expressed in N C^{-1} or in V m^{-1}.)

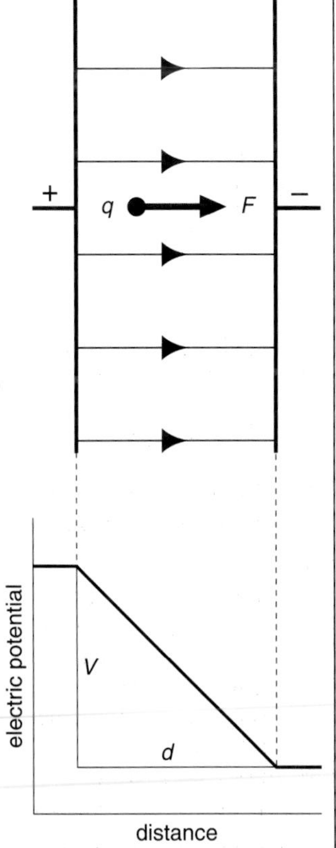

B14 Capacitors and fields

Capacitance

Capacitors store small amounts of electric charge. For information on their practical uses, see B20, C15, and C16.

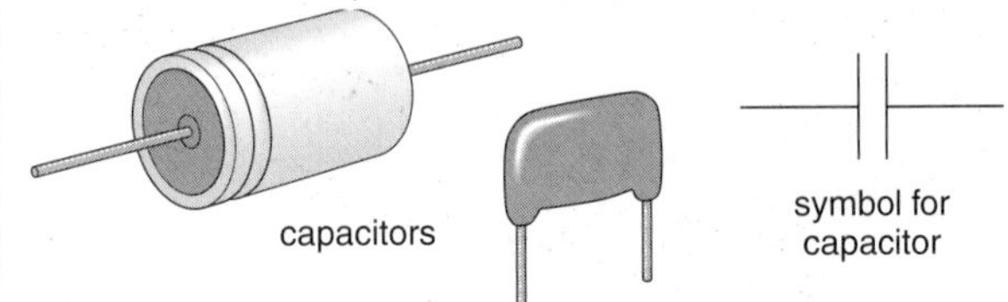

A capacitor can be charged by connecting a battery across it. The higher the PD V, the greater the charge Q stored. Experiments show that $Q \propto V$. Therefore, Q/V is a constant.

The ***capacitance*** C of a capacitor is defined as follows:

$$\text{capacitance} = \frac{\text{charge}}{\text{PD}} \qquad \text{In symbols } C = \frac{Q}{V}$$

The higher the capacitance, the more charge is stored for any given PD.

Capacitance is measured in $C.V^{-1}$, known as a ***farad*** (F). However, a farad is a very large unit, and the μF (10^{-6} F) is more commonly used for practical capacitors.

Energy stored by a capacitor

Work must be done to charge up a capacitor. Electrical potential energy is stored as a result.

If a charge of 2 C is moved through a *steady* PD of 10 V, then, using equation (3) in B13:

work done $W = QV = 2 \times 10 = 20$ J.

So the stored energy is 20 J. Numerically, this is the area under the graph below.

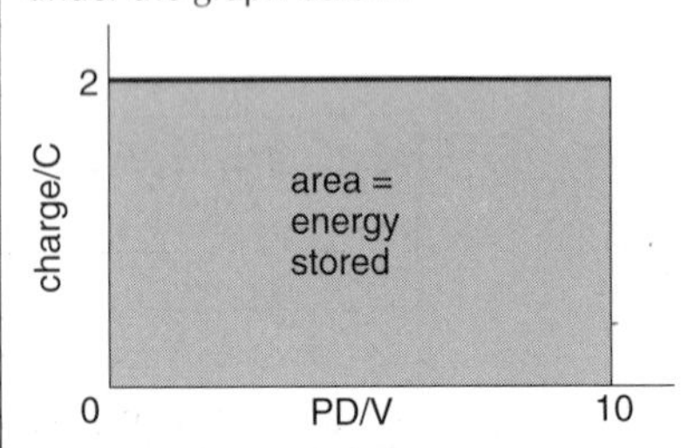

When a capacitor is being charged, Q and V are related as in the graph below. As before, the energy stored is numerically equal to the area under the graph, which is $\frac{1}{2}QV$. As $C = Q/V$, this can be expressed in three ways:

$$\text{energy stored} = \tfrac{1}{2}QV = \tfrac{1}{2}CV^2 = \tfrac{1}{2}Q^2/C$$

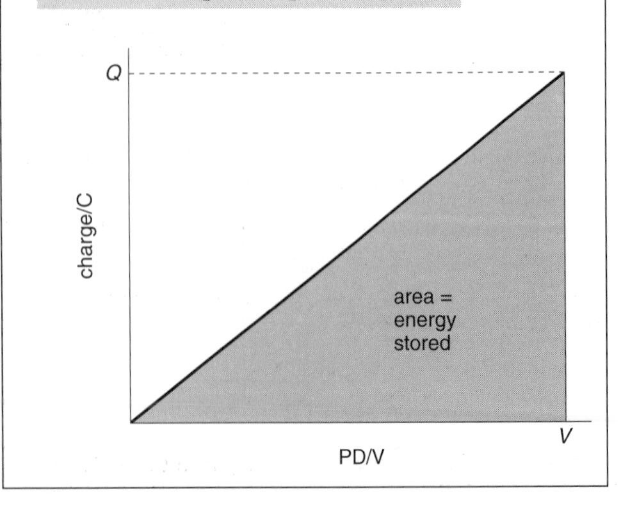

Electric field near a charged plate

On the right, a metal sphere has a charge Q uniformly distributed over its surface. The electric field E near the surface is given by equation (2) in B13:

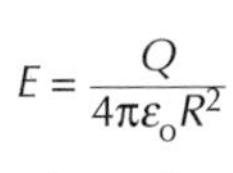

$$E = \frac{Q}{4\pi\varepsilon_0 R^2}$$

But the surface area of the sphere $A = 4\pi R^2$. So:

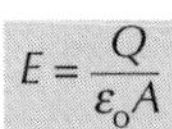

$$E = \frac{Q}{\varepsilon_0 A} \qquad (1)$$

charge Q
surface area A

This equation also applies to a flat, charged metal plate of surface area A.

Parallel plate capacitor

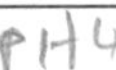

The simplest form of capacitor is made up of two parallel metal plates, separated by an air gap.

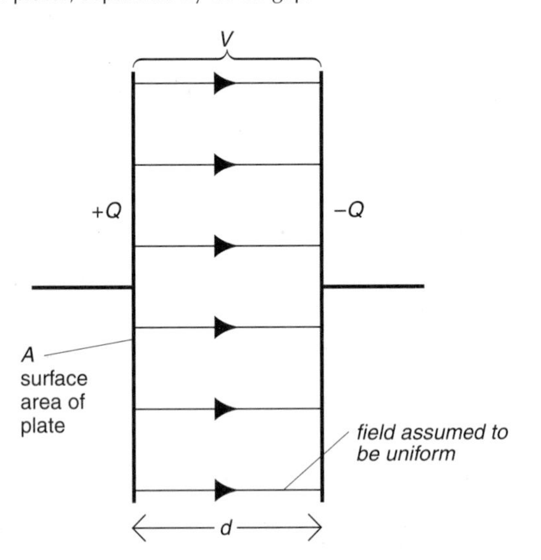

The capacitor above has been connected to a battery so that the PD across its plates is V. As a result, it is storing a charge Q. (This means that charge Q has been transferred, leaving $-Q$ on one plate and $+Q$ on the other.)

From equation (1) above $\quad E = Q/\varepsilon_0 A$
From equation (5) in B13 $\quad E = V/d$
From these, it follows that $Q/V = \varepsilon_0 A/d$

But $C = \dfrac{Q}{V}$ $\quad$ So $C = \dfrac{\varepsilon_0 A}{d}$ $\quad$ (2)

From the above equation, note:

- $C \propto A$, so a larger plate area gives a higher C.
- $C \propto 1/d$, so a smaller plate separation gives a higher C.

Dielectric

If the gap between the capacitor plates is filled with a material such as polythene, the capacitance is increased. Any insulating material which has this effect is called a ***dielectric***.

The ***relative permittivity*** ε_r of the dielectric is the factor by which the capacitance is increased. For polythene, $\varepsilon_r = 2.3$. With a dielectric present, equation (2) becomes:

$$C = \frac{\varepsilon_r \varepsilon_0 A}{d} \qquad (3)$$

Discharge of a capacitor

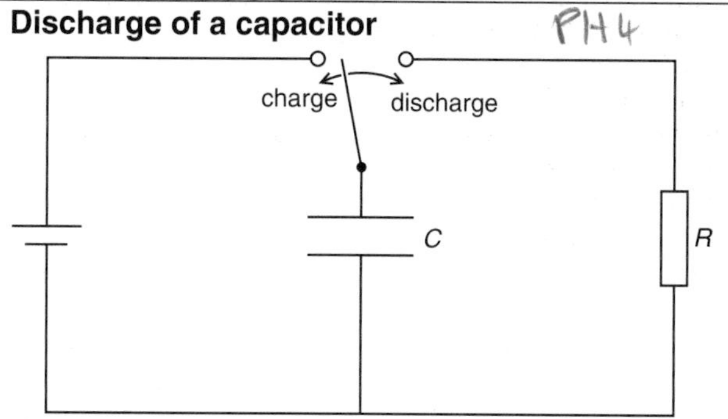

The capacitor above is charged from a battery and then discharged through a resistance R.

Graph A shows how, during discharge, the charge Q decreases with time t, according to the following equation:

$$Q = Q_0 e^{-t/RC} \qquad \text{where e} = 2.718$$

RC is called the ***time constant***. (It equals the time which the charge would take to fall to zero if the initial rate of loss of charge were maintained.) Increasing R or C gives a higher time constant, and therefore a slower discharge.

The gradient of the graph at any time t is equal to the current at that time.

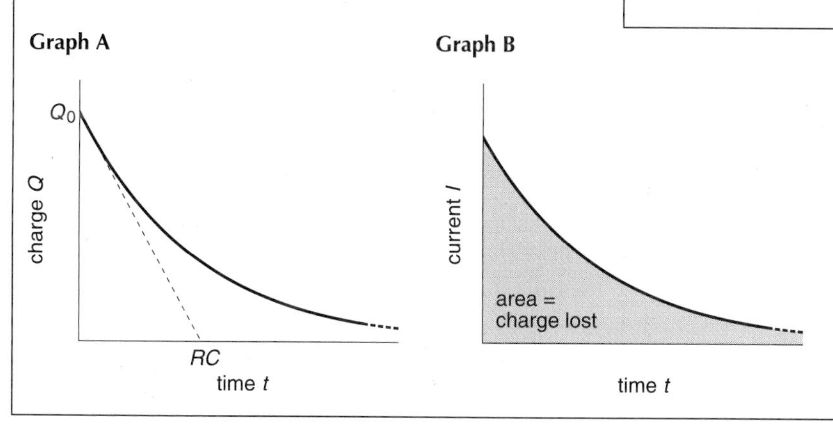

Graph B shows how the current decreases with time. The area under the graph is numerically equal to the charge lost.

Note:

- Each graph is an ***exponential decay curve***, with the same characteristics as a radioactive decay curve. A ***half-life*** can be calculated in the same way (see B33).

Practical capacitors

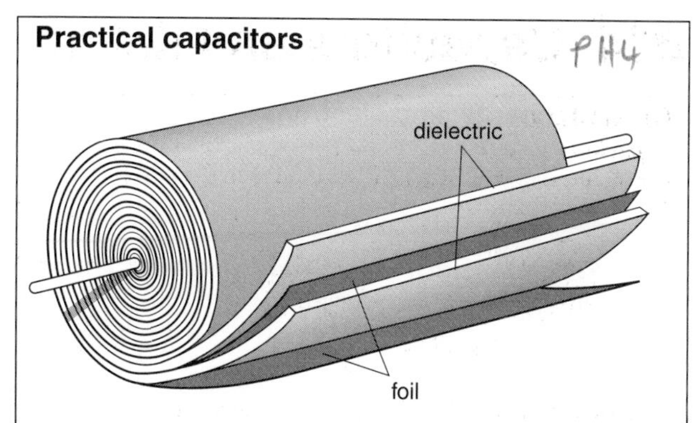

Equation (3) shows that, for a high C, a capacitor needs a high A, high ε_r, and low d. In practice, this is achieved by rolling up two long strips of foil with a thin dielectric between them.

In ***electrolytic capacitors***, the dielectric is formed by the chemical action of a current. This gives a very thin dielectric, and a very high capacitance. But the capacitor must always be used with the same plate positive, or the chemical action is reversed.

Capacitors have a ***maximum working voltage*** above which the dielectric breaks down and starts to conduct.

Capacitors in series

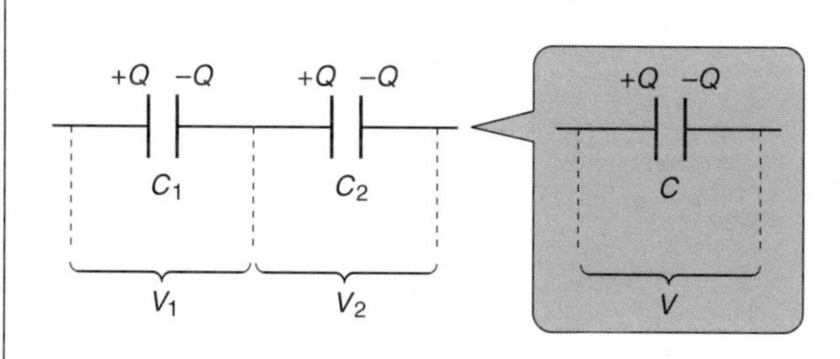

If C_1 and C_2 have a total capacitance of C, then C is the single capacitance which could replace them.

Two capacitors in series store only the same charge Q as a single capacitor. So $V = Q/C$, $V_1 = Q/C_1$, and $V_2 = Q/C_2$.

But $V = V_1 + V_2$ So $\dfrac{Q}{C} = \dfrac{Q}{C_1} + \dfrac{Q}{C_2}$

$$\frac{1}{C} = \frac{1}{C_1} + \frac{1}{C_2}$$

For example, if $C_1 = 3\ \mu F$ and $C_2 = 6\ \mu F$, then $1/C = 1/3 + 1/6 = 1/2$. So $C = 2\ \mu F$.

Capacitors in parallel

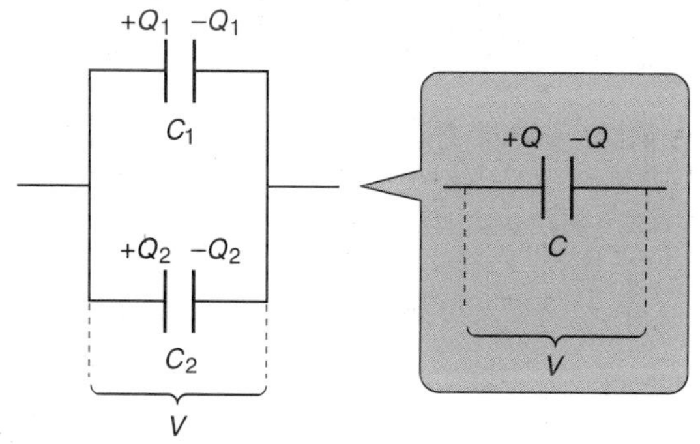

If C_1 and C_2 have a total capacitance of C, then C is the single capacitance which could replace them.

Capacitors in parallel each have the same PD across them. So $Q = CV$, $Q_1 = C_1V$, and $Q_2 = C_2V$.

Together, the capacitors act like a single capacitor with a larger plate area. So $Q = Q_1 + Q_2$

$\therefore \quad CV = C_1V + C_2V$

$\therefore \quad C = C_1 + C_2$

For example, if $C_1 = 3\ \mu F$ and $C_2 = 6\ \mu F$, then $C = 9\ \mu F$.

B15 Current and resistance

Current, charge, and electrons

In a wire, the current is a flow of electrons. If I is the current and Q the charge passing any point in time t, then:

$$Q = It$$

From the above, a current of 1 ampere (A) means that charge is flowing at the rate of 1 coulomb (C) per second.

The charge on an electron $= e = -1.60 \times 10^{-19}$ C.

Therefore, 1 C is the charge carried by $1/e$ electrons, i.e. 6.24×10^{18} electrons. So a flow of 6.24×10^{18} electrons per second gives a current of 1 A. However, as e is negative, an electron flow to the *right* is a current to the *left*.

Resistance

If a conductor has resistance, then energy is *dissipated* (changed to internal energy) when a current passes through.

The PD V (in V) across a conductor, current I (in A) through it, and its resistance R (in Ω) are linked by this equation:

$$R = \frac{V}{I}$$

If a conductor obeys ***Ohm's law***, its resistance is constant for any given temperature (i.e. R is independent of V).

The link between I and V can be investigated using the circuit below. Graphs for three different components are shown. (A negative V means that the DC supply connections have been reversed.)

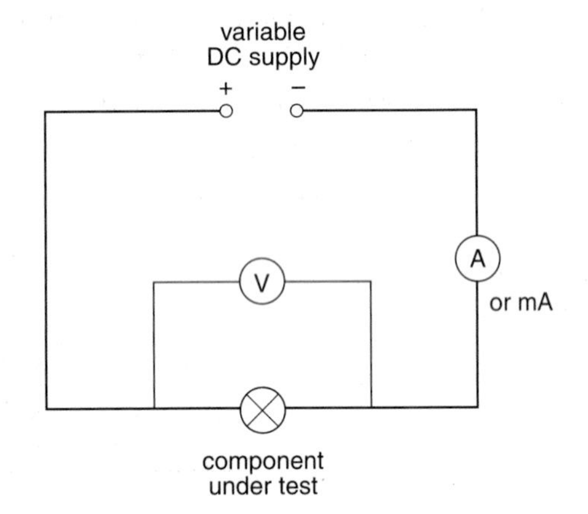

Current and drift speed

Most electrons are bound to their atoms. However, in a metal, some are ***free electrons*** which can move between atoms. When a PD is applied, and a current flows, the free electrons are the ***charge carriers***.

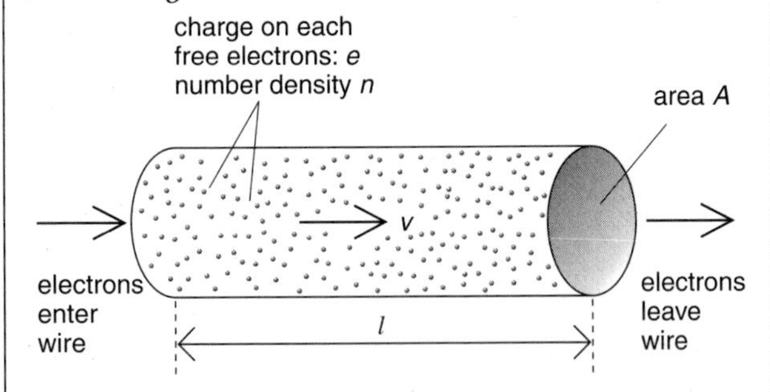

In the wire above, free electrons (each of charge e) are moving with an average speed v. n is the ***number density*** of free electrons: the number per unit volume (per m^3).

In the wire the number of free electrons $= nAl$
So total charge carried by free electrons $= nAle$

As time = distance/speed:
time taken for all the free electrons to pass through A
$= l/v$

As current I = charge/time $\quad I = \dfrac{nAle \times v}{l}$

$\therefore \quad I = nAev$

v is called the ***drift speed***. Typically, it can be less than a millimetre per second for the current in a wire.

The ***current density*** J is the current per unit cross-sectional area (per m^2).

$J = \dfrac{I}{A}$ so $J = nev$

Note:

- The number density of free electrons is different for different metals. For copper, it is 8×10^{28} m^{-3}.
- When liquids conduct, ions are the charge carriers. The above equations apply, except that e and n must be replaced by the charge and number density of the ions.

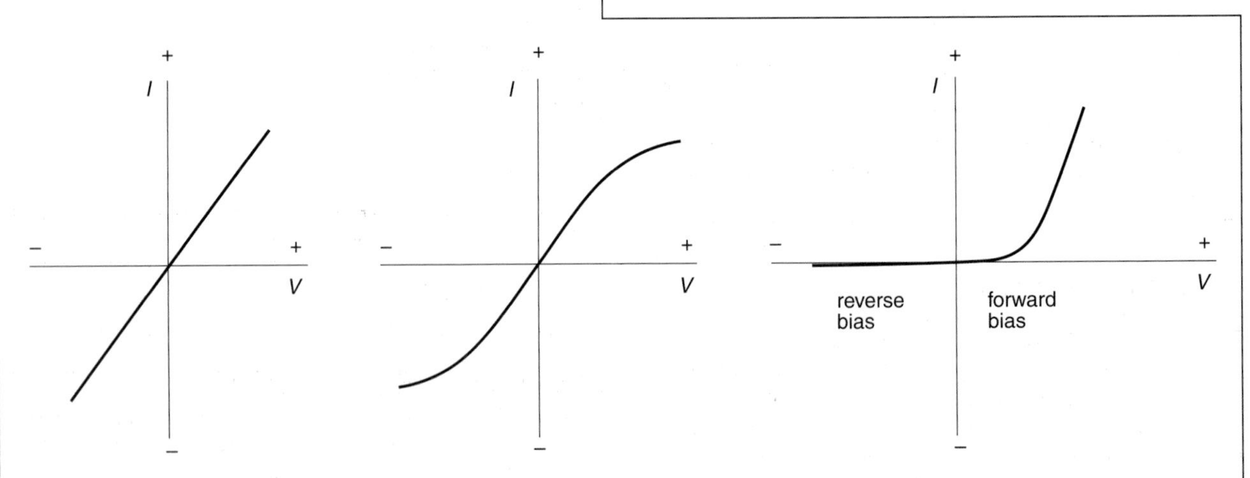

Wire (metal) kept at constant temperature V/I is constant, so R is constant.

Bulb filament (metal) As the current rises the filament heats up. V/I increases, so R increases.

Diode (semiconductor) R is very high in one direction. It is much lower in the other direction, and decreases as the current rises.

Resistance and temperature

A conducting solid is made up of a ***lattice*** of atoms. When a current flows, electrons move through this lattice.

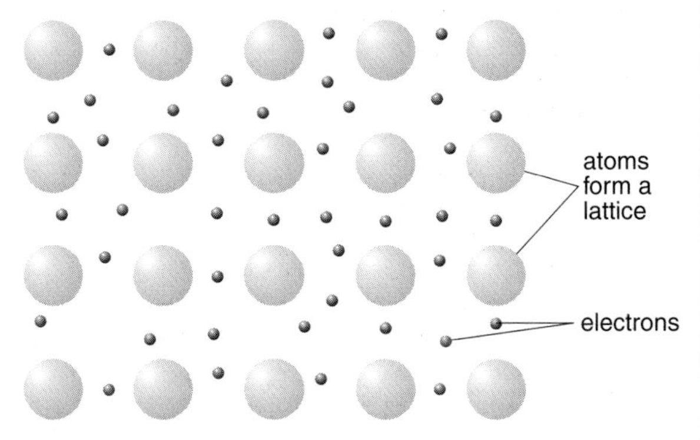

Metals When free electrons drift through a metal, they make occasional collisions with the lattice. These collisions are inelastic and transfer energy to the lattice as internal energy. That is why a metal has resistance. If the temperature of a metal rises, the atoms of the lattice vibrate more vigorously. Free electrons collide with the lattice more frequently, which increases the resistance.

Semiconductors (e.g. silicon) At low temperature, the electrons are tightly bound to their atoms. But as the temperature rises, more and more electrons break free and can take part in conduction. This easily outweighs the effects of more vigorous lattice vibrations, so the resistance decreases. At around 100–150 °C, ***breakdown*** occurs. There is a sudden fall in resistance – and a huge increase in current. That is why semiconductor devices are easily damaged if they start to overheat.

The conduction properties of a semiconductor can be changed by ***doping*** it with tiny amounts of impurities. For example, a diode can be made by doping a piece of silicon so that a current in one direction increases its resistance while a current in the opposite direction decreases it.

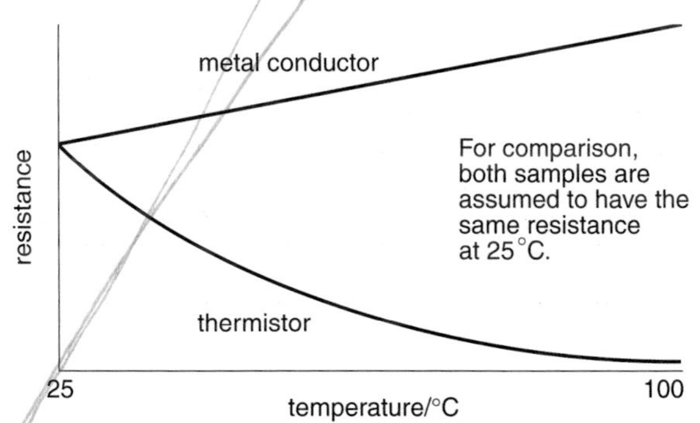

The graphs above are for a typical metal conductor and one type of thermistor. The thermistor contains semiconducting materials.

Superconductivity

When some metals are cooled towards absolute zero, a ***transition temperature*** is reached at which the resistance suddenly falls to zero. This effect is called ***superconductivity***. It occurs when there is no interaction between the free electrons and the lattice, and is explained by the quantum theory. Some specially-developed metal compounds have transition temperatures above 100 K.

If an electromagnet has a superconducting coil, a huge current can be maintained in it with no loss of energy. This enables a very strong magnetic field to be produced.

Energy transfer

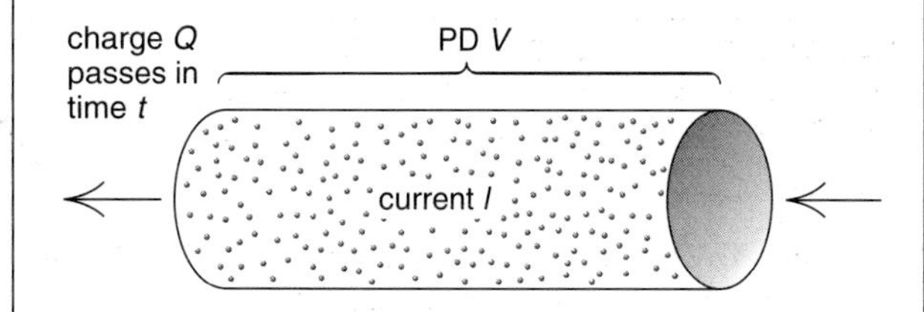

Above, charge Q passes through a resistor in time t. Work W is done by the charge, so energy W is transformed – the electrons lose electrical potential energy and the lattice gains internal energy (it heats up).

W, Q and V are linked by this equation (see also B13):

$$W = QV$$

But $Q = It$, so $W = VIt$ (1)

Applying $V = IR$ to the above equation:

$W = I^2Rt$ and $W = V^2t/R$ (2)

For example, if a current of 2 A flows through a 3 Ω resistor for 5 s, $W = 2^2 \times 3 \times 5 = 60$ J. So the energy dissipated is 60 J. *Double* the current gives *four* times the energy dissipation.

Note:

- Equation (1) can be used to calculate the total energy transformation whenever electrical potential energy is changed into other forms (e.g. KE and internal energy in an electric motor). Equations (2) are only valid where *all* the energy is changed into internal energy. Similar comments apply to the power equations which follow.

As power $P = W/t$, it follows from (1) and (2) that:

$P = VI$ $P = I^2R$ $P = V^2/R$

Resistivity

The resistance R of a conductor depends on its length l and cross-sectional area A:

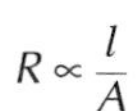

$$R \propto \frac{l}{A}$$

This can be changed into an equation by means of a constant, ρ, known as the ***resistivity*** of the material:

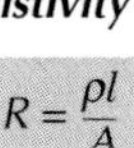

$$R = \frac{\rho l}{A}$$

With this equation, the resistance of a wire can be calculated if its dimensions and resistivity are known.

Resistivites, in Ω m

copper 1.55×10^{-8} aluminium 2.50×10^{-8}

Conductance and conductivity

If a PD V is applied across a conductor, and a current I flows, then $V = IR$. However, as V is the cause of the current and I is the effect, it is more logical to write this as:

$$I = \frac{1}{R} \times V$$

$1/R$ is called the ***conductance***. $1/\rho$ is the ***conductivity***.

(1)

B16 Analysing circuits

Note: in this unit, the symbol E stands for EMF and not electric field strength.

Kirchhoff's first law

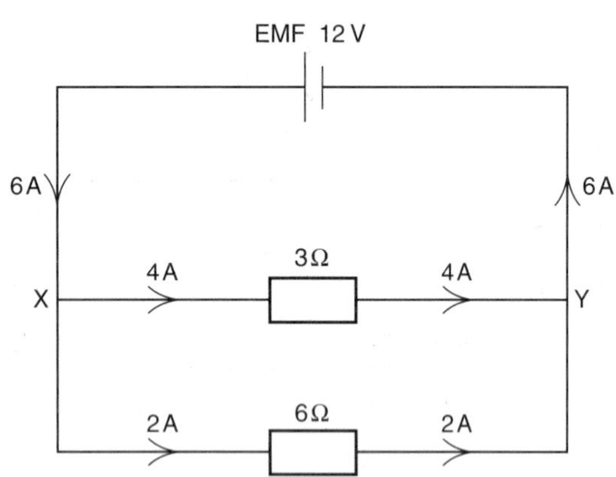

The currents at junctions X and Y above illustrate a law which applies to all circuits:

total current out of junction = total current into junction

This is known as ***Kirchhoff's first law***. It arises because, in a complete circuit, charge is never gained or lost. It is conserved. So the total rate of flow of charge is constant.

Kirchhoff's second law

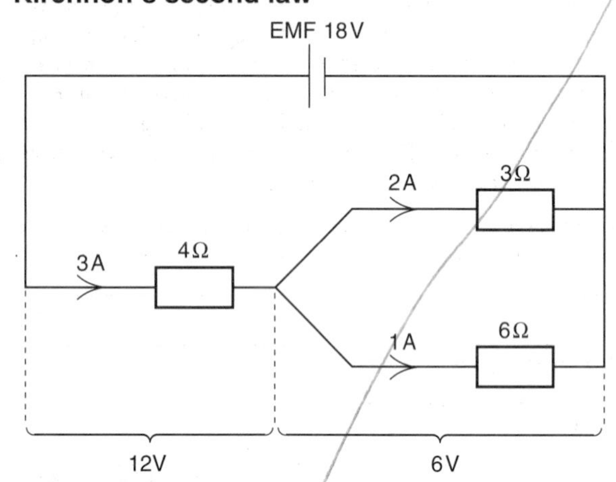

The arrangement above is called 'a circuit'. But, really, there are *two* complete circuits through the battery. To avoid confusion, these will be called *loops*.

In the circuit above, charge leaves the battery with electrical potential energy. As the charge flows round a loop, its energy is 'spent' – in stages – as heat. The principle that the total energy supplied is equal to the total energy spent is expressed by ***Kirchhoff's second law***.

Round any closed loop of a circuit, the algebraic sum of the EMFs is equal to the algebraic sum of the PDs (i.e. the algebraic sum of all the IRs).

Note:

- From the law, it follows that if sections of a circuit are in parallel, they have the same PD across them.
- 'Algebraic' implies that the direction of the voltage must be considered. For example, in the circuit on the right, the EMF of the right-hand battery is taken as *negative* (–4 V) because it is opposing the current. Therefore:

algebraic sum of EMFs $= 18 + (-4) = +14$ V
algebraic sum of IRs $= (2 \times 3) + (2 \times 4) = +14$ V

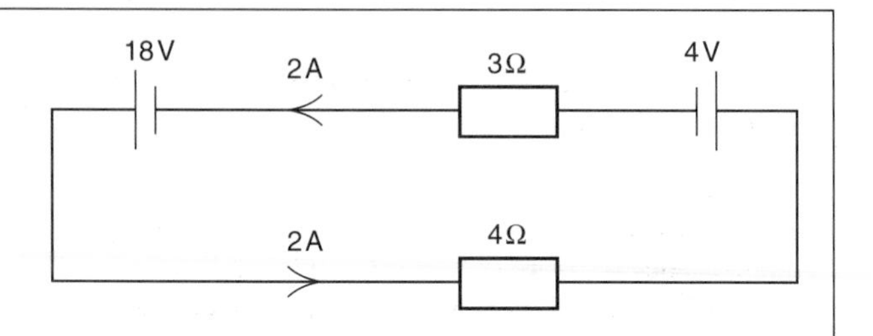

Resistors in series

If R_1 and R_2 below have a total resistance of R, then R is the single resistance which could replace them.

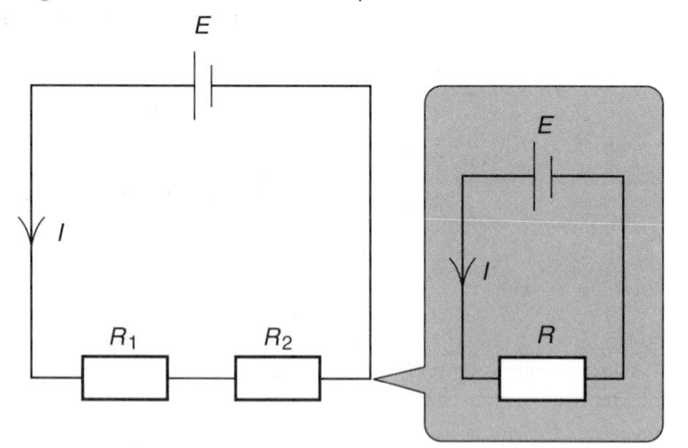

From Kirchhoff's first law, all parts of the circuit have the same current I through them.

From Kirchhoff's second law $E = IR$ and $E = IR_1 + IR_2$.

So $IR = IR_1 + IR_2$

$\therefore$ $R = R_1 + R_2$

For example, if $R_1 = 3\ \Omega$ and $R_2 = 6\ \Omega$, then $R = 9\ \Omega$.

Resistors in parallel

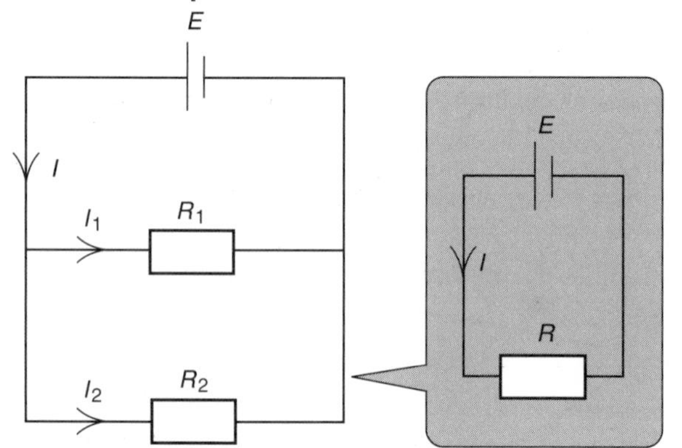

From Kirchhoff's second law (applied to the various loops):

$E = IR$ and $E = I_1R_1$ and $E = I_2R_2$

From Kirchhoff's first law $I = I_1 + I_2$.

So $\dfrac{E}{R} = \dfrac{E}{R_1} + \dfrac{E}{R_2}$

$\therefore$ $\dfrac{1}{R} = \dfrac{1}{R_1} + \dfrac{1}{R_2}$

For example, if $R_1 = 3\ \Omega$ and $R_2 = 6\ \Omega$,
$1/R = 1/3 + 1/6 = 1/2$. So $R = 2\ \Omega$.

Internal resistance

On the opposite page, it was assumed that each battery's output PD (the PD across its terminals) was equal to its EMF. In reality, when a battery is supplying current, its output PD is *less* than its EMF. The greater the current, the lower the output PD. This reduced voltage is due to energy dissipation in the battery. In effect, the battery has ***internal resistance***. Mathematically, this can be treated as an additional resistor in the circuit.

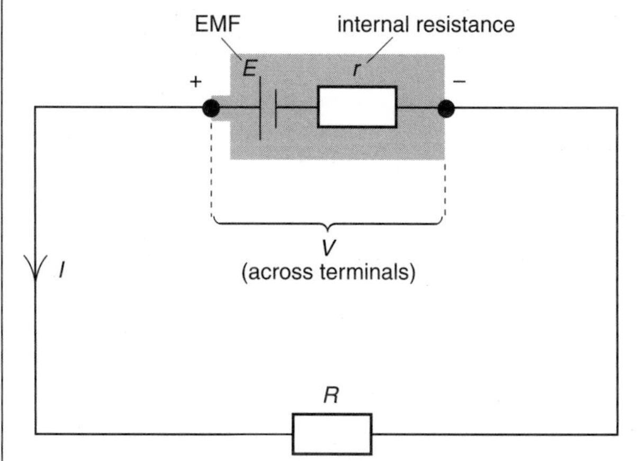

The battery above is supplying a current I to an external circuit. The battery has a constant internal resistance r.

From Kirchhoff's second law $E = IR + Ir$

But $V = IR$, so $E = V + Ir$

So $V = E - Ir$ (1)

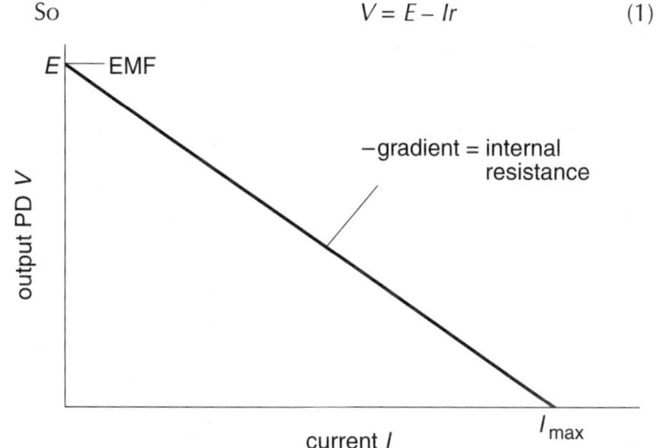

The graph above shows how V varies with I. Unlike earlier graphs, V is on the vertical axis.

Note:

- When I is zero, $V = E$. In other words, when a battery is in ***open circuit*** (no external circuit), the PD across its terminals is equal to its EMF
- When R is zero, V is zero. In other words, when the battery is in ***short circuit*** (its terminals directly connected), its output PD is zero. In this situation, the battery is delivering the maximum possible current, I_{max}, which is equal to E/r. Also, the battery's entire energy output is being wasted internally as heat.
- As $I_{max} = E/r$, it follows that $r = E/I_{max}$. So the gradient of the graph is numerically equal to the internal resistance of the battery.

If both sides of equation (1) are multiplied by I, the result is $VI = EI - I^2r$. Rearranged, this gives the following:

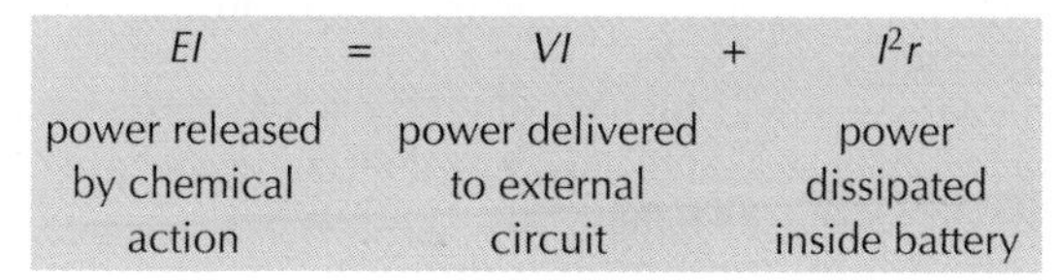

EI	=	VI	+	I^2r
power released by chemical action		power delivered to external circuit		power dissipated inside battery

Potential divider

A ***potential divider*** or ***potentiometer*** like the one below passes on a fraction of the PD supplied to it.

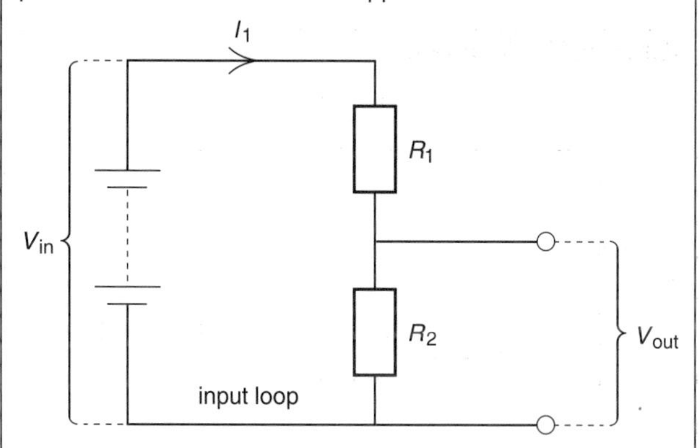

In the input loop above, the total resistance = $R_1 + R_2$.

So $I = V_{in}/(R_1 + R_2)$

But $V_{out} = IR_2$, so $V_{out} = \left(\dfrac{R_2}{R_1 + R_2}\right)V_{in}$

For example, if R_1 and R_2 are both 2 kΩ, then $R_2/(R_1 + R_2)$ works out at 1/2, so V_{out} is a half of V_{in}.

Note:

- The above analysis assumes that no external circuit is connected across R_2. If such a circuit is connected, then the output PD is reduced.

In electronics, a potential divider can change the signals from a sensor (such as a heat or light detector) into voltage changes which can be processed electrically. For example, if R_2 is a thermistor, then a rise in temperature will cause a fall in R_2, and therefore a fall in V_{out}. Similarly, if R_2 is a ***light-dependent resistor*** (**LDR**), then a rise in light level will cause a fall in R_2, and therefore a fall in V_{out}.

Potential dividers are not really suitable for high-power applications because of energy dissipation in the resistors.

Balanced PDs

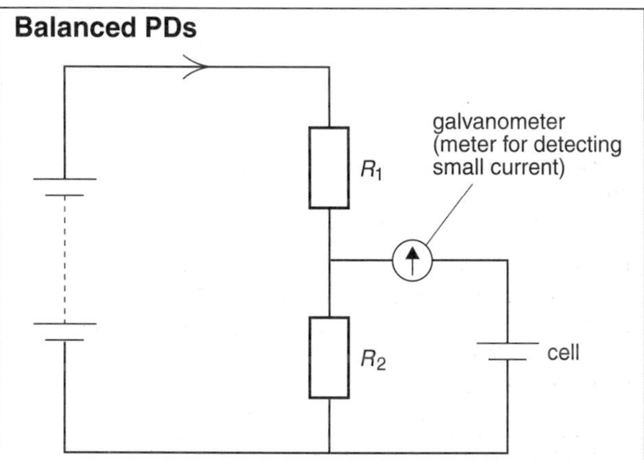

Above, a cell has been connected across the output of a potential divider, and the values of R_1 and R_2 adjusted so that the galvanometer reads zero. This happens when the PD across R_2 exactly balances the cell's output PD.

The above method can be used to compare the EMFs of different cells. It has several advantages.

- The cell is effectively in open circuit, so the PD across the cell's terminals is equal to its EMF
- As the meter is only being used to test for zero current, it does not need an accurately calibrated scale.
- A very sensitive meter can be used.

B17 Magnetic fields and forces

Magnetic field patterns

Any electric current has a magnetic field around it. Examples are shown in the cross-sectional diagrams below.

Single flat coil
Near any section of wire, the field direction is given by Maxwell's screw rule (see A5).

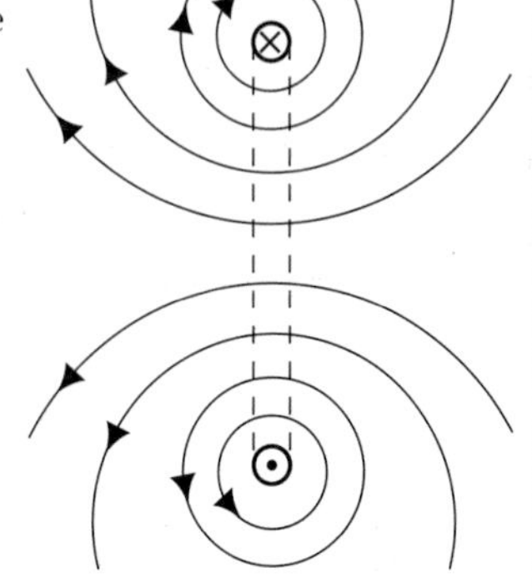

Opposing flat coils
A ***neutral point*** (N on the right) is the point where one magnetic field cancels another.

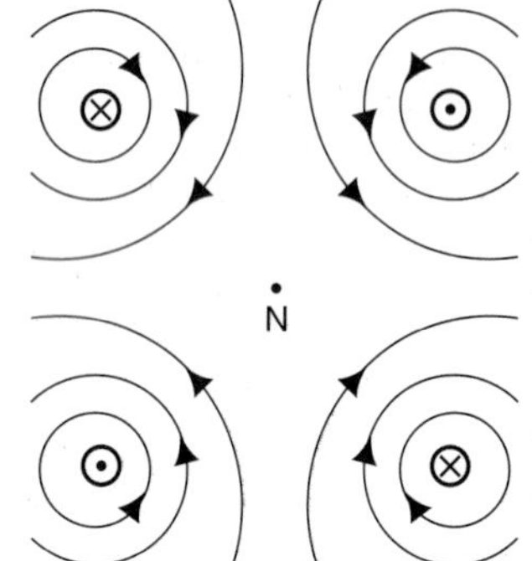

Magnetic force and flux density

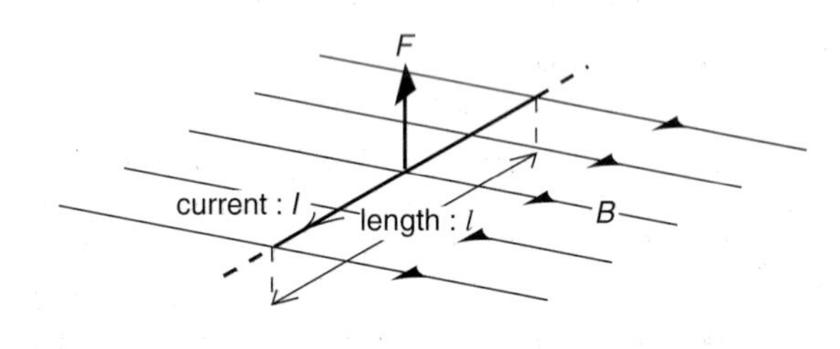

Above, a current-carrying wire is at right-angles to a uniform magnetic field. The field exerts a force on the wire. The direction of the force is given by Fleming's left-hand rule (see A5). The size of the force depends on the current I, the length l in the field, and the strength of the field. This effect can be used to define the magnetic field strength, known as the ***magnetic flux density***, B:

$$F = BIl \qquad (1)$$

B is a vector. The SI unit of B is the ***tesla*** (T). For example, if the magnetic flux density is 2 T, then the force on 2 m of wire carrying a current of 3 A is $2 \times 2 \times 3 = 12$ N.

If a wire is not at right angles to the field, then the above equation becomes:

$$F = BIl\sin\theta$$

where θ is the angle between the field and the wire. As θ becomes less, the force becomes less. When the wire is *parallel* to the field, $\sin\theta = 0$, so the force is zero.

Measuring magnetic flux density

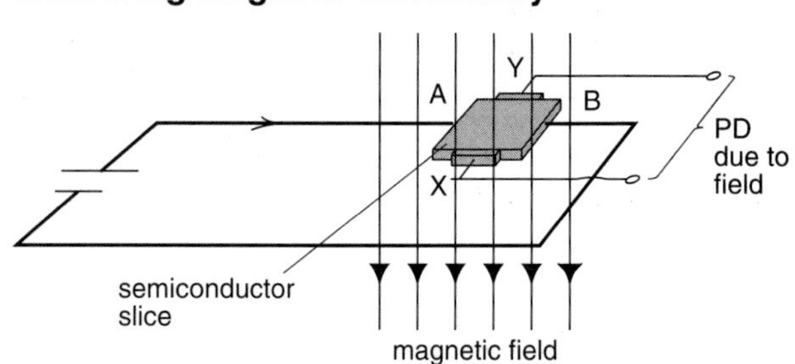

Magnetic flux density can be measured using a ***Hall probe.*** This contains a small slice of semiconductor material, as shown above. When a current is passed between A and B, the drifting charge carriers (see B15) experience a sideways force from the magnetic field. This pushes them sideways, causing a PD between X and Y which can be measured with a sensitive meter. The higher the magnetic flux density, the greater the force on the charge carriers and the higher the PD. A semiconductor is used because the charge carriers move faster than in a metal, for any given current, and this gives a higher PD.

Before it can be used, a Hall probe must be calibrated by finding the meter reading produced by a field of known B.

Torque on a current-carrying coil

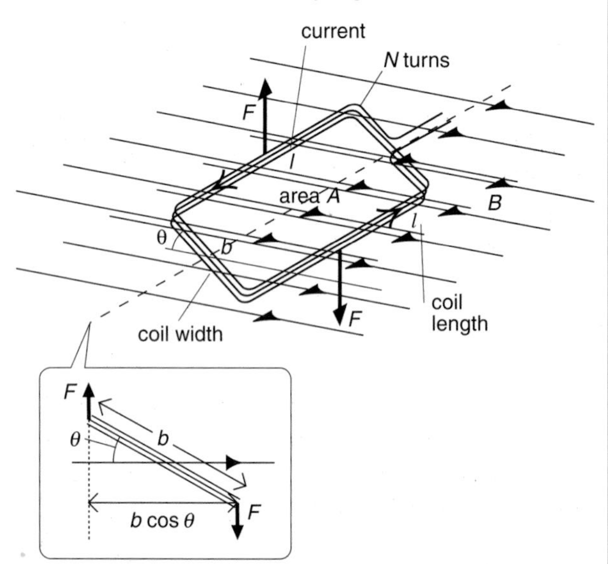

Above, applying equation (1), there is a total upward force F of $BIl \times N$ on one edge of the coil and the same downward force on the other. These form a couple of torque T:

$T = Fb\cos\theta$ (see B5) So $T = BIlNb\cos\theta$

But $lb = A$, the coil's area.

So $$T = BIAN\cos\theta$$

Note:

- The equation also applies to a non-rectangular coil.
- When the plane of the coil is parallel to the field, θ is zero, so $\cos\theta = 1$, and the torque is a maximum, $BIAN$.
- When the plane of the coil is at right-angles to the field, the torque is zero.
- T for torque should not be confused with T for tesla.
- Forces on the near and far ends of the coil do not have moments about the turning axis.

The Biot Savart law, and μ_o

On the right, a short length δl of thin wire, carrying a current I, causes a magnetic flux density δB at P. According to the ***Biot Savart law***:

$$\delta B \propto \frac{I\delta l \sin\theta}{r^2}$$

With a suitable constant, this can be turned into an equation:

$$\delta B = \frac{kI\delta l \sin\theta}{r^2}$$

For a vacuum (and effectively for air), the value of k is 10^{-7} T m A^{-1}. However, in practice, another constant μ_o is used, and the above equation is rewritten as follows:

$$\delta B = \frac{\mu_o I\delta l \sin\theta}{4\pi r^2} \qquad (2)$$

μ_o is called the ***permeability of free space***. Its value is $4\pi \times 10^{-7}$ T m A^{-1}. This is not found by experiment. It is a *defined* value, linked with the definition of the ampere (see the panel right).

Calculating magnetic flux density

Using equation (2) and calculus, it is possible to derive equations for B near wires and inside coils carrying a current I.

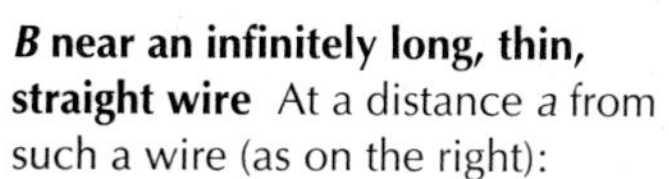

***B* near an infinitely long, thin, straight wire** At a distance a from such a wire (as on the right):

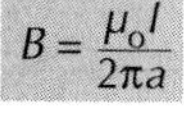

$$B = \frac{\mu_o I}{2\pi a}$$

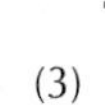

(3)

***B* at the centre of a thin coil** On the axis of such a coil, of N turns and radius r (as on the right):

$$B = \frac{\mu_o NI}{2r}$$

***B* inside an infinitely long solenoid** (coil) The field inside such a solenoid (as on the right) is uniform. If n is the number of turns *per unit length* (per m), then:

$$B = \mu_o nI$$

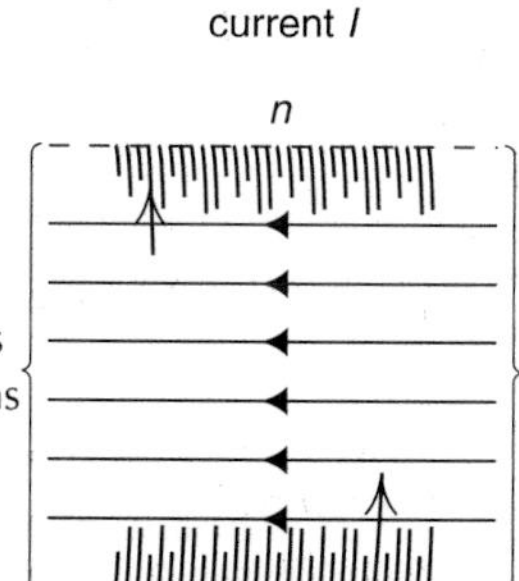

This equation is a reasonable approximation for any solenoid which is at least ten times longer than it is wide.

Force between two current-carrying wires

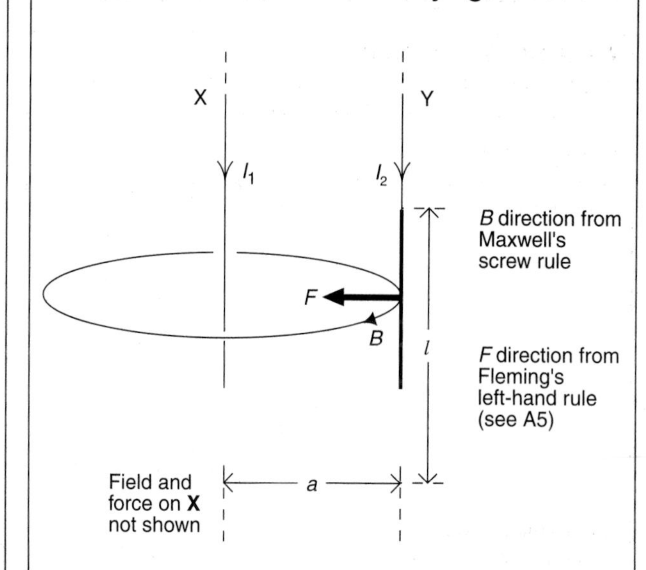

X and Y above are two infinitely long, straight wires in a vacuum. The current in X produces a magnetic field, whose flux density is B at Y. As a result, there is a force on Y. F is the force acting on length l.

From equation (3) $\quad B = \dfrac{\mu_o I_1}{2\pi a}$

From equation (1) $\quad F = BI_2 l$

$$\therefore \qquad F = \frac{\mu_o I_1 I_2 l}{2\pi a} \qquad (4)$$

Note:

- The above equation gives the force of X on Y. Working out the force of Y on X gives exactly the same result.
- If the two currents are in the *same* direction (as above), then the wires *attract* each other. If the two currents are in *opposite* directions, then the wires *repel*.

Defining the ampere

The SI unit of current is defined as follows:

One ampere is the current which, flowing through two infinitely long, thin, straight wires placed one metre apart in a vacuum, produces a force of 2×10^{-7} newtons on each metre length of wire.

Using the various factors in equation (4), the above definition can be expressed in the following form (for simplicity, units have been omitted):

If $I_1 = I_2 = 1$, $a = 1$, and $l = 1$, then $F = 2 \times 10^{-7}$.

Substituting these in equation (4) gives $\mu_o = 4\pi \times 10^{-7}$.

The above definition is not a practical way of fixing a standard ampere. This is done by measuring the force between two current-carrying coils.

***B* inside a solenoid with a core** The value of B is changed by a core. For example, with a pure iron core, B is increased by a factor of about 1000 (depending on the temperature). The previous equation then becomes:

$$B = \mu_r \mu_o nI$$

μ_r is called the ***relative permeability*** of the material. So, for pure iron, μ_r is about 1000.

An electromagnet is a solenoid with a core of high μ_r.

B18 Electromagnetic induction

Magnetic flux

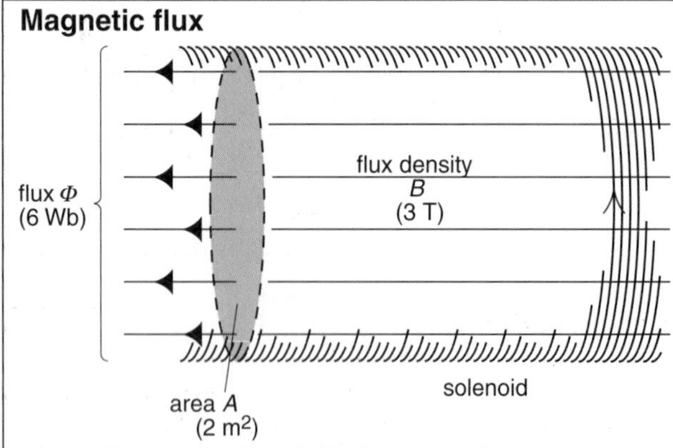

Above, there is a uniform field of magnetic flux density B inside a solenoid of cross-sectional area A. The ***magnetic flux*** Φ is defined by this equation:

flux = flux density × area $\qquad \Phi = BA$

The SI unit of magnetic flux is the ***weber*** (**Wb**). For example, if B is 3 T and A is 2 m^2, then Φ is 6 Wb.

Note:

- Field lines do not really exist, but they can help you visualize what magnetic flux means. In the diagram above, each field line represents a flux of 1 Wb. There are 6 lines altogether, so the flux is 6 Wb. But there are 3 lines per m^2, so the flux density is 3 T.
- With flux, 'density' implies 'per m^2' and not 'per m^3'.
- 1 tesla = 1 weber per metre^2 i.e. 1 T = 1 Wb m^{-2}.

Faraday's law

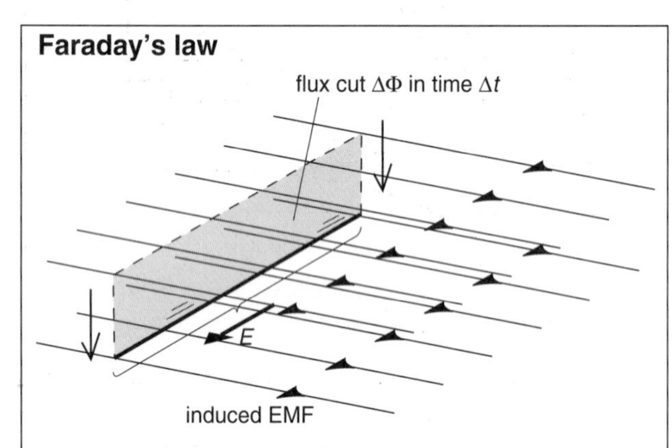

Above, a conductor is moving at a steady speed through a magnetic field. It cuts through flux $\Delta\Phi$ in time Δt. As a result, an EMF E is induced in the conductor. According to ***Faraday's law of electromagnetic induction***, the induced EMF is proportional to the rate of cutting flux:

$$\text{induced EMF} \propto \frac{\text{flux cut}}{\text{time taken}} \qquad E \propto \frac{\Delta\Phi}{\Delta t}$$

With a constant, this can be turned into an equation. The constant is 1 because of the way the units are defined. So:

$$\text{induced EMF} = \frac{\text{flux cut}}{\text{time taken}} \qquad E = \frac{\Delta\Phi}{\Delta t}$$

For example, if 6 Wb of flux are cut in 2 s, E is 3 V.

There is a calculus version of the above equation which also applies if flux is not cut at a steady rate:

$$E = -\frac{d\Phi}{dt} \qquad (1)$$

The significance of the minus sign is explained on the right.

Flux change and flux linkage

Changing flux has exactly the same effect as cutting flux, and the induced EMF is calculated in the same way.

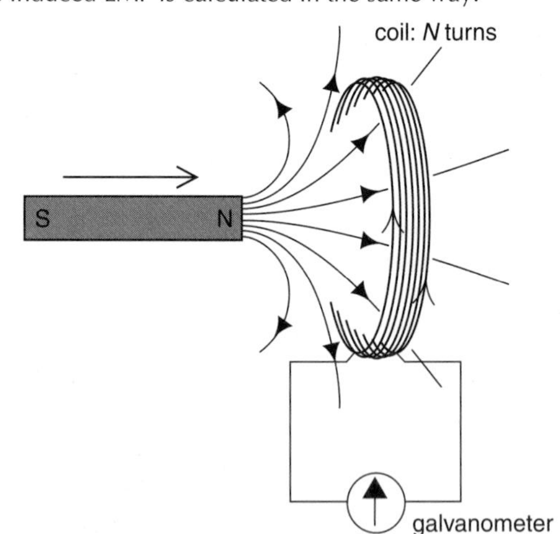

Above, a magnet is moved into a coil. If the flux through the coil changes (at a steady rate) by $\Delta\Phi$ in time Δt, then an EMF of $\Delta\Phi/\Delta t$ is induced *in each turn*. But there are N turns in series. So, the *total* induced EMF E is as follows:

$$E = N\frac{\Delta\Phi}{\Delta t}$$

For example, if the flux changes by 6 Wb in 2 s, and the coil has 100 turns, then the total induced EMF is 300 V.

If there is a flux Φ through a coil of N turns, then $N\Phi$ is called the ***flux linkage***. $N\Delta\Phi$ is the *change* in flux linkage (600 Wb turns, in the previous example). So, the previous equation can be written as follows:

$$\text{induced EMF} = \frac{\text{change in flux linkage}}{\text{time taken}}$$

Lenz's law

According to this law:

If an induced current flows, its direction is always such that it will oppose the change in flux which produced it.

For example, in the diagram above, the induced current causes a N pole at the left end of the coil so that the approaching magnet is repelled. If the magnet is moved the other way, the induced current direction reverses so that there is a pull on the magnet to oppose its motion.

The minus sign in equation (1) comes about because the induced EMF opposes the flux change.

Lenz's law follows from the law of conservation of energy. Energy must be transferred to produce an induced current. So work must be done to make the change which causes it.

Eddy currents When the aluminium disc on the right is spun between the magnetic poles, ***eddy currents*** are induced in it. These set up a magnetic field which pulls on the poles and opposes the motion. So the disc quickly comes to a halt. Electromagnetic braking systems use this effect.

Calculating an induced EMF

The conductor on the right is cutting magnetic flux. It moves a distance of 4 m in 6 s, at a steady speed. From the data supplied, the PD across the ends of the conductor can be calculated. (The PD is equal to the induced EMF E.)

area of flux cut = $3 \times 4 = 12\ \text{m}^2$

$\therefore$ flux cut = $BA = 2 \times 12 = 24$ Wb

$\therefore$ PD = $E = \Delta\Phi/\Delta t = 24/6 = 4$ V

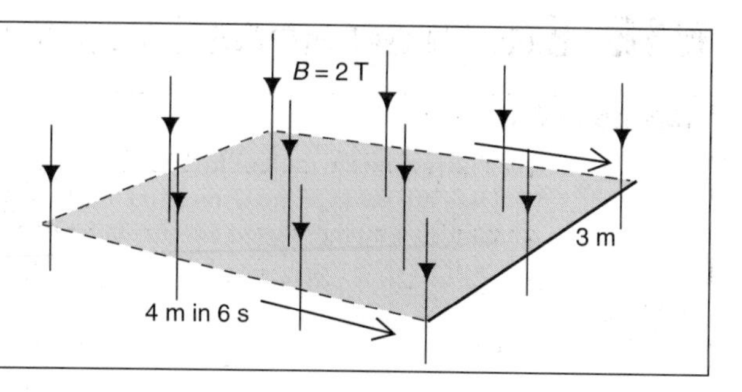

Induced EMF in a rotating coil

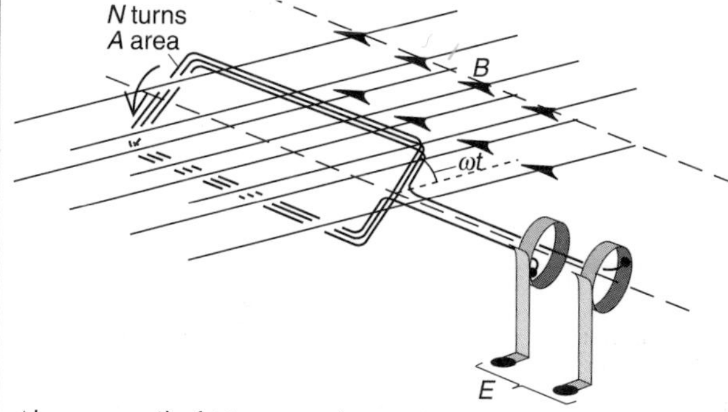

Above, a coil of N turns and area A is rotating at a steady angular velocity ω in a magnetic field of flux density B. In time t, the coil has turned through an angle ωt. For a vertical coil, the flux linkage would be BAN. However, as the coil is an angle to the ωt to the field: flux linkage = $BAN \sin \omega t$.

The induced EMF E can be found by working out the rate of change of flux linkage, using calculus. The result is:

$$E = BAN\omega \cos \omega t$$

The graph shows how E varies with t. The **peak** (maximum) EMF, E_o, occurs when the coil is horizontal and $\cos \omega t = 1$.

So $E_o = BAN\omega$

Increases in B, A, N, and ω all give an increased EMF.

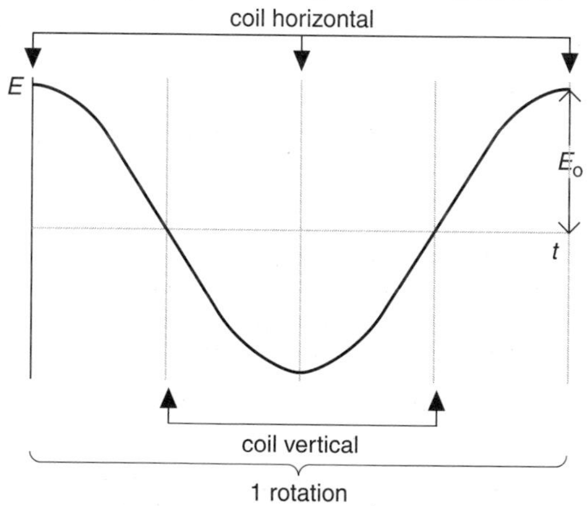

The output from an alternator (see A5) is as shown in the graph above. The current is ***alternating current*** **(AC)**.

Induced EMF in an electric motor (See A5 for motor diagram.) When the coil of a motor is turning, it is cutting magnetic flux. As a result, an EMF is induced which, by Lenz's law, opposes the current. This is known as a ***back EMF***. At switch-on, when the coil is stationary, there is no back EMF, so the current is high. As the motor speeds up, the back EMF rises and the current drops.

For higher B, the coil of a motor is normally wound on an iron-based *armature*. This has a laminated (layered) structure to reduce eddy currents, which waste energy.

Self-induction

When the circuit below is switched on, the current through the coil rises as shown in the graph. The rising current causes a changing flux which induces a back EMF in the coil. By Lenz's law, this opposes the rising current. The effect is called ***self-induction***. The coil is an ***inductor***.

If a back EMF E_b is induced in a coil when the current rises by ΔI in time Δt (at a steady rate) then the ***self-inductance*** L of the coil is given by this equation:

$$\text{back EMF} = L \times \frac{\text{current change}}{\text{time taken}} \qquad E_b = L\frac{\Delta I}{\Delta t} \qquad (2)$$

The unit of self-inductance is the ***henry*** (H). For example, if current is rising at the rate of 2 A s^{-1} in a coil of self-inductance 3 H, then the back EMF is 6 V.

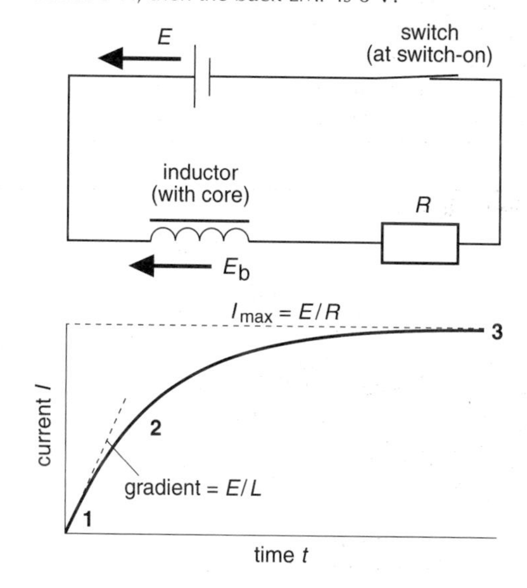

1 At switch-on As the current is zero, the back EMF must balance the supply EMF. So $E_b = E$, and from equation (2), the initial rate of rise of current:

$$\frac{\Delta I}{\Delta t} = \frac{E}{L}$$

2 After switch-on Kirchhoff's second law (see B16) gives the equation linking E_b and I:

$$E - E_b = IR$$

3 At maximum current E_b is zero. So:

$$I = \frac{E}{R}$$

Stored energy When current I flows through an inductor, energy is stored by its magnetic field:

$$\text{stored energy} = \tfrac{1}{2}LI^2$$

At switch-off, the energy is released – often as heat and light from a spark across the switch contacts, caused by the high EMF induced when the current falls rapidly to zero.

B20 Alternating current – 1

AC terms

The graph below shows how the current from an AC supply varies with time. Here are some of the terms used to describe AC. Note the similarities with those used for circular motion and SHM (see B8 and B11).

Frequency f This is the number of cycles per second. The unit is the hertz (Hz). For example, in the UK, the frequency of the AC mains is 50 Hz (50 cycles per second).

Angular frequency ω This is equivalent to angular velocity in circular motion and is measured in rad s^{-1}. As in SHM, it has no direct physical meaning, but is useful in equations. It is defined as follows:

$$\omega = 2\pi f$$

Peak current I_0 This is the maximum current during the cycle. It is the amplitude of the waveform in the graph below.

The current I at any instant is related to the peak current by the following equation (given in two alternative versions):

$I = I_0 \sin \omega t$ and $I = I_0 \sin 2\pi ft$

The graph is an example of a ***sinusoidal*** waveform.

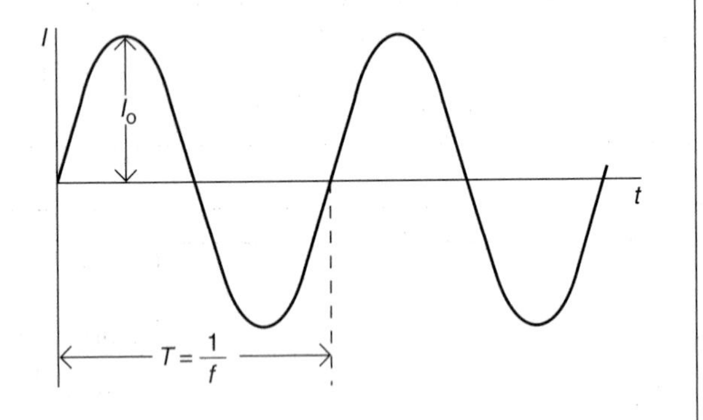

Power dissipated in a resistor

On the right, an alternating current I flows through a resistance R. The power P dissipated in the resistor varies through the cycle. At any instant $P = I^2R$.

But $I = I_0 \sin \omega t$

So $P = I_0^2 R \sin^2 \omega t$

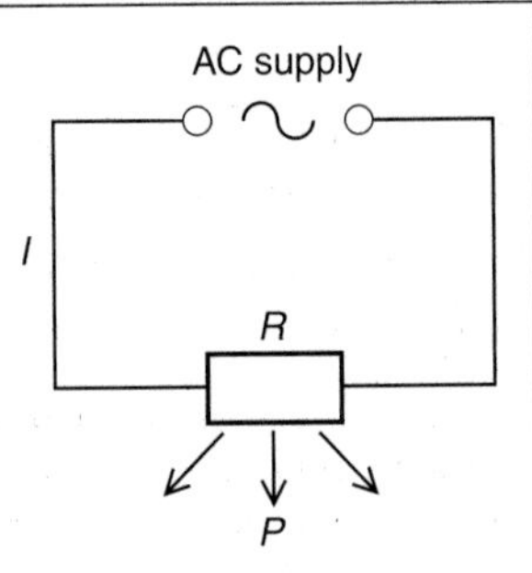

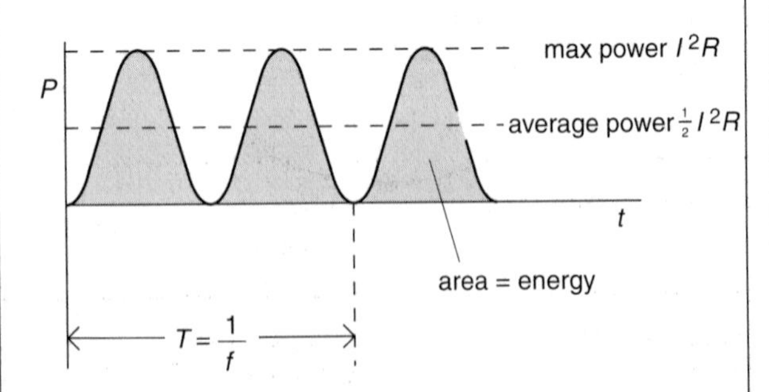

The graph shows how P varies with t. P is always positive because all values of $\sin^2 \omega t$ lie between 0 and 1. Note:

$$\text{average power} = \tfrac{1}{2}\text{maximum power} = \tfrac{1}{2} I_0^2 R$$

RMS voltage and current

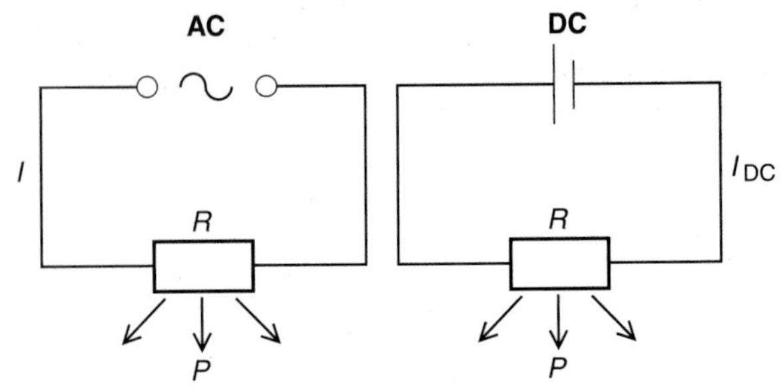

The current from a battery is one-way ***direct current*** **(DC)**. In the DC circuit above, there is a steady current I_{DC} such that power is dissipated in the resistor at exactly the same rate as in the AC circuit. So:

$$I_{DC}^2 R = \tfrac{1}{2} I_0^2 R$$

From which it follows that $I_{DC} = I_0/\sqrt{2}$.

In the AC circuit, the ***root mean square (RMS) current*** is equal to I_{DC}. So it is equal to the steady current which gives the same power dissipation as the alternating current. (It is so named because it is the square root of the mean of I^2 throughout the sinusoidal cycle.) So:

$$I_{RMS} = \frac{I_0}{\sqrt{2}}$$

Similarly, for the alternating PD of peak value V_0:

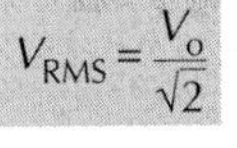

$$V_{RMS} = \frac{V_0}{\sqrt{2}}$$

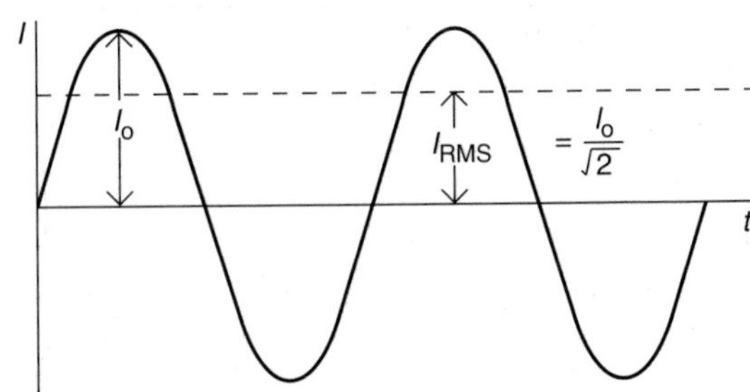

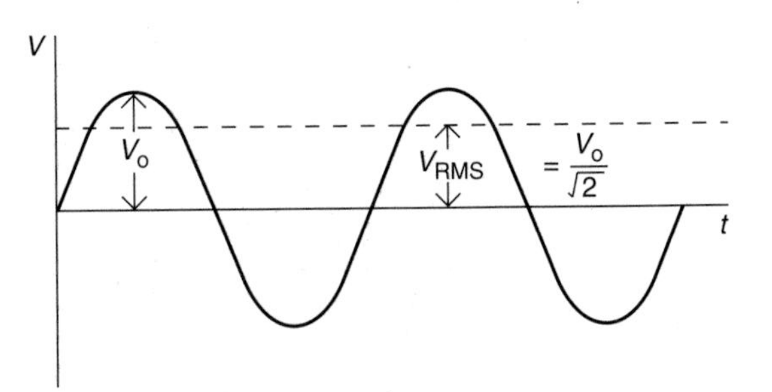

The graphs above show how the alternating V across a resistor, and I through it, vary with time. The resistor is assumed to obey Ohm's law.

Note:

- When the PD is zero, the current is zero. And when the PD is at its peak, the current is at its peak. In other words, the PD and current are ***in phase***.
- $R = \dfrac{V}{I} = \dfrac{V_0}{I_0} = \dfrac{V_{RMS}}{I_{RMS}}$
- The average power dissipated $= \tfrac{1}{2} V_0 I_0 = V_{RMS} I_{RMS}$

The UK AC mains voltage of 230 V is a RMS value. The peak voltage = $230 \times \sqrt{2} = 325$ V. In doing calculations on power dissipation, RMS values are normally used because the factor $\tfrac{1}{2}$ does not need to be included in the working.

Reactance of a capacitor

On the right, an alternating PD V is applied across a capacitance C, and an alternating current I flows. It is usual to talk of current 'through' the capacitor even though no charge actually crosses the gap between the plates.

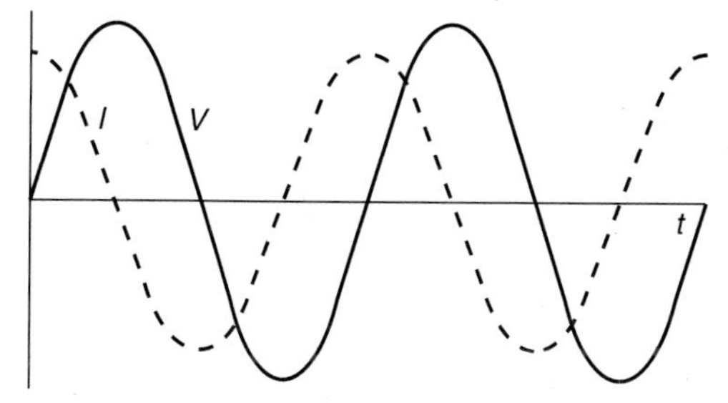

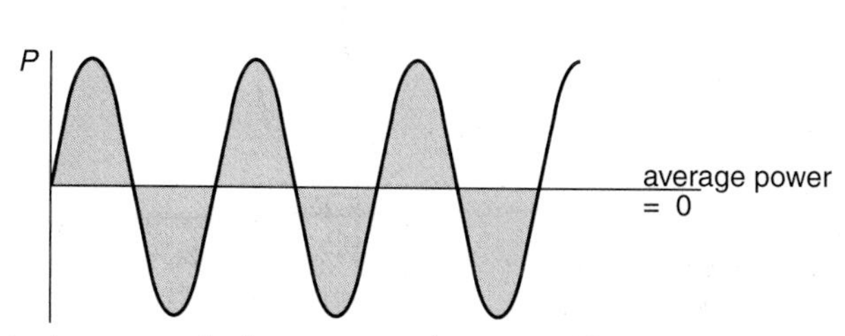

In the top graph, the current peaks are at earlier times than the PD peaks: the current *leads* the applied PD by $\frac{1}{4}$ of a cycle. So the current is a maximum when the PD is zero, and vice versa. The bottom graph shows that the average power is zero, so no power is dissipated. All energy stored by the capacitor is returned to the supply.

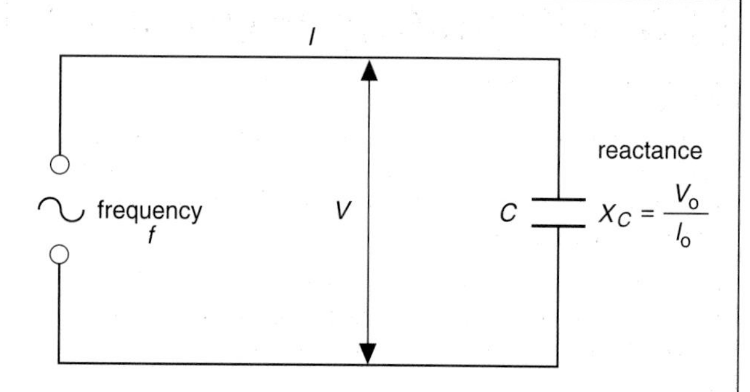

V_o/I_o is called the ***reactance*** of the capacitor. As with resistance, the unit of reactance is the ohm (Ω). However, if a component has only reactance (and no resistance),

- the current and PD are out of phase by $\frac{1}{4}$ of a cycle,
- no power is dissipated.

If X_C is the reactance of a capacitor:

$$X_C = \frac{1}{2\pi fC}$$

Note that the reactance depends on the frequency. As f increases, the reactance *decreases*. For DC ($f = 0$), the reactance is infinite. So a capacitor 'blocks' DC.

Calculating reactance If a 1000 μF capacitor is in an AC mains circuit, of frequency 50 Hz:

$$X_C = \frac{1}{(2\pi \times 50 \times 1000 \times 10^{-6})} = 3.2\ \Omega$$

Reactance of an inductor

On the right, AC flows through an inductance L.

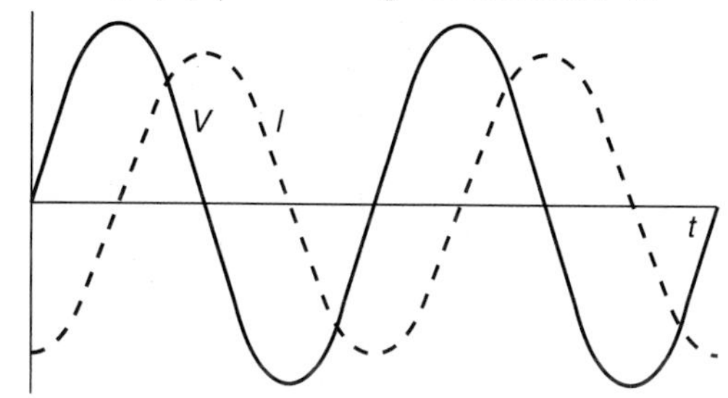

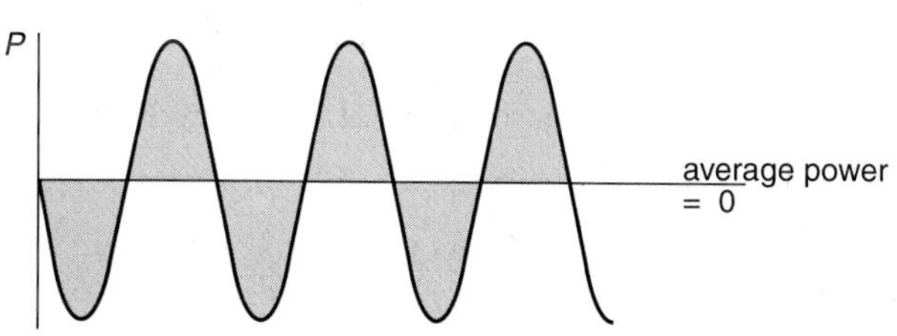

The current *lags* behind the PD by $\frac{1}{4}$ of a cycle. The current is a maximum when the PD is zero, and vice versa.

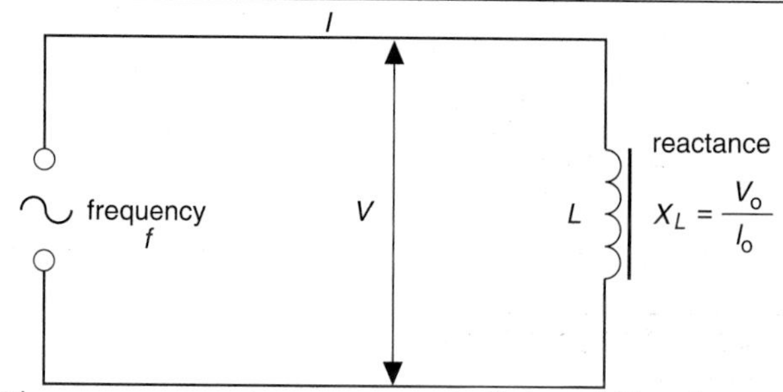

The average power is zero, so none is dissipated. Therefore, the inductor has reactance.

If X_L is the reactance of an inductor:

$$X_L = 2\pi fL$$

The reactance depends on the frequency, but in the opposite way to that of a capacitor. As f increases, the reactance of an inductor *increases*. For DC ($f = 0$), the reactance is zero.

Calculating reactance If a 22 mH inductor is in an AC mains circuit, of frequency 50 Hz:

$$X_L = 2\pi \times 50 \times 22 \times 10^{-3} = 6.9\ \Omega$$

resistor R	resistance = R (in Ω)	resistance *independent* of f	average power dissipated $= I_{RMS}^2 R$
capacitor C	reactance (in Ω) $= \frac{1}{2\pi fC}$	reactance *decreases* with f	average power dissipated $= 0$
inductor L	reactance (in Ω) $= 2\pi fL$	reactance *increases* with f	average power dissipated $= 0$

B20 Alternating current – 2

Using phasors for AC

An alternating current or voltage can be represented by a rotating vector, called a ***phasor***. Above, I_o is rotating anticlockwise at a steady angular velocity ω. Its projection I on the vertical axis is given by $I = I_o \sin \omega t$, the same as the equation for the current I in an AC circuit (see B19).

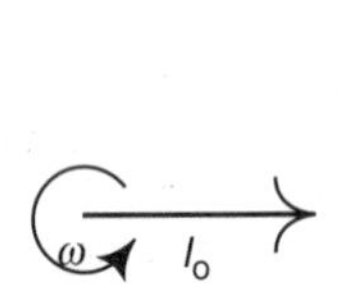

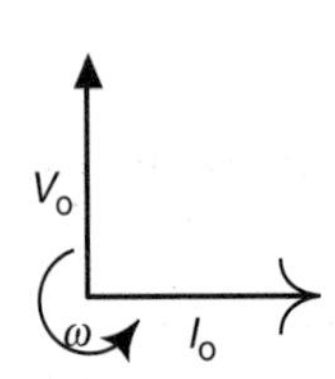

The vector above left represents an alternating current. The anticlockwise rotation is shown. The circle and axes have been omitted for simplicity.

The two vectors above right represent a PD leading a current by $\frac{1}{4}$ cycle (90°), as for an inductor.

Resistance and reactance vectors

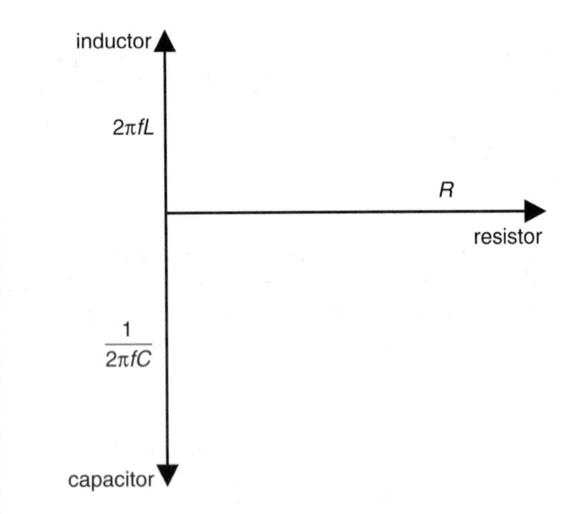

In analysing AC circuits, it is useful to represent resistances and reactances by vectors, even though they are not alternating. You interpret each vector as follows:

- The *length* represents the *magnitude* of the resistance or reactance (in Ω).
- The *direction* indicates the *phase* of the PD relative to a right-pointing current vector. Above, for example, the $2\pi fL$ vector points upwards, so, for an inductor, the PD leads the current by $\frac{1}{4}$ cycle.

Impedance

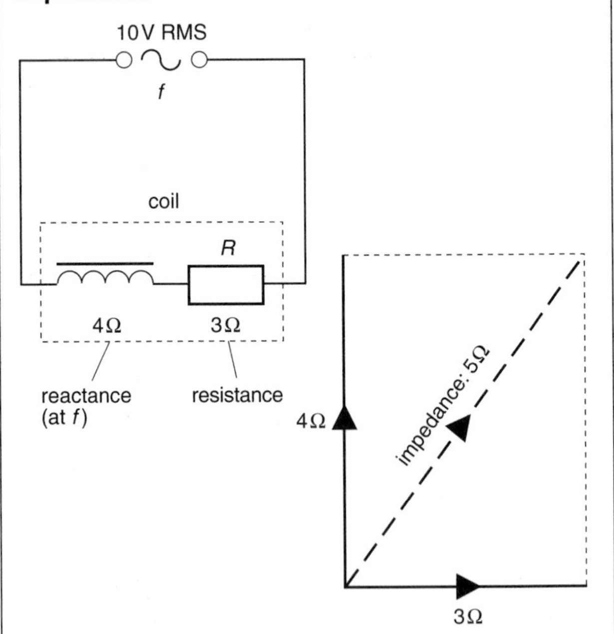

In the circuit above, the coil has a resistance of 3 Ω and a reactance of 4 Ω. By vector addition (see B4), the resultant is 5 Ω. This is called the ***impedance*** of the coil.

If there is a PD V across a device, and a current I through it, then the impedance Z is given by the following:

$$Z = \frac{V_{RMS}}{I_{RMS}} \quad \text{and} \quad Z = \frac{V_o}{I_o}$$

(V_o = peak PD)
(I_o = peak current)

From the first equation, the current in the circuit above can be calculated:

$$I_{RMS} = \frac{V_{RMS}}{Z} = \frac{10}{5} = 2\text{ A}$$

Power dissipated Only the resistive part of the impedance dissipates power. So:

power dissipated in coil = $P = I_{RMS}{}^2 R = 2^2 \times 4 = 16$ W

Phase angle Φ This is the phase difference between the PD and the current. If Φ is known, the power dissipated, above, can also be worked out using the impedance:

$$P = I_{RMS}{}^2 \times Z \cos \Phi$$

$\cos \Phi$ is called the ***power factor***.

Transformers

Transformers increase or decrease alternating voltage (see A5 for diagram and principle). Provided there is no flux leakage from the core:

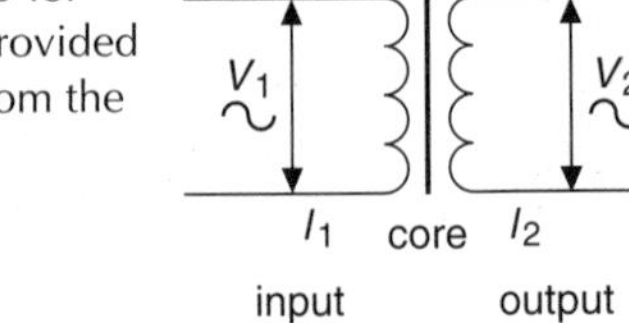

$$\frac{V_2}{V_1} = \frac{N_2}{N_1}$$

In an ideal transformer, the power output is equal to the power input. In practice, a transformer wastes some power (as heat). Two reasons for this are:

- coil resistance
- the changing flux induces eddy currents (see B18) in the core. The core is laminated (layered) to reduce these.

For a practical transformer $V_2 I_2 = eV_1 I_1$

where e is the efficiency (typically over 0.95).

Resonance in an *RCL* circuit

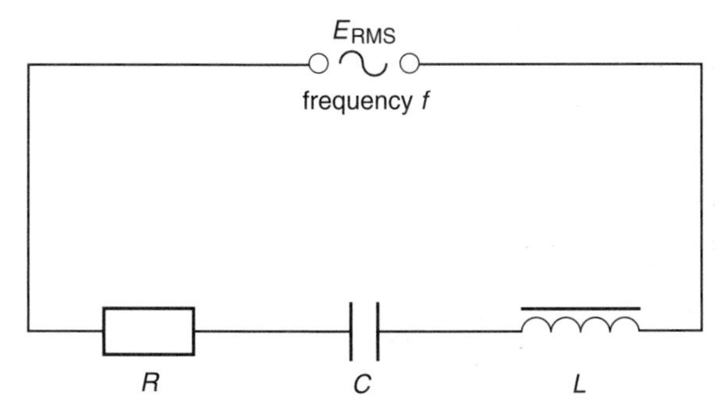

In the circuit above, if the supply frequency is increased, the reactance of L rises, while that of C falls. At a certain frequency f_r, the two reactances cancel, as shown in the vector diagram below. The total impedance is then a minimum, so the current is a maximum. This is an example of ***resonance*** (see B11). f_r is the ***resonant frequency***.

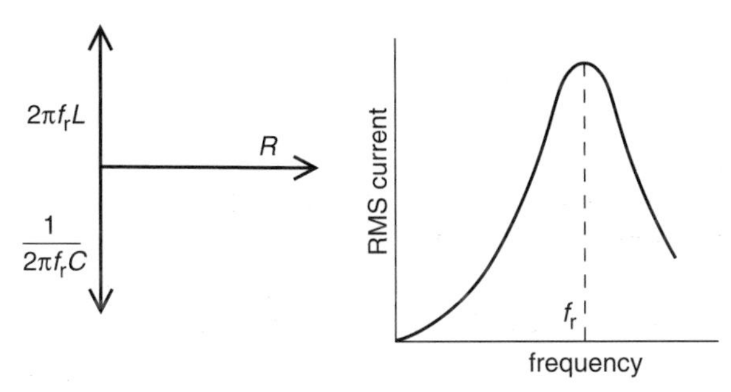

At resonance $\quad 2\pi f_r L = \dfrac{1}{2\pi f_r C}$

$$\therefore \quad f_r = \frac{1}{2\pi\sqrt{LC}}$$

Also, the circuit behaves as if only R is present. So:

- the total impedance is R,
- the phase angle is zero i.e. V and I are in phase,
- the RMS current is E_{RMS}/R.

In radios and TVs, resonant circuits are used to select particular frequencies from a range of incoming ones.

Supplying AC for the mains

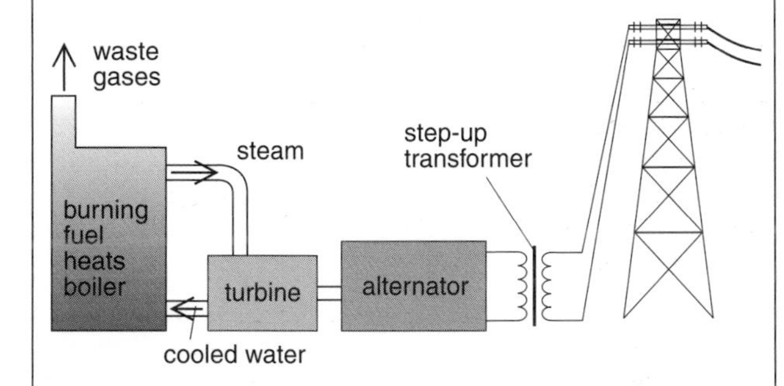

Mains AC is generated in power stations. The layout of a typical fuel-burning station is shown above. The power is fed into a distribution network called the ***Grid***.

Power is sent across country through overhead lines at very high voltage (typically 400 000 V). The voltage is increased to this level by transformers and then reduced again at the far end. As power = voltage × current, transmitting at a higher voltage means a lower current and, therefore, less power wasted as heat because of line resistance.

Rectification

Low voltage DC equipment can use mains power, provided the voltage is reduced, and the AC is converted to DC. Turning AC into DC, is called ***rectification***.

Half-wave rectification The circuit below reduces the alternating voltage, and then uses a diode to block the backwards part of the alternating current. The DC output is in half-wave pulses with zero PD between.

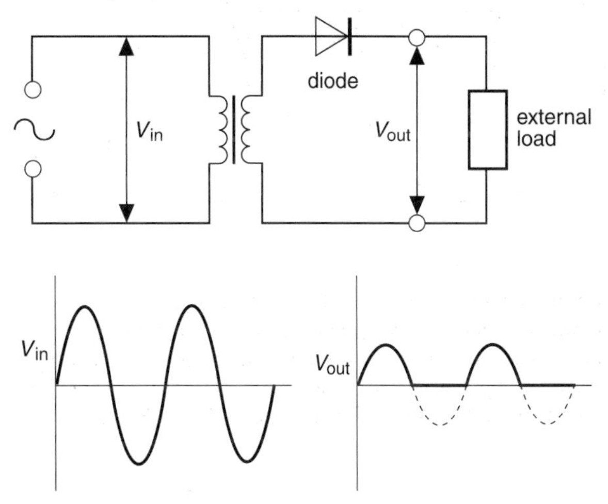

Full-wave rectification The four diodes in the circuit below form a ***bridge rectifier***. In one half of the AC cycle, diodes A conduct and diodes B block. In the other half, diodes B conduct and diodes A block. The effect is to reverse the backwards parts of the AC.

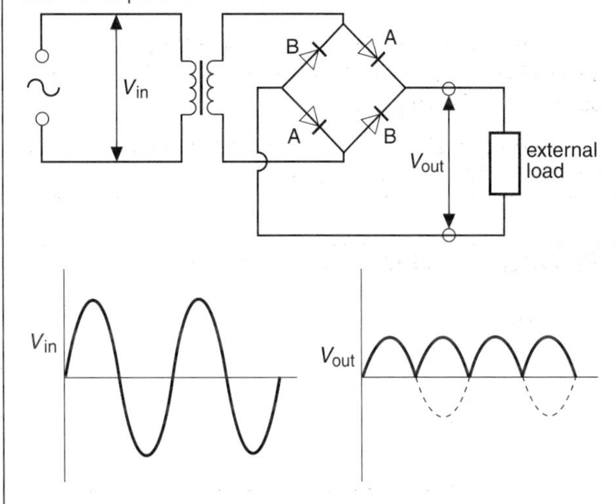

Smoothing The output from a rectifier circuit can be smoothed by connecting a large capacitor across it, as below. The capacitor charges up during the forward peaks, then releases its charge in between.

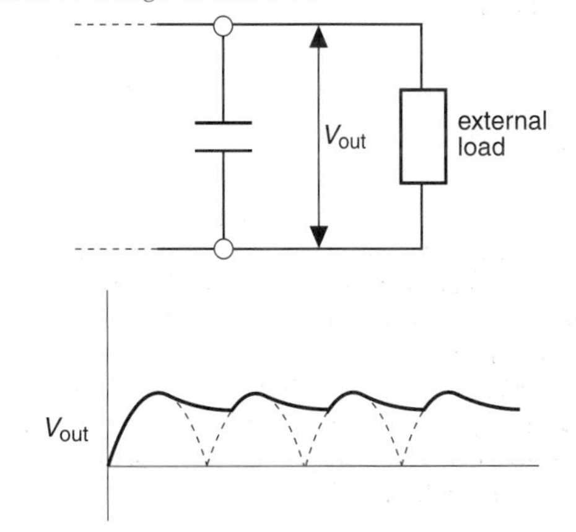

B21 Charged particles in motion

Producing an electron beam

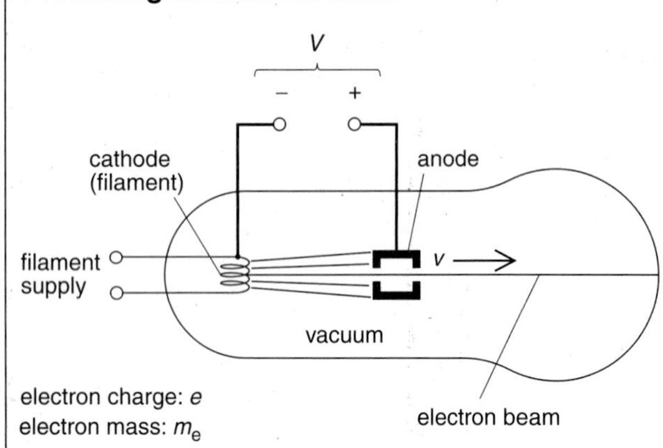

In the vacuum tube above, electrons are given off by a hot tungsten filament. The effect is called ***thermionic emission***. The electrons gain kinetic energy (KE) as they are pulled from the ***cathode*** (–) to the ***anode*** (+). Some pass through the hole in the anode and emerge as a narrow beam, at speed v. Electrons in a beam are sometimes called ***cathode rays*** because they come from the cathode.

As an electron (charge e) moves from cathode to anode:

KE gained = work done = charge × PD = eV (see B13)

So $\frac{1}{2} m_e v^2 = eV$

Electron gun This is a device which produces a narrow beam of electrons. It uses the principle described above. In many electron guns, the cathode is an oxide-coated plate, heated by a separate filament.

Electronvolt (eV) This is a unit often used for measuring particle energies. 1 eV is the energy gained by an electron when moving through a PD of 1 V.

If an electron (1.60×10^{-19} C) moves through 1 V:
KE gained = charge × PD = $1.60 \times 10^{-19} \times 1$ J

So $1 \text{ eV} = 1.60 \times 10^{-19}$ J

Deflection of electrons by an electric field

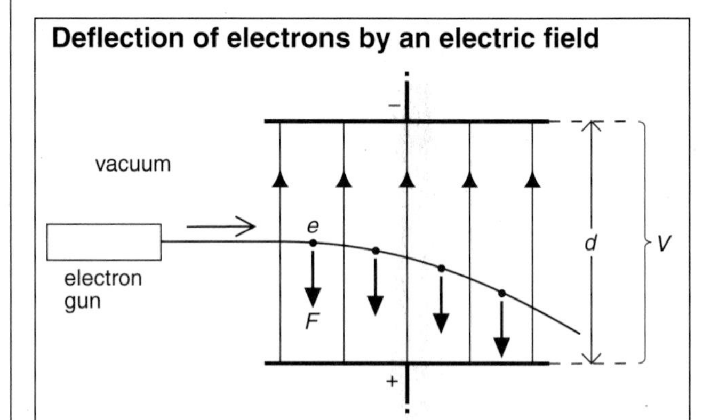

Above, electrons pass between two horizontal plates. The electric field strength between the plates is V/d (see B13).

force F on electron = electric field strength × charge

So $F = \dfrac{Ve}{d}$

Note:
- The force on the electron does not depend on its speed.
- The force is always in line with the electric field.
- The path of the electrons is a *parabola* (just as it is for the thrown ball in B3).

Magnetic force on a moving charge

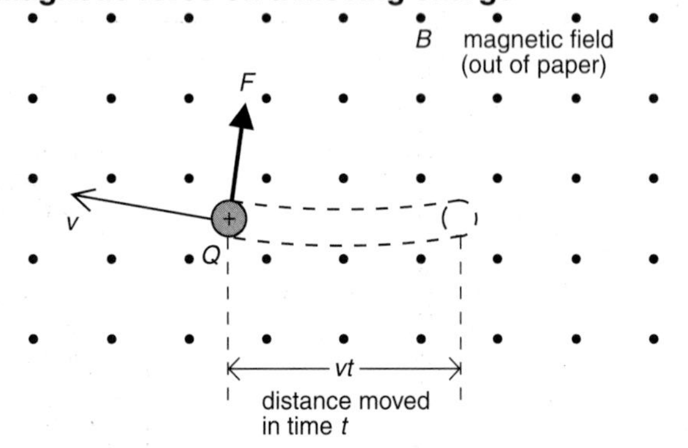

Above, a particle of charge Q, is moving at a steady speed through a uniform magnetic field. In time t, it travels a distance vt. So it is equivalent to a current Q/t in a wire of length vt. According to equation (1) in B17, the force on a current-carrying wire is BIl. Applying this to the above:

force $F = B \times \dfrac{Q}{t} \times vt$

So $F = BQv$ (1)

Note:
- As the speed increases, the force increases.
- The direction of the force is given by Fleming's left-hand rule (see A5).
- If the particle is travelling at an angle θ to the field, then the above equation becomes $F = BQv \sin \theta$.

Deflection of electrons by a magnetic field

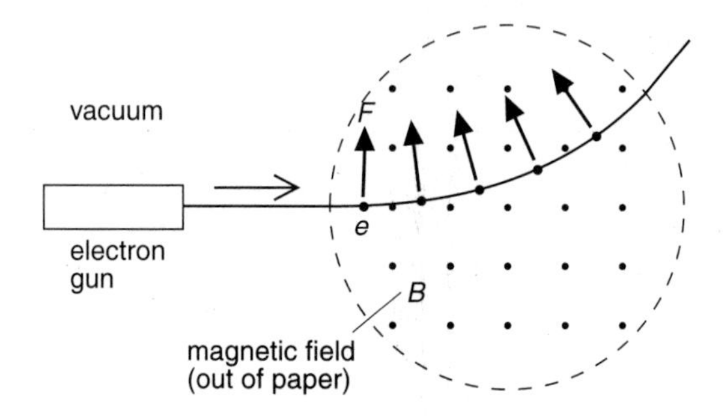

Above, electrons travel at right angles to a uniform magnetic field. The force F on an electron is found by putting Q equal to e in equation (1) on the left. So:

$F = Bev$

Note:
- The force on the electron increases with speed.
- The force is always at right-angles to the direction of motion, as predicted by Fleming's left-hand rule. But in applying this rule, remember that the electron has negative charge, so electron motion to the *right* represents a conventional current to the *left*.
- The path of the beam is *circular* (see next page).

Circular motion in a magnetic field

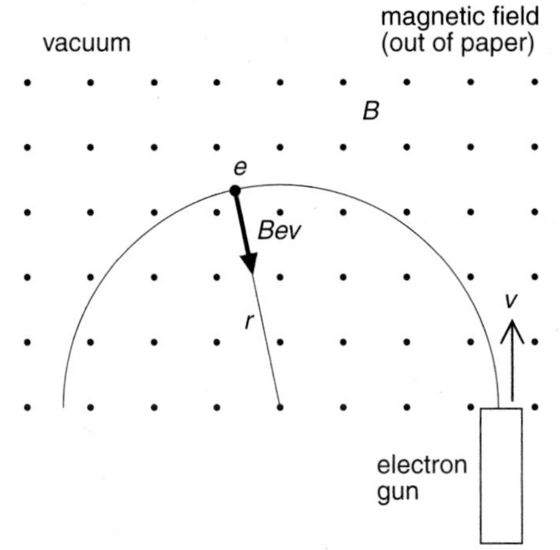

Above, electrons leave the electron gun at speed v. They move in a circle because the magnetic force Bev supplies the necessary centripetal force (see B8). So:

$$Bev = \frac{m_e v^2}{r}$$

$$\text{So} \quad r = \frac{m_e v}{eB} \qquad (2)$$

Note:
- The radius of the circle is proportional to the speed.
- Increasing B decreases the radius.

Specific charge of an electron This an electron's charge per unit mass, e/m_e. Its value is -1.8×10^{11} C kg^{-1}. Methods of measuring it make use of the above equation.

Ion beams If atoms lose electrons, they become positive ions. These particles also have circular paths in a magnetic field. If Q is the charge on a particle, and m the mass, then equation (2) can be written in this more general form:

$$r = \frac{mv}{QB}$$

Note:
- The radius depends on the specific charge (Q/m). This idea is used in a ***mass spectrometer*** to separate nuclei with different specific charges.

Speed selection

An ion beam may contain ions with a range of speeds. Ions of only one speed can be selected by the method shown below. This uses the principle that the magnetic force on an ion depends on its speed, while the electric force does not:

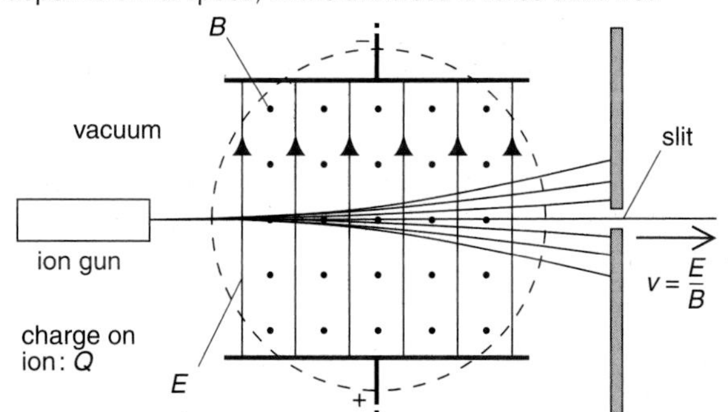

The magnetic field produces an upward force BQv. The electric field produces a downward force EQ. The only ions to pass through the slit are those for which these forces are equal. So, if $EQ = BQv$, the selected speed $v = E/B$. Faster ions are deflected upwards (because BQv is more); slower ions are deflected downwards.

Cathode ray oscilloscope (CRO)

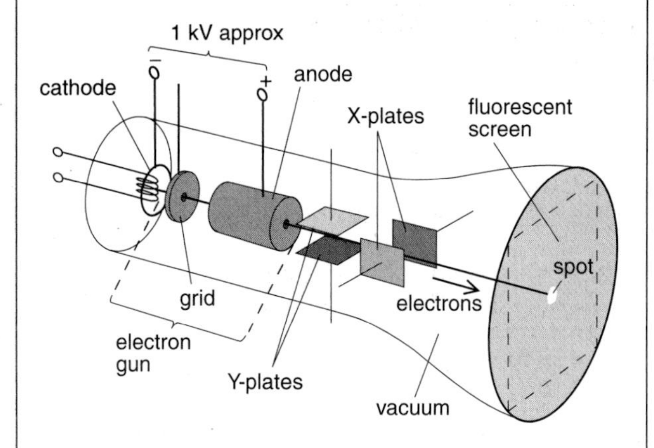

In a CRO, as above, a beam of electrons is used to draw a graph on a screen. The screen is coated with a ***fluorescent*** material, so that it glows where the electrons strike it.

The electrons come from an ***electron gun***. The anode is designed so that it focuses the beam. The flow of electrons and, therefore, the brightness of the spot, is controlled by making the ***grid*** negative relative to the cathode.

The ***Y-plates*** and ***X-plates*** are used to move the beam up and down and side to side. The beam is deflected whenever there is a PD across a set of plates.

Displaying an alternating voltage The line below has two components. Across the Y-plates, an alternating PD, coming from an external source via an amplifier in the CRO, moves the spot up and down. Across the X-plates, a ***time base*** circuit in the CRO changes the PD so that the spot moves from left to right at a steady rate – until it reaches the edge of the screen and flicks back. The result is a graph of PD against time, drawn over and over again.

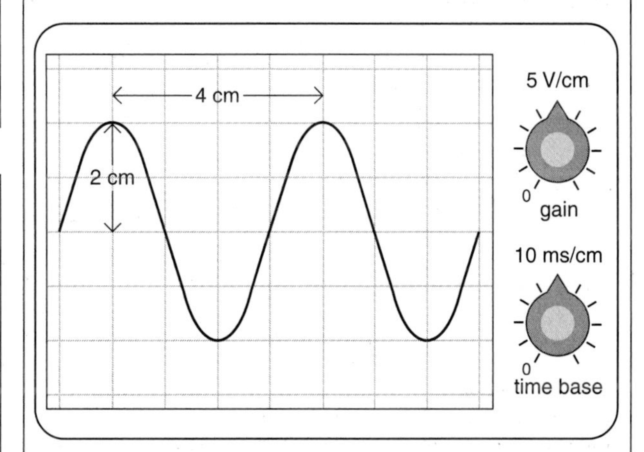

Measuring peak alternating PD The setting on the gain control (above) means that 5 V across the Y-input terminals cause the spot to move 1 cm vertically. On the screen, the amplitude of the wave trace is 2.0 cm. So in this case, the peak voltage is $2.0 \times 5 = 10$ V.

Measuring time and frequency The setting on the time base control (above) means that the spot takes 10 ms to move 1 cm horizontally. On the screen, the wave peaks are 4.0 cm apart. So the time between the peaks = $4.0 \times 10 = 40$ ms (0.04 s). This is the period of the wave cycle. So the frequency = 1/period = 1/0.04 = 25 Hz.

B22 Moving waves

Progressive wave motion

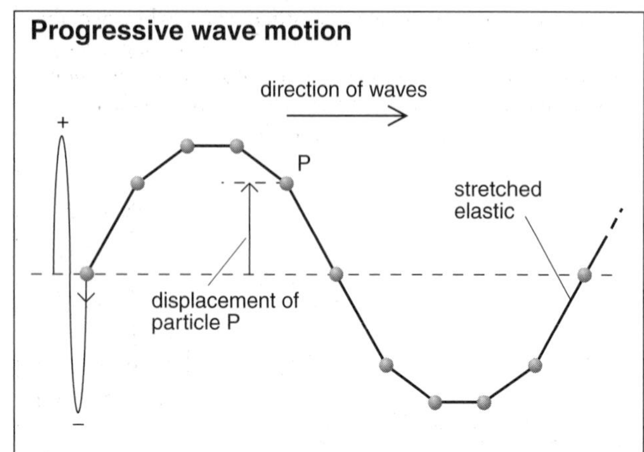

Above is one model of how waves travel. The first particle is oscillated up and down with SHM (see B11). This pulls on the next particle, making it oscillate up and down slightly later, and so on, along the line. As a result, ***progressive*** (moving) waves are seen travelling from left to right. The waves in this case are ***transverse*** (see A6) because the oscillations are at right-angles to the direction of travel.

The ***displacement*** of a particle at any instant is measured from the centre line, with a + or – to indicate an *upward* or *downward* direction.

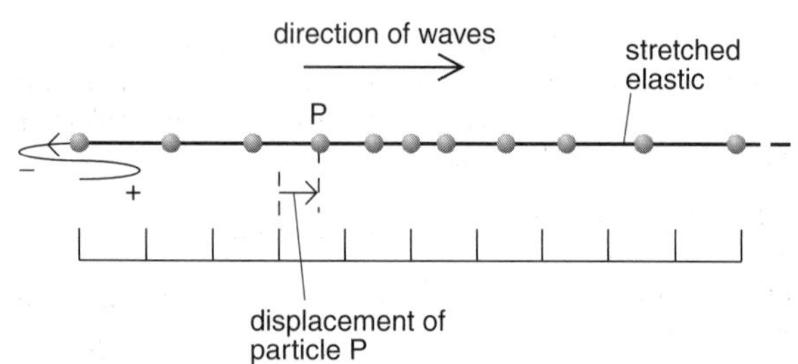

With ***longitudinal*** waves as above, the oscillations are in the direction of travel (see A6). So a particle can have a displacement to the *right* (+) or *left* (–).

The speed of waves depends on the properties of the ***medium*** (material) through which they are travelling. For example, if the particles above are lighter, or the elastic tighter, then each particle is affected more rapidly by the one before, so the wave speed is greater.

The speed of electromagnetic waves

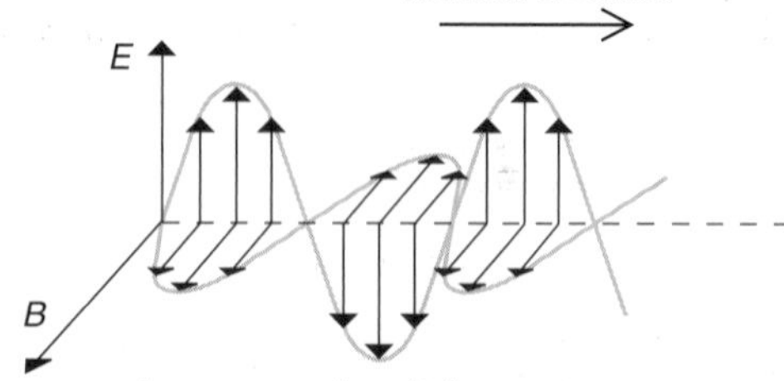

Electromagnetic waves such as light (see A6) are transverse waves. However, it is not particles which oscillate, but an electric field (E) coupled with a magnetic field (B), as shown above. The speed of the waves through space, called the ***speed of light***, depends on the permittivity ε_o and permeability μ_o of a vacuum (see B13 and B17):

$$\text{speed of light (in vacuum) } c = \frac{1}{\sqrt{\varepsilon_o \mu_o}} = 3.0 \times 10^8 \text{ m s}^{-1}$$

Refraction of light waves

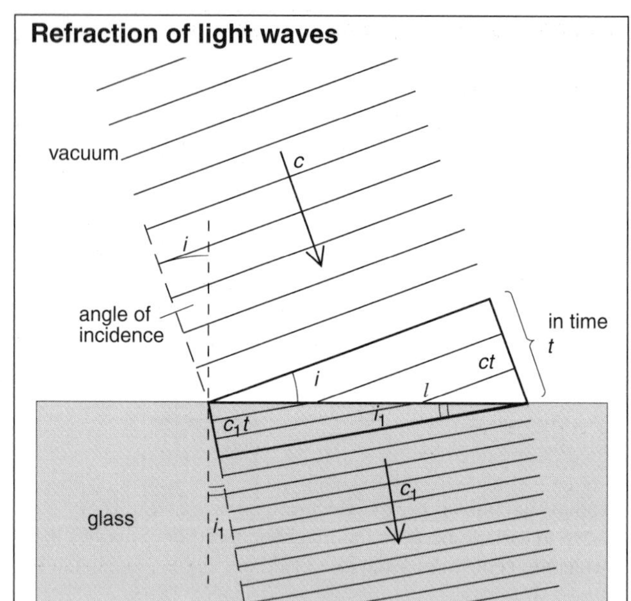

Above, light waves are shown as a series of lines called ***wavefronts***. All points on a wavefront are in phase. As the waves enter the glass, their speed slows from c to c_1. As a result, ***refraction*** (bending) occurs. In time t, one side of the beam travels a shorter distance in the glass (c_1t) than the other side does in the vacuum (ct). From the triangles in the diagram:

$$\sin i = \frac{ct}{l} \quad \text{and} \quad \sin i_1 = \frac{c_1t}{l} \quad \therefore \quad \frac{c}{c_1} = \frac{\sin i}{\sin i_1} = n_1$$

n is a constant called the ***refractive index*** of the medium (glass).

When light enters a typical glass, its speed slows from 3.0×10^8 m s^{-1} to 2.0×10^8 m s^{-1}. So, from the above equation, the refractive index of the glass is 1.5. Water does not slow light so much. Its refractive index is 1.3.

Note:
- $\sin i_1 \propto \sin i$.
- The refraction at an air-glass boundary is effectively the same as at a vacuum-glass boundary.
- The refractive index is slightly different for different wavelengths, which is why dispersion occurs (see A6).

On the right, light passes from one medium into another (of greater refractive index in this case). The wave direction is indicated by a single ray. The following equation applies:

$$\frac{c_1}{c_2} = \frac{\sin i_1}{\sin i_2} = {}_1n_2 \qquad (1)$$

${}_1n_2$ is the ***relative refractive index*** for light passing from medium 1 to medium 2. It can be shown that:

$${}_1n_2 = n_2/n_1$$

From this and equation (1), it follows that:

$$n_1 \sin i_1 = n_2 \sin i_2 \quad \text{and} \quad n_1c_1 = n_2c_2$$

Note:
- The equation above left is known as **Snell's Law**.
- n for a vacuum (or air) = 1.
- By the ***principle of reversibility***, a ray from B to A has the same path as one from A to B.

  So $\quad {}_2n_1 = \dfrac{1}{{}_1n_2}$

Speed, frequency, and wavelength

The waves on the right have a frequency f. So in time $1/f$, they move forward one wavelength, λ. As their speed c equals distance (λ) divided by time ($1/f$):

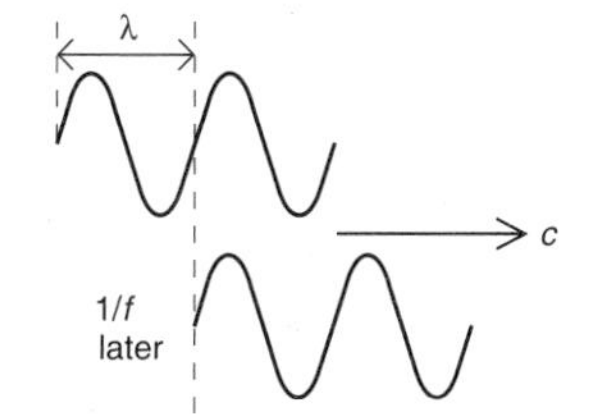

$$c = f\lambda$$

When refraction occurs, the frequency of the waves is unchanged. However, if the speed decreases, it follows from the above equation that the wavelength must also decrease.

Critical angle

On the right, light travels towards a boundary with a medium of lower refractive index. i_c is the ***critical angle*** (see A6). For angles greater than this, all the light is reflected by the surface and none is refracted. There is ***total internal reflection***.

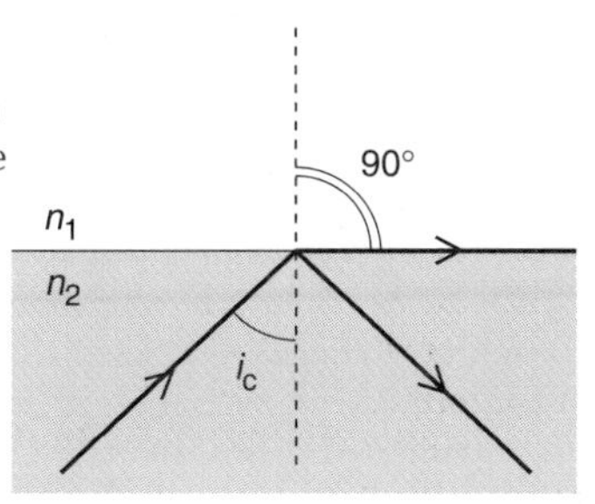

From equation (1)

$${}_1n_2 = \frac{\sin 90^\circ}{\sin i_c} = \frac{1}{\sin i_c}$$

So $$\sin i_c = \frac{1}{{}_1n_2}$$

For an air-glass boundary, ${}_1n_2$ is effectively equal to n_2. If $n_2 = 1.5$, then $\sin i_c = 1/1.5$. So $i_c = 42^\circ$ for the glass.

Optical fibres

Optical fibres (see also A6) can carry data, in the form of infrared pulses. They make use of total internal reflection.

Step-index multimode fibre This has a core surrounded by a cladding of lower refractive index. In the core, zig-zag paths (modes) of many different lengths are possible, so different pulses may overlap by the time they reach the end.

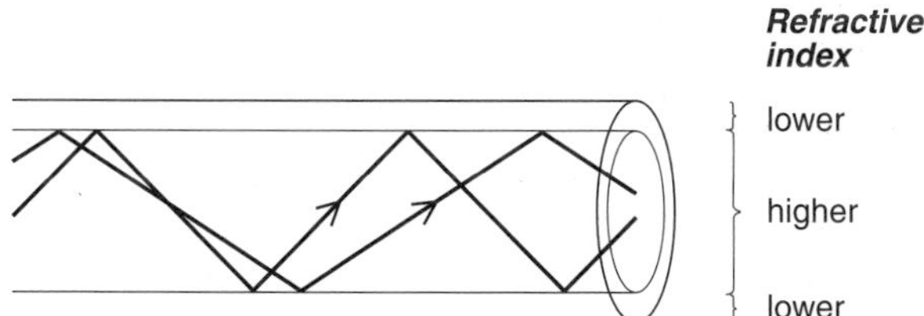

step-index multimode

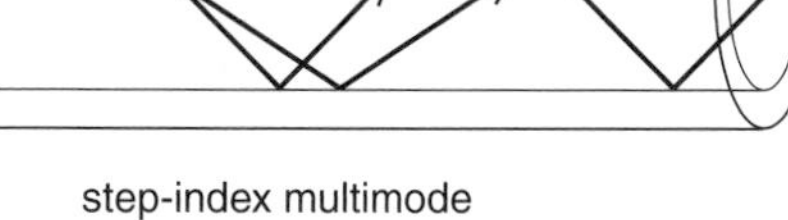

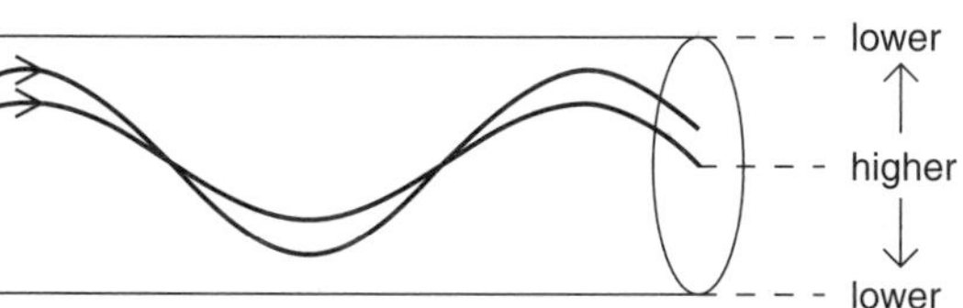

graded-index multimode

Graded-index multimode fibre The refractive index gradually reduces from the centre out. This means that the pulses take curved paths. But the longer paths are faster, so the travel times are about the same for all of them.

Graded-index monomode fibre This has a very narrow core, so that only one path is possible. As a result, the fibre can carry more pulses per second without overlap.

Polarization

In the top diagram on the opposite page, the particles oscillate in a vertical ***plane of vibration***. For a light wave, the plane of vibration is taken as that of the E vector. Light is usually a mixture of waves with different planes of vibration. It is ***unpolarized***. Polaroid transmits light in one plane of vibration only. Light like this is ***polarized***.

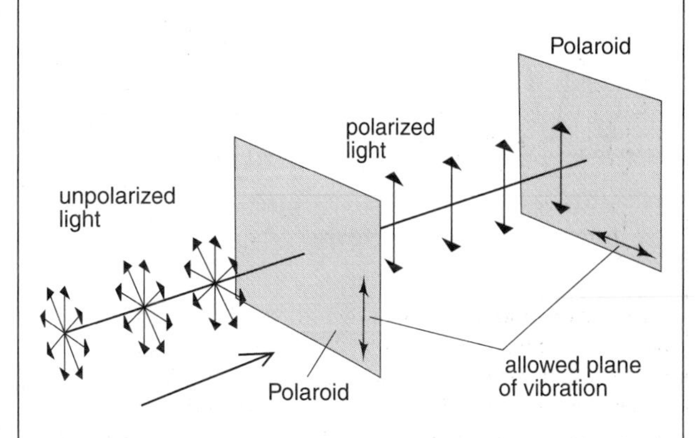

Above, polarized light from one Polaroid strikes a second. The light is blocked because its plane of vibration has no component in the allowed direction.

Only tranverse waves can be polarized. Experiments with Polaroid provide evidence that light waves are transverse.

Polarization by reflection When an unpolarized light ray strikes the surface of a transparent medium such as water, the refracted ray is partly polarized. At most angles, the reflected ray is also partly polarized.

But if the reflected ray is at 90° to the refracted ray, it is *totally* polarized. i_p is the ***polarizing angle***.

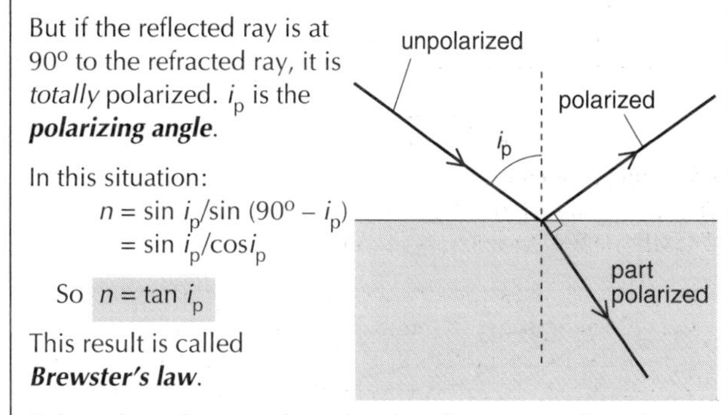

In this situation:

$$n = \sin i_p / \sin (90^\circ - i_p)$$
$$= \sin i_p / \cos i_p$$

So $n = \tan i_p$

This result is called ***Brewster's law***.

Polaroid sunglasses reduce the glare from wet surfaces by blocking the reflected, polarized light.

Intensity

Waves transmit energy. If waves pass through a surface, their ***intensity*** (in W m^{-2}) is calculated like this:

$$\text{intensity} = \frac{\text{power crossing surface}}{\text{area of surface}}$$

Intensity is proportional to $(\text{amplitude})^2$.

On the right, waves are radiating uniformly from a source of power output P. At a distance r from the source, the power is spread over an area $4\pi r^2$. So intensity $I = P/4\pi r^2$

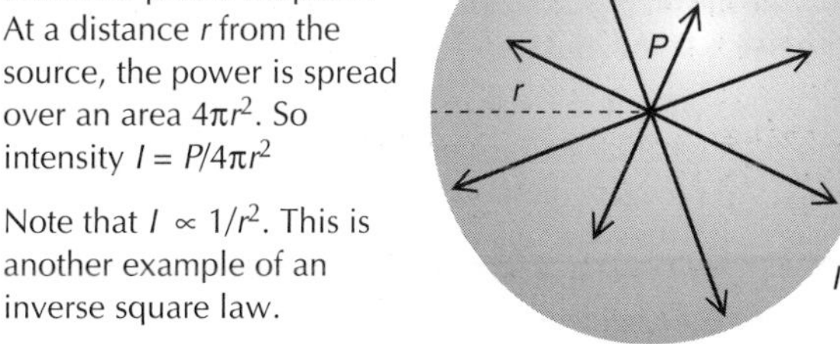

Note that $I \propto 1/r^2$. This is another example of an inverse square law.

B23 Combining waves

Superposition and interference

Two sets of waves can pass through the same point without affecting each other. However, they have a combined effect, found by adding their displacements (as vectors). This is known as the ***principle of superposition***.

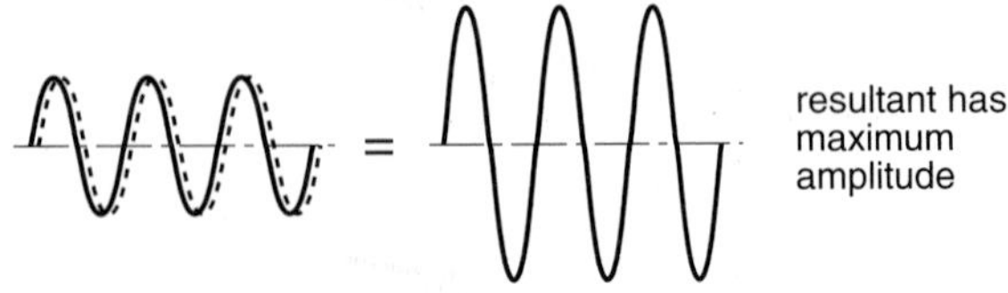

The waves above are *in phase* and reinforce each other. This is called ***constructive interference***.

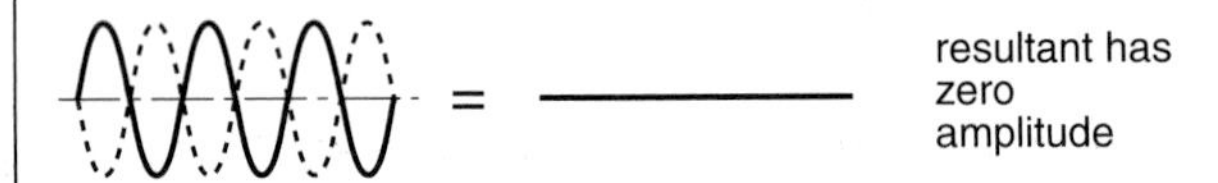

The waves above have a *phase difference* of $\frac{1}{2}$ cycle (180°) and cancel each other. This is called ***destructive interference***.

For interference to be observed:

- The sets of waves must be ***coherent***: there must be a constant phase difference between them. For this, they must have the same frequency.
- The sets of waves must have approximately the same amplitude and plane of vibration.

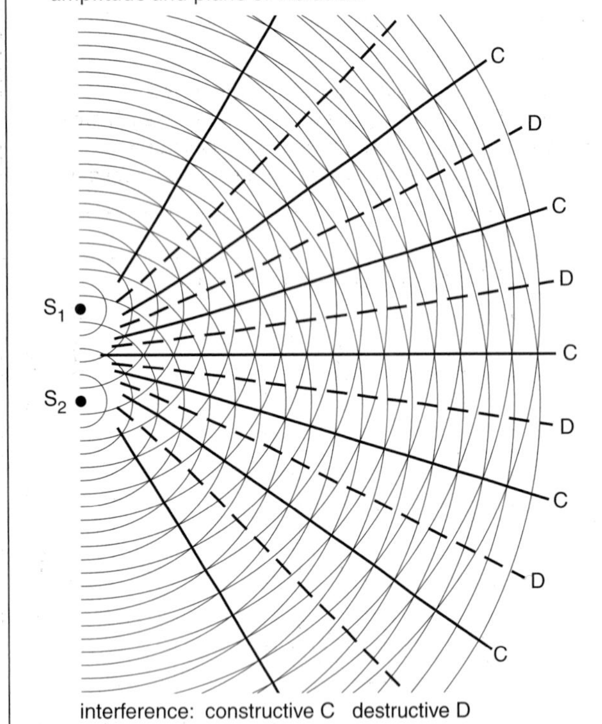

Above, waves from two coherent sources, S_1 and S_2, produce regions of reinforcing and cancelling called an ***interference pattern***. At each point of constructive interference, the path from one source is an exact number of wavelengths longer than from the other source (or the same length). The ***path difference*** is 0 or λ or 2λ, and so on.

Light waves will produce an interference pattern. However, waves from separate sources are not normally coherent, so the two sets of waves must originate from the same source. Light of one frequency (and therefore of one wavelength and colour) is called ***monochromatic light***. A laser emits monochromatic light which is coherent across its beam.

Double-slit experiment

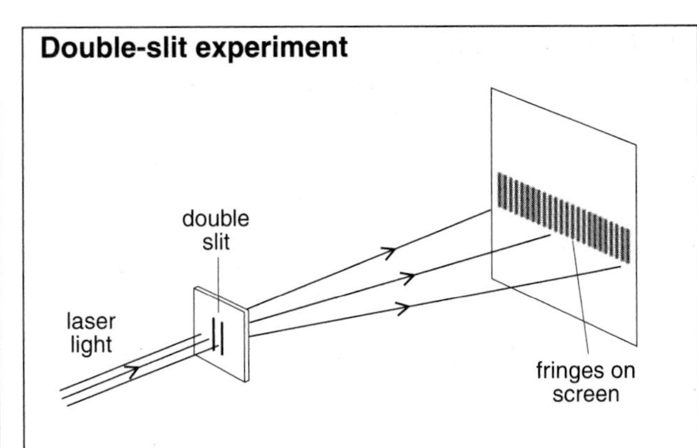

Above, light waves from a laser spread out from two slits (typicaly less than $\frac{1}{2}$mm apart). The interference pattern produces a series of bright and dark ***fringes*** on the screen. The bright fringes are regions of constructive interference.

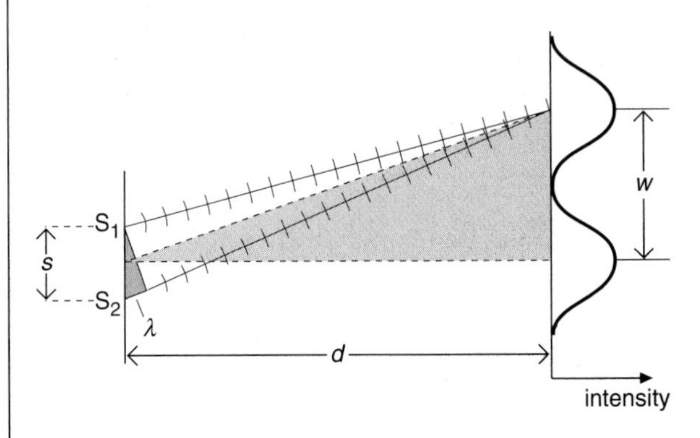

The first bright fringe occurs where the path difference is λ. For small angles, the shaded triangles above are similar, and the following equation applies:

$$\frac{\lambda}{s} = \frac{w}{D}$$

So: $w = \frac{\lambda D}{s}$ w is the ***fringe spacing***

Note:

- The fringe spacing is increased if the slits are closer together or light of longer wavelength is used.
- By measuring w, D, and s, the wavelength of light can be found using the above equation. Light wavelengths range from 7×10^{-7} m (red) down to 4×10^{-7} m (violet).

Single-slit diffraction

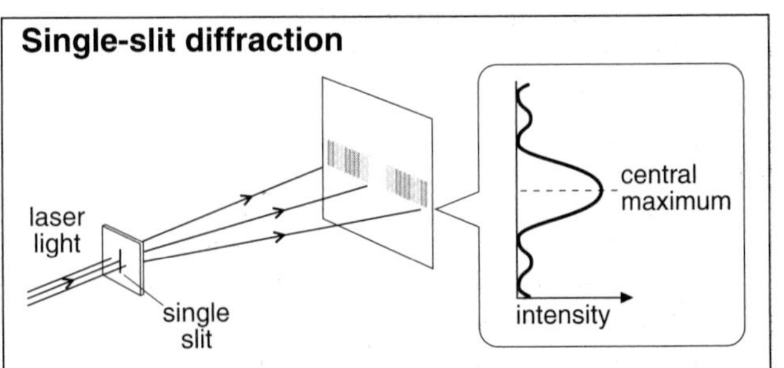

The spreading of light from a slit is an example of ***diffraction*** (see A6). Interference occurs between the different waves diffracted by the slit. The result is a pattern as above. The pattern becomes wider if the slit is made narrower or light of longer wavelength is used.

In optical instruments, diffraction limits the amount of detail in the image (see B24).

Diffraction grating

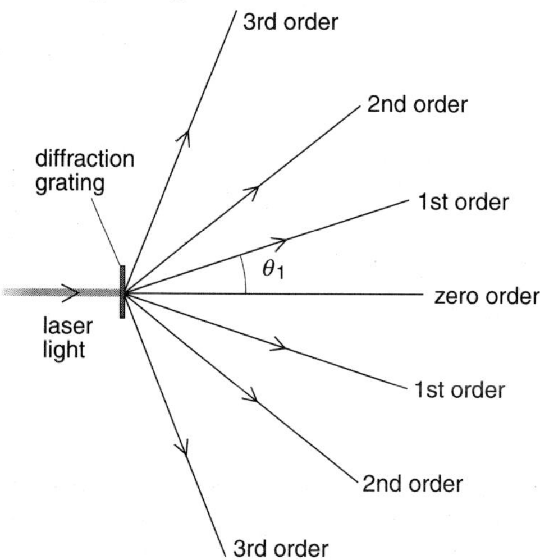

A ***diffraction grating,*** as above, has many slits (typically, 500 per mm). Constructive interference produces sharp lines of maximum intensity at set angles either side of a sharp, central maximum. In between, destructive interference gives zero or near-zero intensity. To identify the lines, they are each given an ***order number*** (0, 1, 2 etc.).

A close-up of part of the grating is shown above. d is the ***grating spacing***. θ_1 is the angle of the first order maximum. In this case, the path difference for any two adjacent slits is one wavelength, λ. From the triangles:

$\sin \theta_1 = \frac{\lambda}{d}$ So: $d \sin \theta_1 = \lambda$

For higher orders, the path differences are 2λ, 3λ etc. The following equation gives values of θ for all orders:

$$d \sin \theta = n\lambda$$

where n is the order number (0, 1, 2 etc.).

Note:

- If d, θ_1 and n are known, λ can be calculated.
- A longer wavelength gives a larger angle for each order.
- If the incoming light is a mixture of wavelengths (e.g. white), each order above zero becomes a spectrum.

Stationary waves in a stretched string

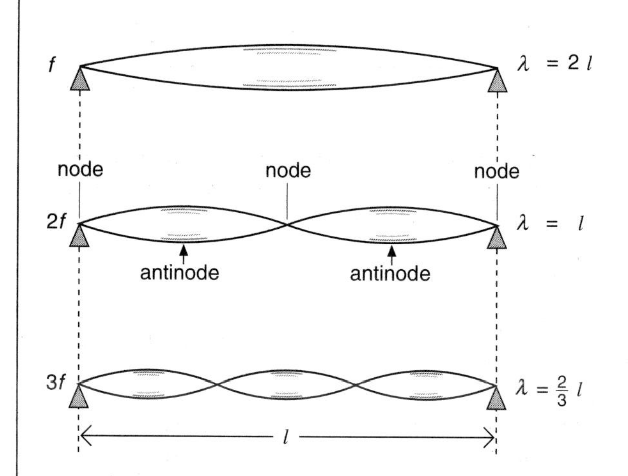

A stretched string can vibrate in various ***modes***, some of which are shown above. Each has a different frequency. The waves produced are known as ***stationary waves***. At ***nodes***, the amplitude of the oscillation is always zero. At ***antinodes***, it is always a maximum.

Stationary waves are produced by the superposition of two sets of progressive waves (of equal amplitude and frequency) travelling in opposite directions. For example, when a stretched string is vibrated, waves travel along the string, reflect from the ends, and are superimposed on waves travelling the other way.

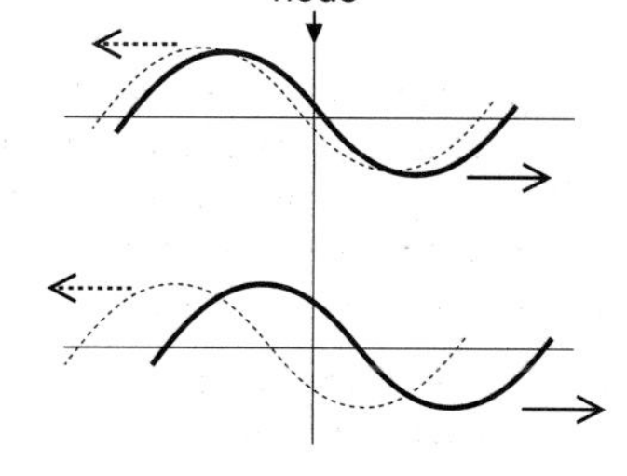

On the right, you can see how a node is formed. As one wave moves to the right and the other to the left, the + and – displacements always cancel, so the resultant displacement is zero.

Stationary waves in an air column

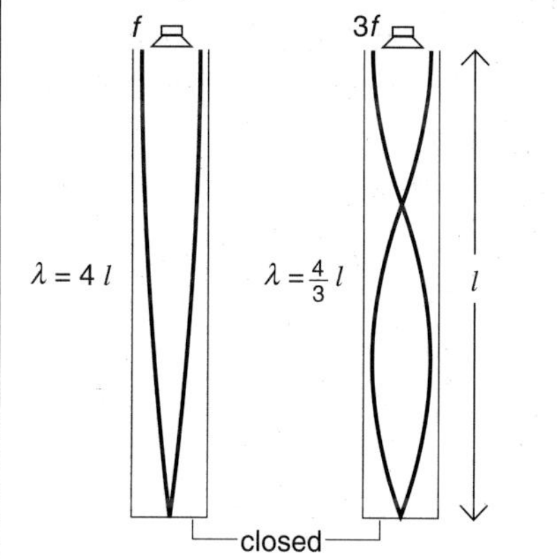

If a sound source is placed near the open end of a pipe, there are certain frequencies at which stationary waves are set up in the air column and the sound intensity reaches a maximum. This is another form of ***resonance*** (see also B11). Three examples are shown above.

Note:

- Sound waves are *longitudinal*. The 'waves' in each pipe are a *graphical representation* of the amplitude.
- Where the end of a pipe is open, there is an antinode. Where the end of a pipe is closed, there is a node.
- Knowing the frequency needed to produce resonance, and the wavelength from the pipe length, the speed of sound c can be calculated using $c = f\lambda$.

B24 Using mirrors and lenses

Plane mirrors, and images

On the right, rays from one point on an object reflect from a plane (flat) mirror. To the eye, the rays seem to come from a point behind the mirror. The same process occurs with rays from other parts of the object. As a result, an image is seen. (For simplicity, ray diagrams like this usually only show the rays coming from one point.)

The image in a plane mirror is known as a ***virtual image*** because no rays pass through it. Some optical instruments bring rays to a focus to form a ***real image***. This type of image can be picked up on a screen.

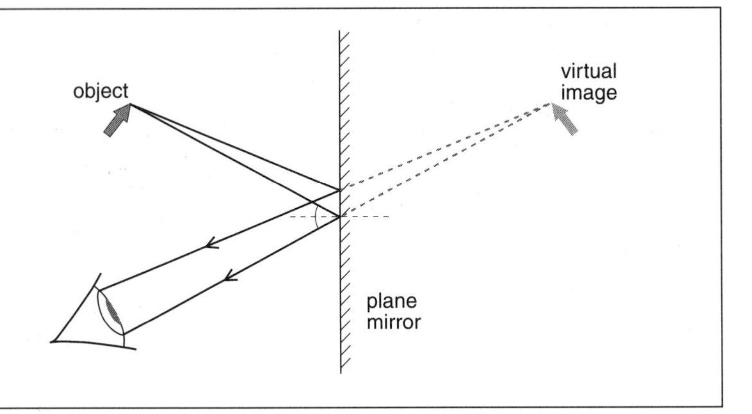

Convex and concave lenses

The diagrams on the right show how a convex and a concave lens each refract incoming rays parallel to the axis. Outgoing rays either converge towards or diverge from a ***principal focus***, F. Rays can come from either side, so there is another principal focus, F′, in an equivalent position on the opposite side of each lens. P is the ***optical centre***.

Note:

- In the rest of this unit, lenses are assumed to be thin, with no distorting effects. Diagrams will show refraction occuring at a line through the optical centre.

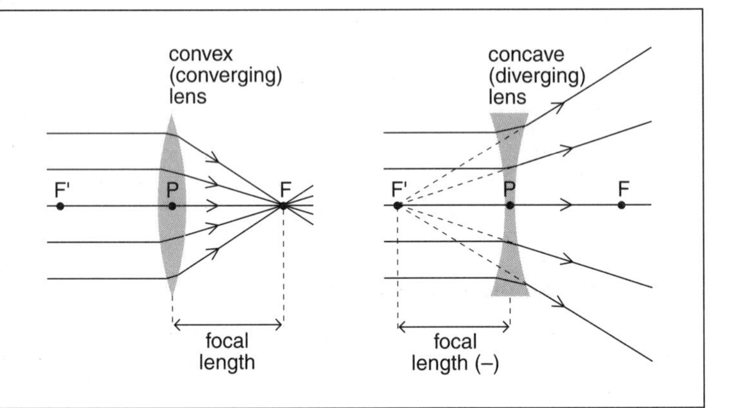

Convex lens equations

On the right, three rays have been used to show a convex lens forming a real, inverted image of an object:

1 A ray parallel to the axis is refracted through F.
2 A ray though P is undeviated (straight).
3 A ray through F′ is refracted parallel to the axis.

From pairs of similar triangles in the diagram, it is possible to link the object distance u, the image distance v and the focal length f with an equation:

$$\frac{1}{u}+\frac{1}{v}=\frac{1}{f} \qquad (1)$$

For example, for a lens of focal length 20 cm, the equation predicts that an object 60 cm from the lens will produce an image 30 cm from it, because:

$$\frac{1}{60}+\frac{1}{30}=\frac{1}{20}$$

Linear magnification *m* This is defined as follows:

$$\text{linear magnification} = \frac{\text{height of image}}{\text{height of object}}$$

By comparing similar triangles in the diagram above right:

$$m=\frac{v}{u} \qquad (2)$$

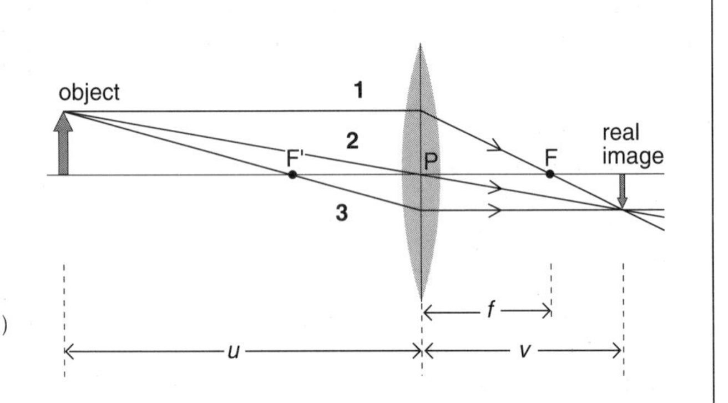

If the object above is moved towards F′, the image distance increases and the image gets larger. When u is $2f$, v is also $2f$, and the image and object are the same size ($m = 1$).

Convex lens as a magnifier

If u is less than f, a convex lens produces a virtual, upright, magnified image as on the right. Equation (1) applies, but the *virtual* image gives a *negative* value for v. For example if f is 20 cm, and u is 15 cm, solving the equation gives $v = -60$ cm. This tells you that there is a virtual image 60 cm from the lens. Also, as $v/u = -4$, the image is four times the height of the object.

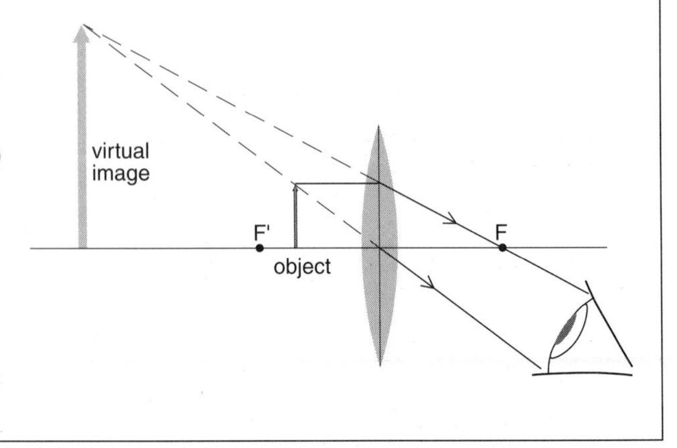

Refracting telescopes

In the telescope on the right, the ***objective*** lens focuses light from a distant object, to form a real image just on the principal focus of the ***eyepiece*** lens. The eyepiece lens then forms a virtual, magnified image of this real image. Set like this, the telescope is in ***normal adjustment.***

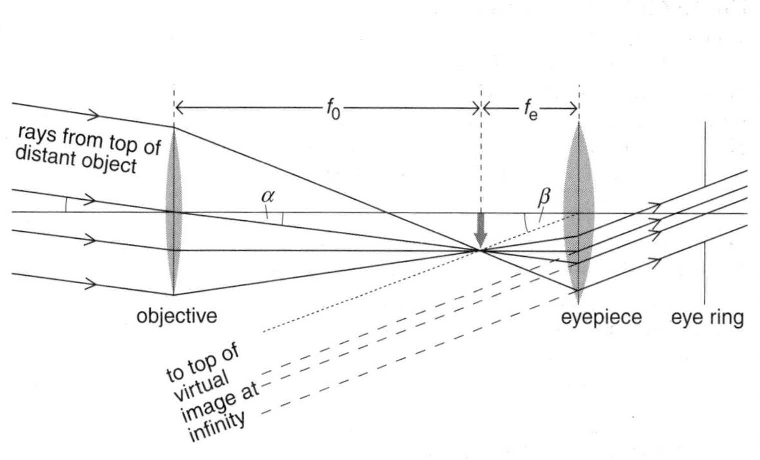

Angular magnification – This is defined as the ratio of the two angles β and α in the diagram on the right:

$$\text{angular magnification} = \frac{\beta}{\alpha}$$

From triangles in the diagram, it can be shown that:

$$\text{angular magnification} = \frac{f_o}{f_e}$$

For example, if the focal lengths of the objective and eyepiece lenses are 100 cm and 5 cm respectively, then the angular magnification (in the above setting) is 20.

Note, in the above diagram:

- The final image is inverted.
- For the widest angle of view, the eye is placed in the ***eye ring*** position (the position where the eyepiece forms a real image of the objective lens).
- By moving the eyepiece, the real image can be formed just inside its principal focus. The final, virtual image is then closer to the eye. However, it is more straining for the eye to look at this image for a long time.

Aperture The diameter of the objective lens is called its ***aperture***. It is difficult to make wide-aperture lenses which do not give a distorted image. But if this problem is solved, a wider aperture gives:

1 a brighter image,
2 a greater resolving power (see below).

Resolving power This is $1/\theta_{min}$, where θ_{min} is the smallest angle between two points such that their images can just be *resolved* (seen separately and unmerged).

Diffraction limits the resolving power because a telescope's objective lens acts rather like a wide slit (see B23). As a result, the images of two 'point' stars will each appear as tiny, circular fringe systems with intensities as below.

According to the ***Rayleigh criterion***, two images are just resolved if the central maximum of one coincides with the first minimum of the other. Increasing the aperture D gives less spread-out fringe systems and a greater resolving power ($\approx D/\lambda$).

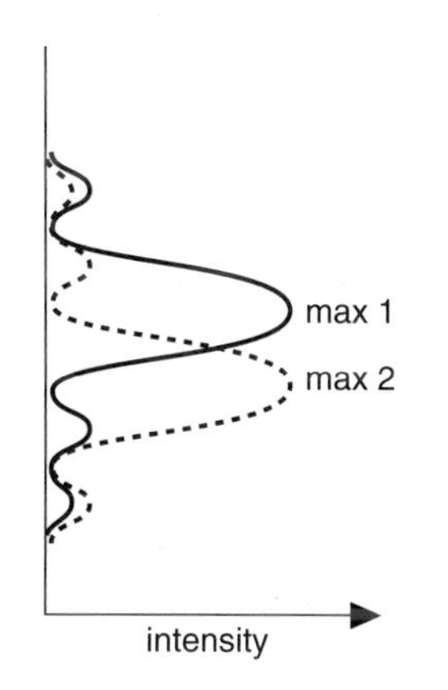

Reflecting prisms

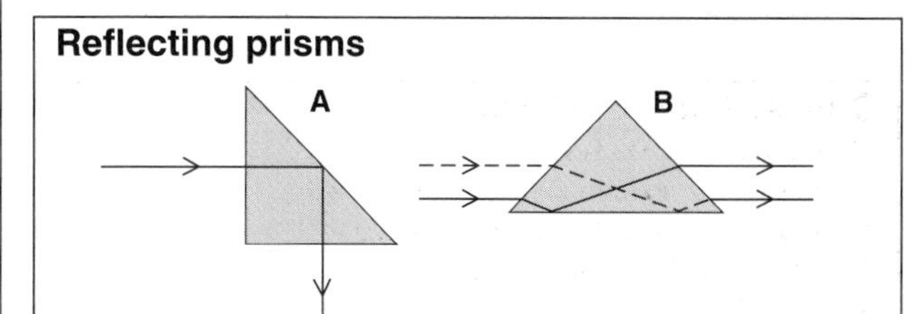

In prisms A and B above, total internal reflection occurs, (see B22). Prism B inverts the beam. Some binoculars contain prisms like this to compensate for the inverting effect of the lens system. (Binoculars are two telescopes side by side.)

Lens and mirror equations

Concave mirrors are *converging* systems, with similar image-forming properties to convex lenses.

Convex mirrors are *diverging* systems, with similar image-forming properties to concave lenses.

Equations (1) and (2) on the opposite page apply to all thin lenses and mirrors. However, when using them, note:

- *Converging* systems have *positive* focal lengths.
- *Diverging* systems have *negative* focal lengths.

Reflecting telescopes

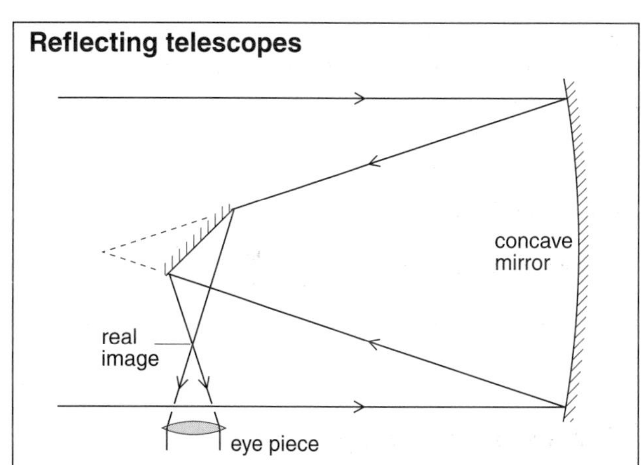

In large-aperture telescopes, the rays are brought to a focus by a concave mirror rather than an objective lens. With a mirror, support can be provided at the back to stop it flexing, and it is easier to reduce image distortion. Often, there is no eyepiece. The real image is formed either on a photographic plate, for later enlargement, or on a ***charge-coupled device (CCD)*** which stores it electronically.

B25 Solids, stresses, and strains

Deformation

The particles of a solid may be atoms, or molecules (groups of atoms), or ions (see A3). They are held closely together by electric forces of attraction.

When external forces are applied to a solid, its shape changes: ***deformation*** occurs. This alters the relative positions of its particles. There are two types of deformation, as described on the right.

Elastic deformation If the deformation is ***elastic***, then the material returns to its original shape when the forces on it are removed.

Plastic deformation If the deformation is ***plastic***, then the material does not return to its original shape when the forces on it are removed. For example, Plasticine takes on a new shape when stretched.

Solid structures

Solids can be classified into three main types, according to how their particles are arranged.

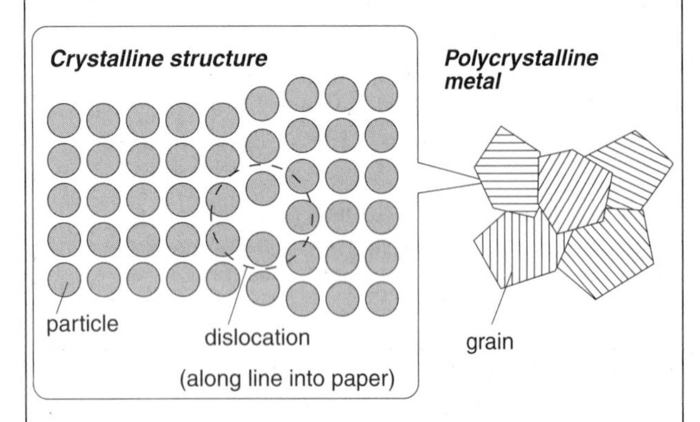

Crystalline solids The particles are in a regular, repeating pattern. They may form a single crystal, as with a diamond. However, there may be millions of tiny crystals joined together. Most metals have this ***polycrystalline*** structure. Their crystals, called ***grains***, can be as small as 10^{-2} mm.

Crystal structures normally have imperfections in them called ***dislocations***. These allow particles to change their relative positions, so the solid is more easily deformed.

Amorphous (glassy) solids The particles have no regular pattern (except over very short distances). Glass and wax have structures like this.

Polymers These materials have long-chain molecules, each of which may contain many thousands of atoms. The molecules are formed from the linking of short units called ***monomers***. In a polymer, the chains may be coiled up and tangled like spaghetti. Depending on the amount of tangling, a polymer may be described as ***semi-crystalline*** or ***amorphous***.

Rubber and wool are natural polymers. Plastics, such as nylon and artificial rubber, are synthetic polymers.

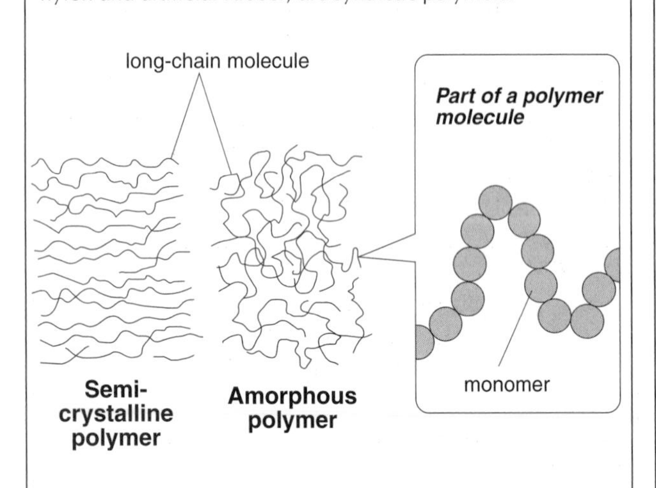

Stress and strain

On the right, a wire of cross-sectional area A is under tension from a force F (at each end). The ***tensile stress*** σ on the wire is defined like this:

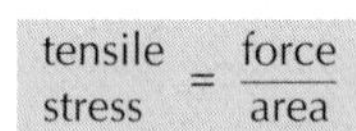

$$\text{tensile stress} = \frac{\text{force}}{\text{area}} \qquad \sigma = \frac{F}{A}$$

The unit of tensile stress is the N m^{-2}.

The wire stretches so that its length l_0 increases by Δl, called its ***extension***. The ***tensile strain*** ε is defined like this:

$$\text{tensile strain} = \frac{\text{extension}}{\text{original length}} \qquad \varepsilon = \frac{\Delta l}{l_0}$$

Tensile strain has no units.

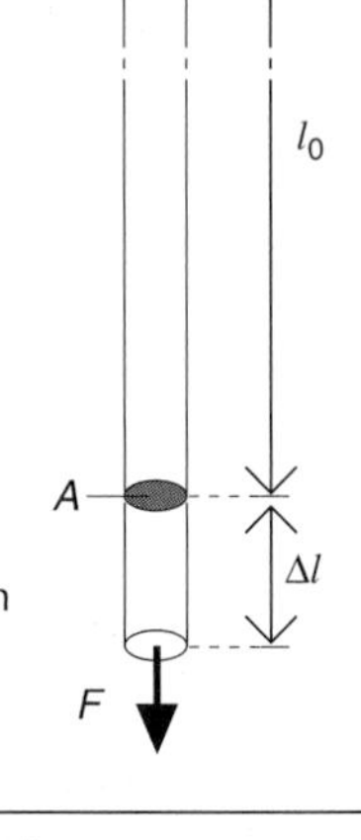

Note:
- There are stresses and strains linked with compression and twisting. On these pages however, the word stress or strain by itself will imply the tensile type.

Hooke's law

The graph below shows how stress varies with strain when a metal wire (steel) is stretched until it breaks.

Note:
- By convention, strain is plotted along the horizontal axis.
- The sequence O to E is described in detail on the next page.

If a material obeys **Hooke's law** then, for an *elastic* deformation, the strain is proportional to the stress.

The wire obeys Hooke's law up to point A.

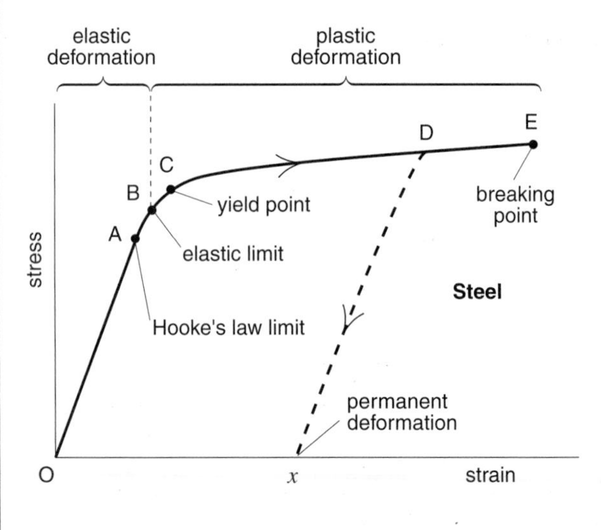

Young's modulus

For a material which obeys Hooke's law, stress/strain is a constant. This constant is called ***Young's modulus***, E:

$$\text{Young's modulus} = \frac{\text{tensile stress}}{\text{tensile strain}} \qquad E = \frac{\sigma}{\varepsilon}$$

Using the equations for σ and ε $\qquad E = \dfrac{Fl_0}{A\Delta l}$

Note:

- l_0 is constant. If E and A are also constant, $\Delta l \propto F$. So the extension is proportional to the stretching force.
- The above equations can also be used when the material is being compressed.

Typical values for Young's modulus, in Nm^{-2}
steel 21×10^{10} aluminium 7×10^{10}

So, steel is proportionately three times as difficult to stretch as aluminium.

Strain energy

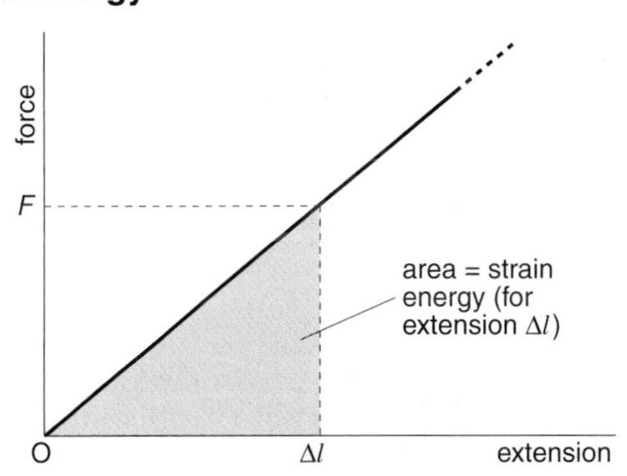

The graph above shows how the extension varies with the stretching force for a material which obeys Hooke's law. The work done for an extension Δl is given by the shaded area (see B12). The area of a triangle = $\frac{1}{2}$ × base × height. So the work done = $\frac{1}{2}$ $F\Delta l$.

As work is done *on* the material, energy is stored *by* the material. This is its ***strain energy***. So:

$$\text{strain energy} = \tfrac{1}{2}\,F\Delta l$$

Note:

- If Hooke's law is *not* obeyed, the work done is still equal to the area under a force-extension graph. However, the above equation does not apply.

Stretching glass

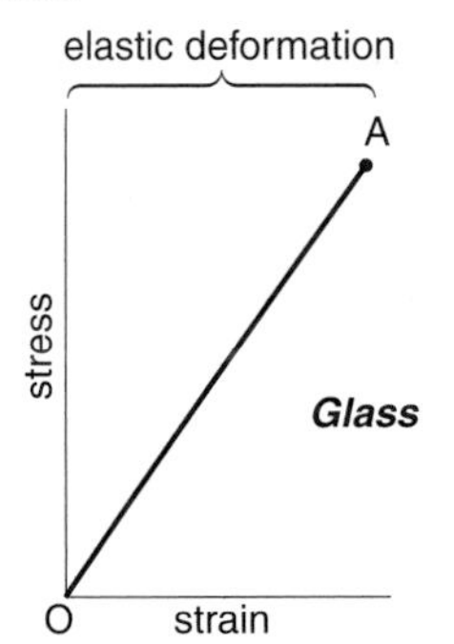

The graph above shows what happens if increasing tensile stress is applied to a glass thread. Elastic deformation occurs until, at point A, a crack suddenly grows, and the glass breaks. A material which behaves like this is said to be ***brittle***. The break is called a ***brittle fracture***.

Stretching a metal

Unlike glass, most metals do not experience brittle fracture when stretched because dislocations tend to stop cracks growing and spreading. The following descriptions refer to the graph for a steel wire on the opposite page.

O to B The deformation of the wire is elastic.

B This is the ***elastic limit***. Beyond it, the deformation becomes plastic as layers of particles slide over each other. If the stress were removed at, say, point D, the wire would be left with a permanent deformation (strain x on the axis).

C this is the ***yield point***. Beyond it, little extra force is needed to produce a large extra extension. If a material can be stretched like this, it is said to be ***ductile***.

E The wire develops a thin 'neck', then a ***ductile fracture*** occurs. The highest stress just before the wire breaks is called the ***ultimate tensile stress***.

Fatigue If a metal is taken through many cycles of *changing* stress, a fatigue fracture may occur before the ultimate tensile stress is reached. Fatigue fractures are caused by the slow spread of small cracks.

Creep This is the deformation which goes on happening in some materials if stress is maintained. For example, unsupported lead slowly sags under its own weight.

Stretching rubber

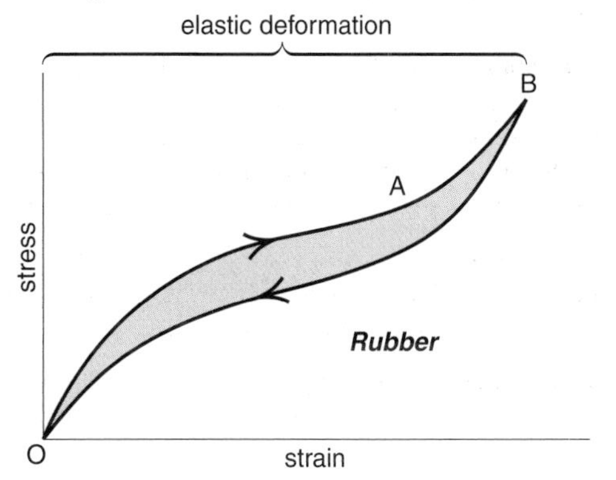

The graph shows what happens if increasing stress is applied to a rubber cord, and then released before the breaking point. Rubber does not obey Hooke's law. Also, much higher strains are possible than in steel or glass. For example, if the extension is twice the original length, the strain is 2.

O to A The molecular chains in the rubber are being uncoiled and straightened.

A to B The chains are almost straight, so the rubber is becoming proportionately more difficult to stretch.

B to A The rubber contracts when the stress is removed.

During this cycle of extension and contraction, energy is lost as heat. The effect is called ***elastic hysteresis***. The shaded area represents the energy lost per unit volume.

Bending

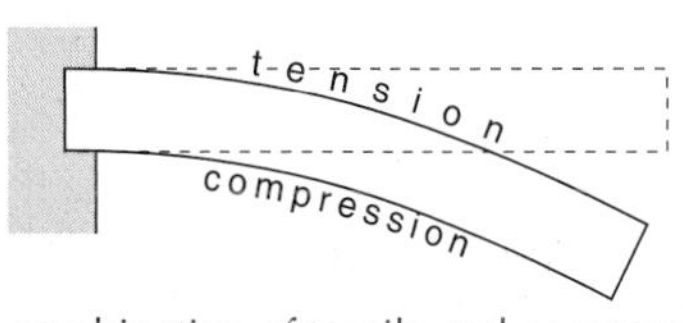

Bending is a combination of tensile and compressive strain as shown here.

B26 Liquid and gas pressure

Density, volume, mass, and weight

The links between the above four quantities are useful when dealing with problems on pressure.

If a material of uniform density ρ has a mass m and occupies a volume V, then:

$$\rho = \frac{m}{V}$$ (see A1)

In the diagram in the panel below, the column of liquid has a depth h and a base area A. In this case:

volume of liquid = hA

mass of liquid = ρhA (because $m = \rho V$)

weight of liquid = ρghA (because weight = mg)

Pressure in a liquid

If a liquid exerts a force F on an area A (at right-angles to it), then the pressure p is given by this equation:

$$p = \frac{F}{A}$$ (see A1)

Note:

- If the area A is vanishingly small, the above equation gives the *pressure at a point* in a liquid.
- Pressure is a scalar, *not* a vector (though the force it creates is a vector).
- The unit of pressure is the pascal (Pa). 1 Pa = 1 N m^{-2}.

The liquid on the right has a density ρ. The weight of the liquid column exerts a downward force F on the base area A.

F = weight of column
$= \rho ghA$
(see previous panel)

But $p = F/A$.

So $p = \rho gh$

The above equation gives the pressure p at a depth h in a liquid of density ρ.

Note:

- The pressure acts in *all* directions (see A1). However, the force produced is at right-angles to any area in contact.
- The pressure does *not* depend on the area A. In the liquid below, all points at the same depth h are at the same pressure, ρgh.

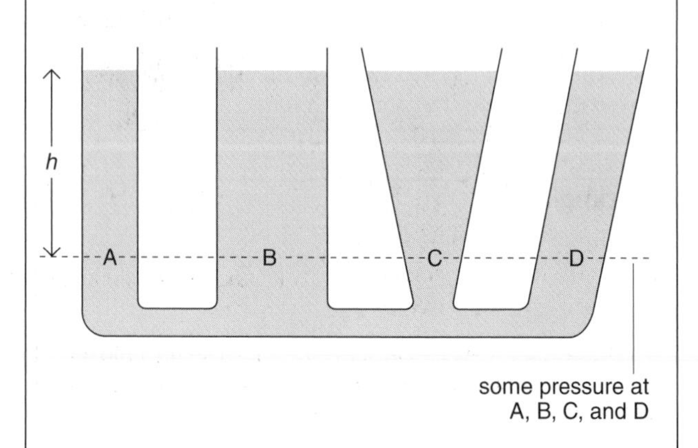

Transmitting pressure

Liquids and gases are called ***fluids*** because they can flow.

According to ***Pascal's principle***, a pressure applied to any part of an enclosed fluid is transmitted to all other parts. This principle is used in ***hydraulic machines*** like the oil-filled jack below.

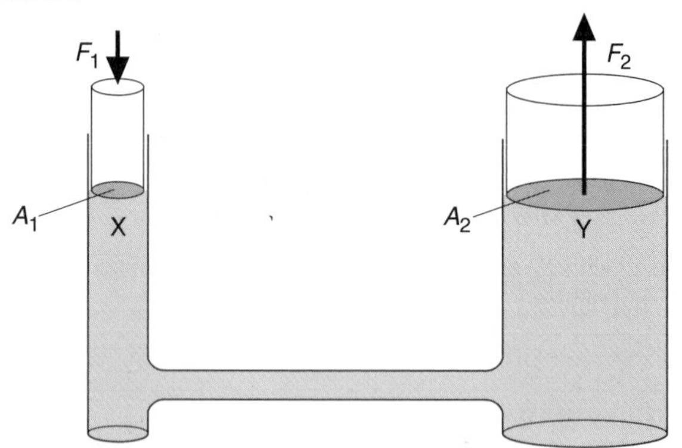

In the above system:

pressure at X (due to force F_1 acting on A_1) = F_1/A_1

So, by Pascal's principle pressure at Y = F_1/A_1

But pressure at Y = F_2/A_2

So $$\frac{F_2}{F_1} = \frac{A_2}{A_1}$$

Note:

- The pressures at X and Y would *not* be the same if their levels were different. There would be ρgh to allow for.
- Pressure is only transmitted without reduction if the liquid is static, and not flowing (see C8).

Barometer

Atmospheric pressure can be measured using a simple barometer like the one on the right. The space at the top of the glass tube is a vacuum, so the pressure there is zero. The column of mercury in the tube is supported by the pressure of the atmosphere outside. The greater the pressure, the longer the column.

atmospheric pressure
= pressure at X

$= \rho gh$

Standard atmospheric pressure (at sea level) will support a column of mercury 0.76 m long. As g is 9.81 N kg^{-1} and the density of mercury is 13.6×10^3 kg m^{-3}:

standard atmospheric pressure = $13.6 \times 10^3 \times 9.81 \times 0.76$
$= 1.01 \times 10^5$ Pa

The ***millibar* (mb)** is a unit of pressure used in meteorology. 1 mb = 100 Pa. So, standard atmospheric pressure = 1.01×10^3 mb.

U-tube manometer

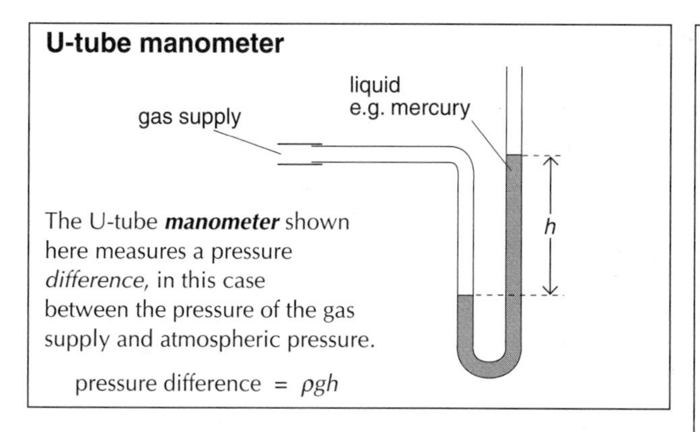

The U-tube ***manometer*** shown here measures a pressure *difference*, in this case between the pressure of the gas supply and atmospheric pressure.

pressure difference $= \rho gh$

Upthrust and Archimedes' principle

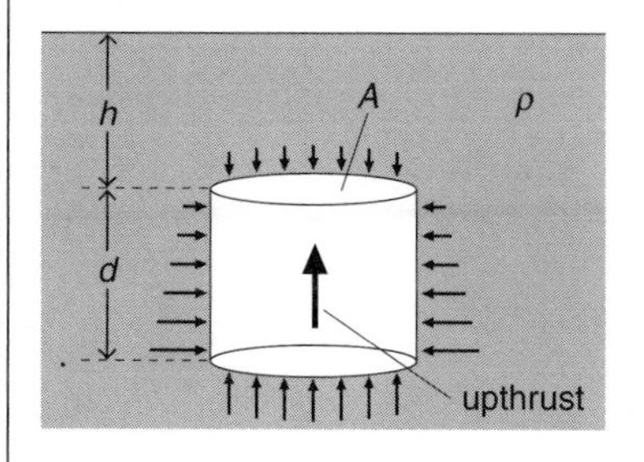

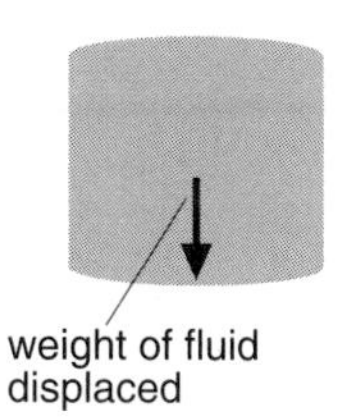

The cylinder above is immersed in a fluid (in this case, a liquid). As a result, fluid is ***displaced***. The mass of fluid displaced is ρdA.

The pressure on the bottom of the cylinder is greater than on the top, so the upward force on the cylinder is greater than the downward force. The *resultant* upward force is the difference between the two. It is called the ***upthrust***.

upward force $= \rho g(h + d)A$

downward force $= \rho ghA$

So upthrust $= \rho g(h + d)A - \rho ghA = \rho gdA$

But $\rho gdA =$ weight of fluid displaced

So **upthrust = weight of fluid displaced**

This is known as ***Archimedes' principle***.

Note:

- The principle applies to all fluids (liquids *and* gases).
- The principle applies to an immersed object of any shape, including one which is only partly immersed.

Floating stability

The upthrust on a boat is the resultant of many forces distributed over the immersed part of its hull. The point at which the upthrust acts is called the ***centre of buoyancy***. It is where the centre of gravity of the displaced fluid would be, and its position changes when the hull rolls.

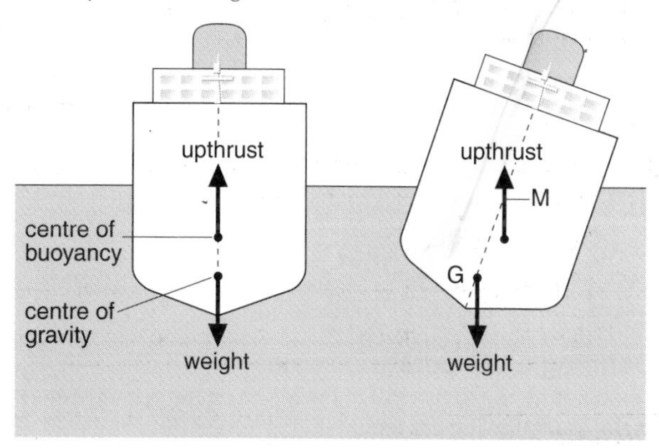

The boat above is in a position of stable equilibrium (see B5). If it starts to roll to one side, the upthrust and the weight form a couple which turns it back again.

The ***metacentre*** (M) is the point where the line of the upthrust meets the centre line of the boat. For stable equilibrium, the metacentre must be *higher* than the centre of gravity (G).

For *maximum* stability the metacentre must be as *high* as possible and the boat loaded so that its centre of gravity is as *low* as possible. (In practice, this is not always desirable because a boat which recovers too rapidly from wave rocking can make passengers sea sick.)

If a boat is loaded so that the metacentre is below the centre of gravity, as on the right, then the equilibrium is unstable. Once the boat has started to roll, the upthrust and the weight form a couple which continues to roll the boat over.

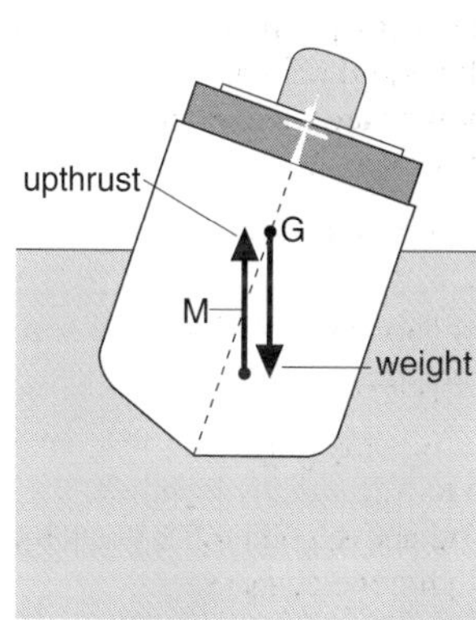

Flotation

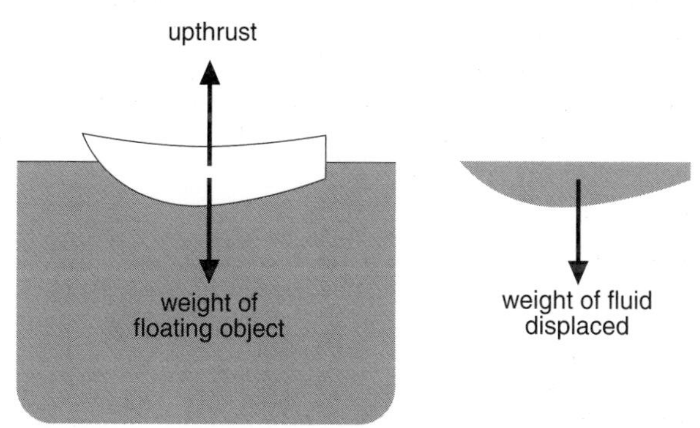

The forces on the boat above are in equilibrium (see B5), so, weight of boat = upthrust on boat. But, by Archimedes' principle, upthrust = weight of fluid displaced. So:

weight of floating object = weight of fluid displaced

This is known as the ***principle of flotation***.

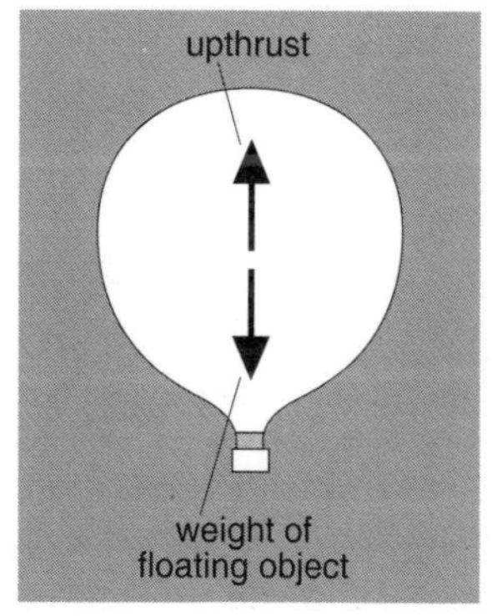

A given volume of hot air weighs less than the same volume of cold air because it has a lower density.

A hot-air balloon like the one above just floats in the cold air around it when the total weight of hot air, fabric, and load is equal to the weight of cold air displaced.

B27 Temperature

Temperature and thermal equilibrium

Objects A and B are in contact. If heat flows from A to B, then A is at a higher ***temperature*** than B.

When the heat flow from A to B is zero, the two objects are in ***thermal equilibrium*** and at the same temperature.

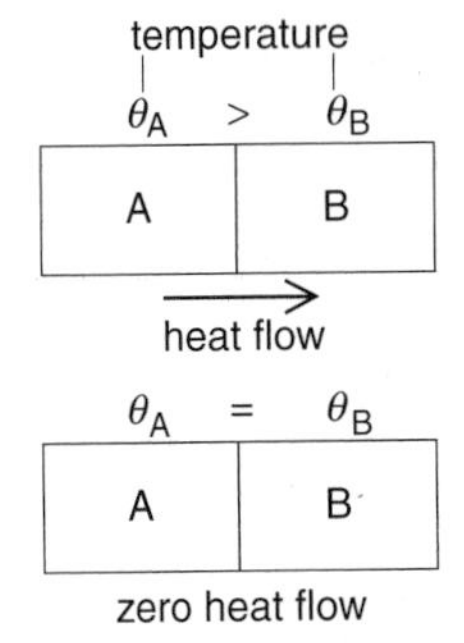

The zeroth law of thermodynamics states that if objects A and B are each in thermal equilibrium with an object C, then they are also in thermal equilibrium with each other.

Note:
- Any objects in thermal equilibrium are at the same temperature.
- Thermodynamics deals with the links between heat and other forms of energy. The zeroth law is so named because the first and second laws of thermodynamics (see B28) had already been stated when the need for a more basic law was realised.

Defining a temperature scale

Temperature is a 'degree of hotness'. To define a temperature scale, the following are required:

Thermometric property This is some property of a material that varies continuously with hotness. For example:
- the length of a column of mercury in a glass capillary tube (the mercury expands when heated, as shown in the diagram on the right),
- the resistance of a coil of platinum wire,
- the pressure of a trapped gas kept at fixed volume.

Fixed points These are *defined* reference points against which other temperatures can be judged. For example, on the Celsius scale:
- The *lower* fixed point (0 °C) is the ***ice point***. This is the temperature of pure, melting ice at standard atmospheric pressure.
- The *upper* fixed point (100 °C) is the ***steam point***. This is the temperature of the steam above pure boiling water at standard atmospheric pressure.

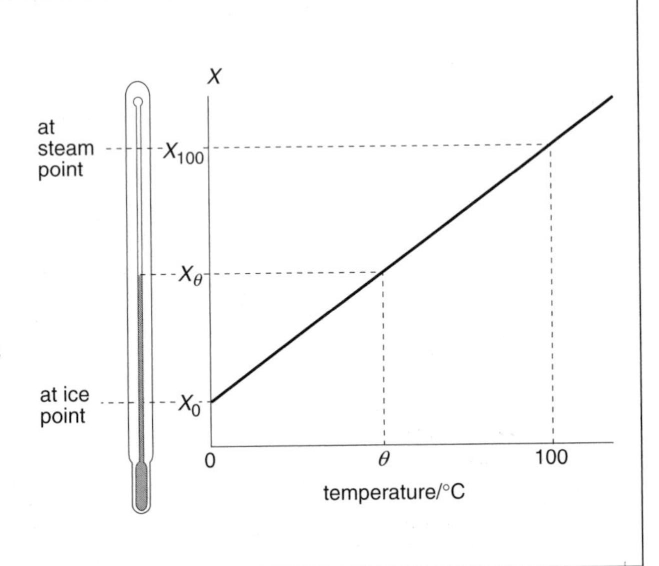

Linear link The graph above right shows how the length X of a column of mercury varies with temperature on the mercury-in-glass Celsius scale. The scale is *defined* such that the relationship between X and temperature is linear.

If X_θ is the length at some unknown temperature θ, and X_0 and X_{100} are the lengths at the ice and steam points respectively, then θ is given by the following equation:

$$\frac{\theta}{100} = \frac{X_\theta - X_0}{X_{100} - X_0}$$

For example, if $X_0 = 20$ mm, $X_\theta = 30$ mm, and $X_{100} = 40$ mm, then $\theta = 50$ °C. In this case, the length is exactly half way between its values at the ice and steam points, so the temperature is exactly half way between 0 °C and 100 °C.

Note:
- In the above equation, X can represent the value of *any* thermometric property.
- Scales based on different thermometric properties must, by definition, agree at the fixed points. But they do not necessarily agree at any other points. (In practice, the thermometric properties listed above give close agreement within the 0–100 °C range.)

Thermodynamic temperatures

The ***Kelvin scale*** (see A3) is a thermodynamic scale, related to the average kinetic energy per particle (e.g. molecule), and not to any thermometric property. Its definition, in terms of the efficiency of a reversible heat engine, is theoretical and cannot be used practically. However, its scale divisions closely match those of a constant-volume gas thermometer (see next page).

On the Kelvin scale:
- ***Absolute zero*** is 0 kelvin (0 K). This is the temperature at which all substances have minimum internal energy.
- The ice point is 273.15 K.

The Celsius thermodynamic temperature θ of an object is linked to its Kelvin temperature T by this equation:

$$\frac{\theta}{°\mathrm{C}} = \frac{T}{\mathrm{K}} - 273.15$$

In the above, 273 is adequate for most purposes.

Thermometers

Different types of thermometer are described on the right. Some give a direct reading. With others, the temperature must be worked out from other measurements. Before a thermometer can be used, it must be *calibrated* by marking on scale divisions or by preparing a system for converting readings into temperatures. For accurate calibration, a constant-volume gas thermometer is used as a standard.

Type of thermometer	Principle	Range/K	Advantages (+) Disadvantages (–)
mercury-in-glass (see opposite page)	When the temperature rises, mercury expands and moves further up a capillary tube.	234 to 700	+ Portable – Not very accurate – Fragile
constant-volume gas 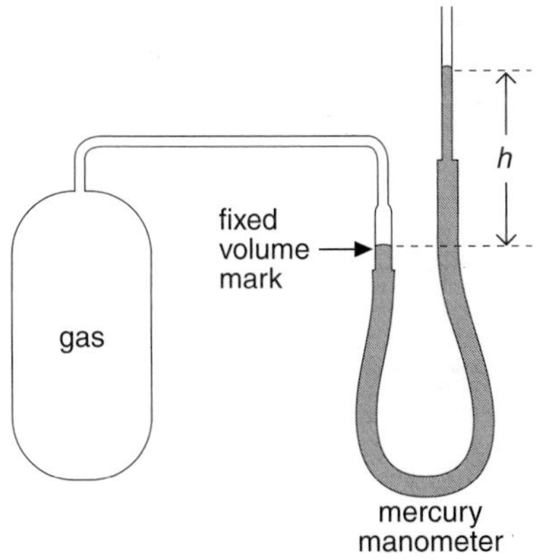	The bulb contains a fixed mass of hydrogen, helium, or nitrogen gas. When the temperature rises, the pressure of the gas rises, and a larger height difference h is needed in the manometer to keep the gas at fixed volume. (The open limb of the manometer can be raised to achieve this.) The pressure of the gas is equal to $\rho g h$ plus atmospheric (see B26).	3 to 1750	+ Wide range + Accurate, sensitive + Used as a standard – Not direct reading – Slow response; not suitable for varying temperatures – Cumbersome, fragile
platinum resistance 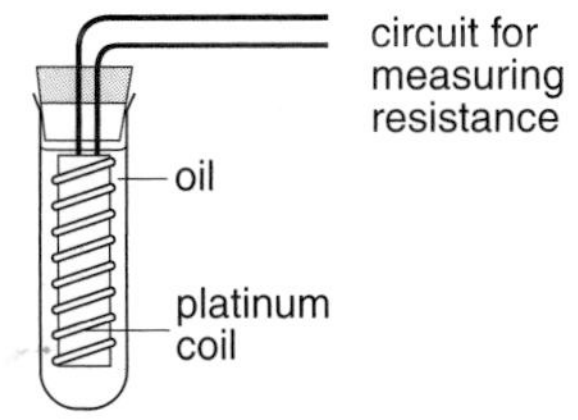	When the temperature rises, the resistance of the platinum coil rises. The resistance is measured accurately with a circuit which makes use of balanced PDs.	25 to 1750	+ Wide range + Accurate, sensitive – Not direct reading – Slow response; not suitable for varying temperatures
thermistor 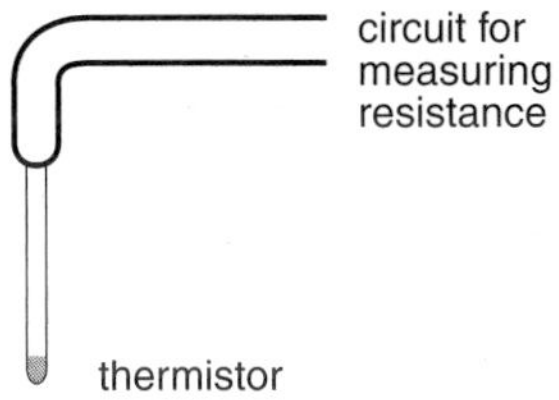	When the temperature rises, the resistance of the thermistor falls. The resistance is measured using a circuit which can include a meter calibrated in degrees.	250 to 450	+ Can be linked to other circuits or computer – Limited range – Not very accurate
thermocouple 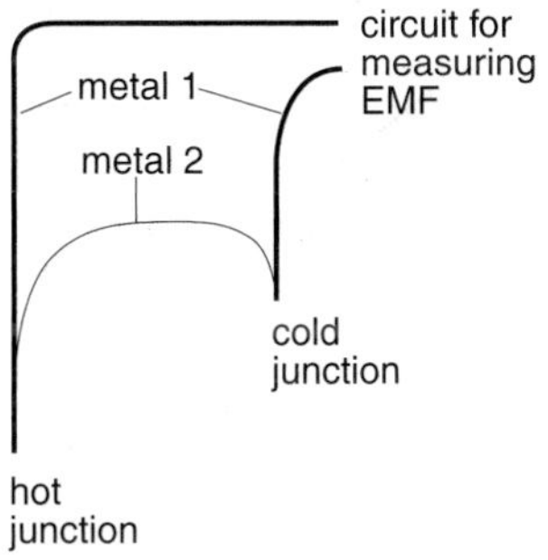	The circuit contains two junctions of dissimilar metals. When one junction is hotter than the other, a small ***thermoelectric*** EMF is generated. The EMF depends on the temperature difference. It is measured using a circuit which can include a meter calibrated in degrees.	80 to 1400	+ Wide range + Small, robust + Quick response + Can be linked to other circuits or computer – Less accurate than constant-volume gas and platinum resistance thermometers
infrared radiation 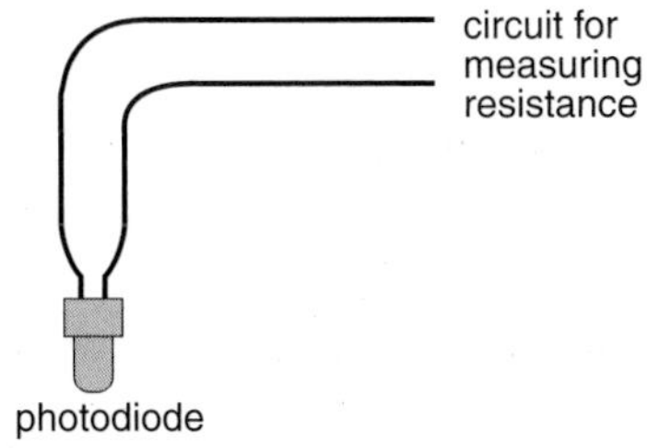	An object gives off more infrared radiation when its temperature rises. This makes the resistance of the photodiode decrease. The resistance is measured using a circuit which can include a meter calibrated in degrees.	225 to 3750	+ No direct contact + Suitable for normal and very high temperatures + Can be linked to other circuits or computer – Less accurate than constant-volume gas and platinum resistance thermometers

B28 Internal energy, heat, and work

Internal energy

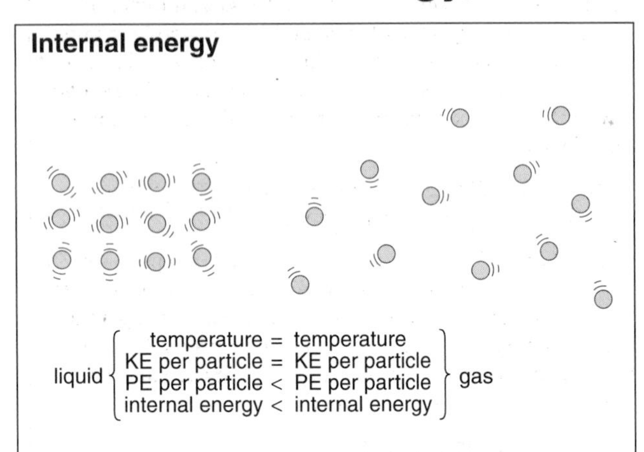

In the liquid, above left, the particles (e.g. molecules) are in motion, so they have kinetic energy (KE). This motion has moved them apart, against the forces of attraction, so they also have potential energy (PE). The total of their KEs and PEs is the ***internal energy*** of the liquid.

Above right, the liquid has become a gas. The temperature is the same as before. So the average KE of each particle due to its linear motion is the same (see A3). However, the average PE is more because of the increased separation of the particles. The gas has more internal energy than the liquid.

The first law of thermodynamics

An object can be given more internal energy:

- by supplying it with heat,
- by doing work on it (i.e. by compressing it) (see A2).

If ΔU is the increase in internal energy when heat Q is supplied to an object *and* work W is done on it, then according to the ***first law of thermodynamics***:

increase in internal energy = heat supplied *to* object + work done *on* object

In symbols $\Delta U = Q + W$

Note:

- The joule is the unit of internal energy, heat, and work.

Heat capacity

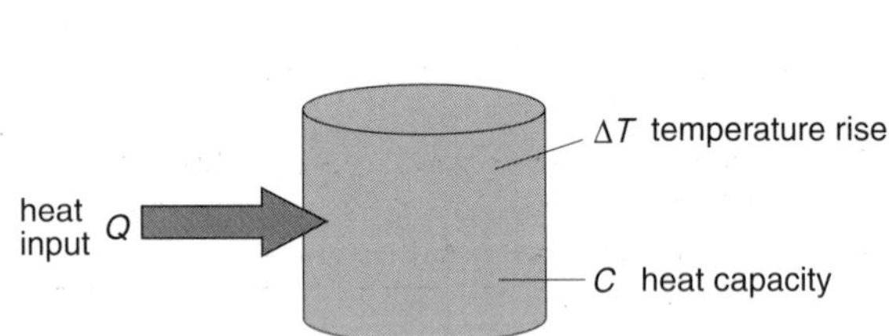

The ***heat capacity*** of an object is given by this equation:

$$\text{heat capacity} = \frac{\text{heat input}}{\text{temperature rise}} \qquad C = \frac{Q}{\Delta T}$$

For example, if a heat input of 4000 J causes a temperature rise of 2 K, then the heat capacity is 2000 J K^{-1}.

When a solid or liquid is heated, it expands very little and does almost no work. So virtually all the heat supplied is used to increase its internal energy. That follows from the first law of thermodynamics. If $W = 0$, then $\Delta U = Q$.

Specific heat capacity

The heat capacity per unit mass is called the ***specific heat capacity*** (see A3 for typical values). If a substance's specific heat capacity is c, then, for a mass m:

$$Q = mc\Delta T \qquad (1)$$

Water has a high specific heat capacity (4200 J kg^{-1} K^{-1}). This makes it a good 'heat storer'. A relatively large heat input is needed for any given temperature rise, and there is a relatively large heat output when the temperature falls.

Measuring *c* for a liquid (e.g. water) This can be done using the equipment below. The principle is to supply a measured mass of liquid with a known amount of heat from an electric heating coil, measure the temperature rise, and calculate c using equation (1).

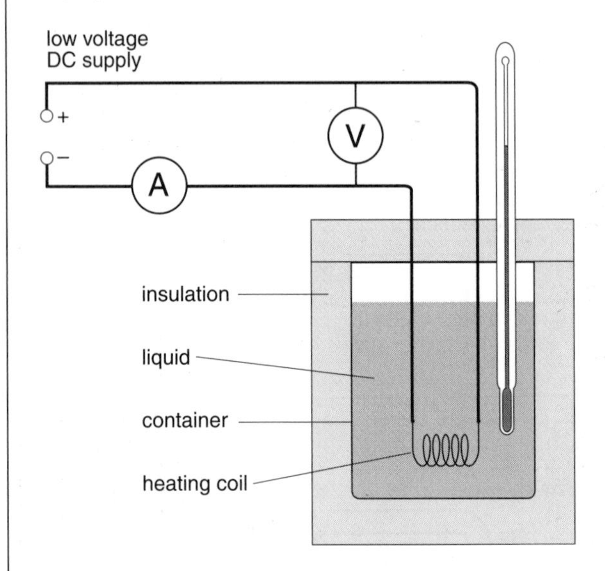

If the PD across the coil is V, and a current I passes for time t, then the electrical energy supplied = VIt (see B15).
If all this energy is supplied as heat, and none is lost:

$$VIt = mc\Delta T$$

Knowing the mass m and temperature rise ΔT of the liquid, its specific heat capacity c can be calculated.

Note:

- When the water heats up, its container does as well. For greater accuracy, this must be allowed for.
- Some heat is lost, despite the insulation. However, there are experiments in which, using different sets of results, heat losses can be eliminated from the calculation.

Measuring *c* for a solid (e.g. a metal) The method is essentially the same as that shown above, except that a solid block is used instead of the liquid. The block has holes drilled in it for an electric heater and a thermometer.

Molar heat capacity

One mole of any substance contains the same number of particles (6.02×10^{23} atoms, ions, or molecules) (see B1).

The ***molar heat capacity*** is the heat capacity per mole, (rather than per unit mass).

Many solids have a molar heat capacity close to 25 J mol^{-1} K^{-1}. This suggests that the heat capacity of a solid depends on the number of particles, rather than on the mass.

Specific latent heat of vaporization

Energy is needed to change a liquid into a gas, even though there is no change in temperature (see A3).

- Most of the energy is needed as extra internal energy (separating the particles means giving them more PE).
- Some energy is needed to do work in pushing back the atmosphere (because the gas takes up more space).

The ***specific latent heat of vaporization*** of a substance is the heat which must be supplied per unit mass to change a liquid into a gas, without change in temperature.

If Q is the heat supplied, m is the mass, and l_v is the specific latent heat of vaporization, then:

$$Q = ml_v \qquad (2)$$

The specific latent heat of vaporization of water is 2.3×10^6 J kg^{-1}. So, to turn 2 kg of water into water vapour (at the same temperature) would require 4.6×10^6 J of heat.

Measuring l_v This can be done using the equipment below. The principle is to supply boiling liquid (e.g. water) with a known amount of heat from an electrical heater, find the mass of vapour formed as a result, and calculate l_v using equation (2). The vapour is cooled, condensed, and collected as a liquid so that its mass can be measured.

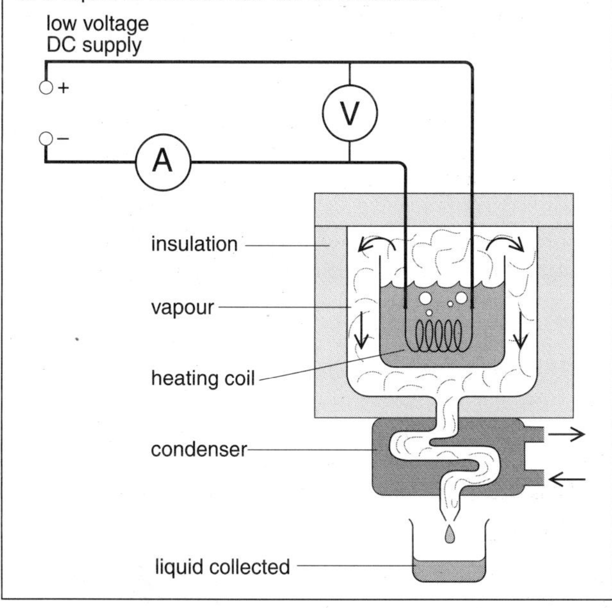

Specific latent heat of fusion

The ***specific latent heat of fusion*** of a substance is the heat which must be supplied per unit mass to change a solid into a liquid, without change in temperature.

If Q is the heat supplied, m is the mass, and l_f is the specific latent heat of fusion, then:

$$Q = ml_f$$

The specific latent heat of fusion of water is 3.3×10^5 J kg^{-1} (about $\frac{1}{7}$ of its specific latent heat of vaporization).

Converting work into heat

Work can be completely converted into heat. For example, if a gas is compressed and then left to cool to its original temperature, its internal energy is unchanged, so $\Delta U = 0$. If W is the work done *on* the gas, then from the first law of thermodynamics, $0 = Q + W$, so $-Q = W$.

Q is the heat supplied *to* the gas, so $-Q$ is the heat given out *by* the gas. It is equal to the work done *on* the gas.

Converting heat into work

Petrol, diesel, jet engines, and the boilers-plus-turbines in powers stations are all ***heat engines***. They convert heat into work. But the process can never be 100% efficient. Some heat must always be wasted. This idea is expressed by the ***second law of thermodynamics***. This can be stated in several forms, one of which is:

No continually-working heat engine can take in heat and completely convert it into work.

Heat naturally flows from a higher to a lower temperature. So, without a temperature difference, there is no flow of heat. All heat engines take heat from one material at high temperature (e.g. a burning petrol-air mixture) and pass on less heat to a material at a lower temperature (e.g. the atmosphere). The difference is converted into work.

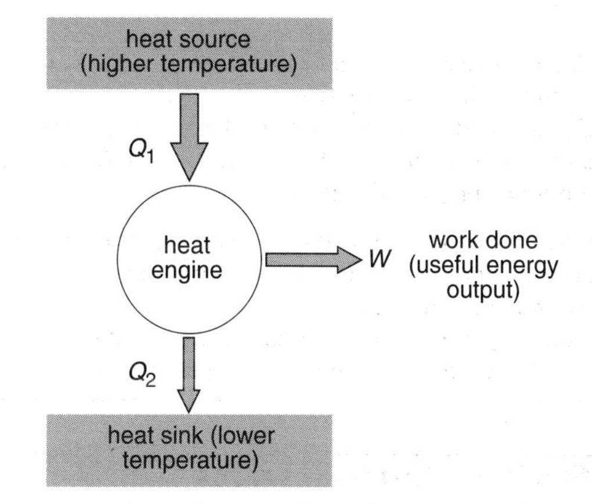

If an engine takes in heat Q_1 from a ***heat source*** and puts heat Q_2 into a ***heat sink***, then the work done $W = Q_1 - Q_2$.

The engine's efficiency is calculated like this (see A2):

$$\text{efficiency} = \frac{\text{useful energy output}}{\text{energy input}} = \frac{W}{Q_1} = \frac{Q_1 - Q_2}{Q_1}$$

An ideal heat engine is one which converts the maximum possible amount of heat into work, so there are no energy losses because of friction. For an engine like this, operating between a source temperature T_1 (in K) and a sink temperature T_2, it can be shown that:

$$\text{efficiency} = \frac{T_1 - T_2}{T_1} \qquad (3)$$

For an ideal heat engine, operating between, say, 1000 K (burning fuel) and 300 K (typical atmospheric temperature):

$$\text{efficiency} = \frac{1000 - 300}{1000} = 0.7, \text{ or } 70\%$$

Efficiencies of real engines are much less than this – for example, 30% for a petrol engine. So, in practice, engines waste more heat than they convert into work.

High and low grade energy

Some forms of energy are more useful for doing work than others. For example, in a large electric motor, electrical energy can be converted into work with very high efficiency. Electrical energy is ***high grade energy***.

By comparison, internal energy is ***low grade energy***. The materials around us contain huge amounts of it, but it is unavailable for useful work unless the material is at a higher temperature than its surroundings. Equation (3) shows that the lower the temperature difference, the more unavailable the energy becomes – the more ***degraded*** it is. The waste heat from an engine is very low grade energy.

B29 The behaviour of gases

Boyle's law

Experiments show that, for a fixed mass of gas at constant temperature, the pressure p decreases when the volume V is increased. A graph of p against V for air is shown on the right.

According to ***Boyle's law***, for a fixed mass of gas at constant temperature, pV = constant.

If pV = constant, then $p \propto 1/V$. So a graph of p against $1/V$ is a straight line through the origin.

Note:
- The value of the constant depends on the mass of the gas and on its temperature. The dashed lines show the effects of raising the temperature.
- Under some conditions, the behaviour of real gases departs from that predicted by Boyle's law (see below).

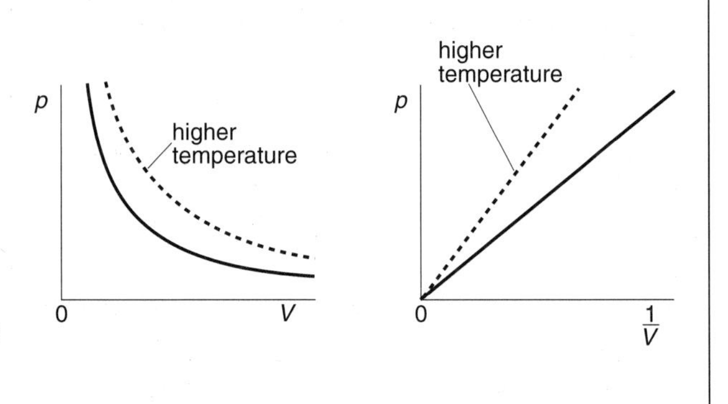

Real and ideal gases

Most common gases are made up of molecules. For convenience, in this unit and the two following, the particles of all gases will be called 'molecules', even if they are single atoms.

An ***ideal gas*** is one which exactly obeys Boyle's law. It can be shown (see B30) that, for such a gas:
- The forces of attraction between the molecules are negligible.
- The molecules themselves have a negligible volume compared with the volume occupied by the gas.

Ideal gases do not exist. However, real gases approximate to ideal gas behaviour at low densities and at temperatures well above their liquefying points.

Ideal gas behaviour is assumed in the rest of this unit.

The pressure law

Before reading this panel, see B27 on temperature.

For a fixed mass of gas at constant volume, the pressure p increases with the Kelvin temperature T, as on the right.

According to the ***pressure law***, for a fixed mass of gas at constant volume:

$$\frac{p}{T} = \text{constant}$$

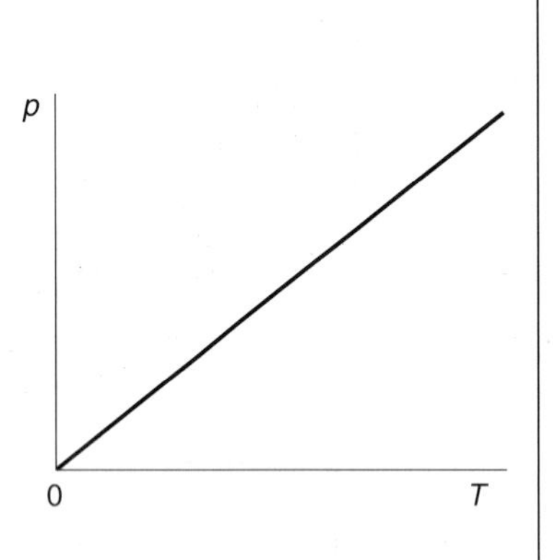

From this equation, $p \propto T$, which is why the graph is a straight line through the origin.

Note:
- The link between p and T can be used to *define* a temperature scale. However, it can be shown that, for an ideal gas, this scale exactly matches a thermodynamic scale based on the same fixed points (see B30).
- The pressure law predicts that the pressure of any ideal gas should be zero at absolute zero. This concept is used to define the zero point (0 K) on the Kelvin scale and to find its Celsius equivalent (–273.15 °C).

Charles's law

For a fixed mass of gas at constant pressure, the volume V increases with the Kelvin temperature T, as on the right.

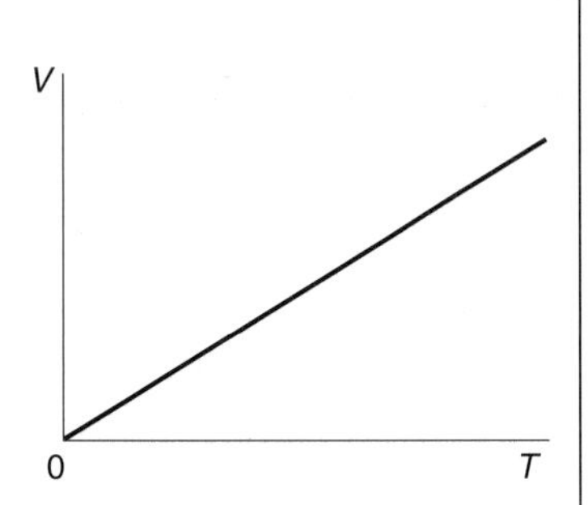

According to ***Charles's law***, for a fixed mass of gas at constant pressure:

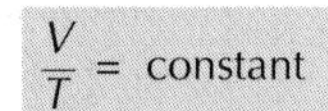

$$\frac{V}{T} = \text{constant}$$

From this equation, $V \propto T$, which is why the graph is a straight line through the origin.

Note:
- Charles's law predicts zero volume at absolute zero. However no real gas behaves like an ideal gas at near-zero volume and temperature.

Equation of state

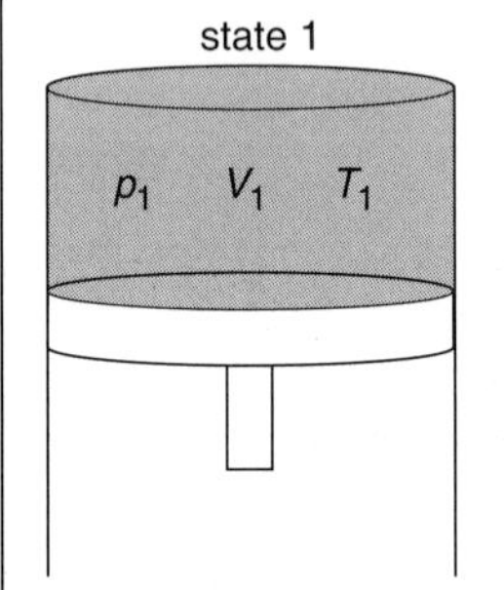

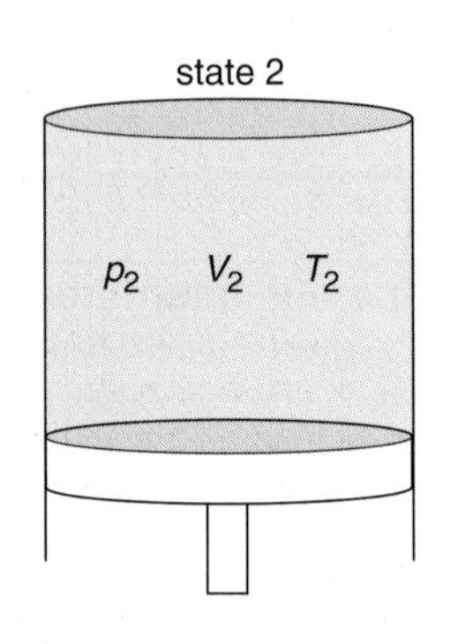

The three gas laws can be combined in a single equation.

If a fixed mass of gas changes from state 1 to state 2, at a different pressure, volume, and Kelvin temperature, as above, then:

$$\frac{p_1 V_1}{T_1} = \frac{p_2 V_2}{T_2}$$

This is called the ***equation of state*** for an ideal gas.

Note, in the above equation:
- If $V_1 = V_2$, then $p_1 V_1 = p_2 V_2$. This is Boyle's law.
- If $V_1 = V_2$, then $p_1/T_1 = p_2/T_2$. This is the pressure law.
- If $p_1 = p_2$, then $V_1/T_1 = V_2/T_2$. This is Charles's law.

The ideal gas equation

From the equation of state, pV/T = constant. The constant can have different values depending on the type and mass of gas. However, if the amount of gas being considered is one mole (6.02×10^{23} molecules) (see B1), then the constant is the same for all gases:

For one mole of any gas $pV = RT$

R is called the ***universal molar gas constant***. Its value is $8.31\ \text{J mol}^{-1}\ \text{K}^{-1}$.

For n moles of any gas $pV = nRT$

Note:

- The number of moles $n = m/M$, where m is the mass of the gas and M is its ***molar mass*** (the mass per mole).

Molar masses of some common gases, in kg mol^{-1}	
hydrogen gas	2×10^{-3}
nitrogen gas	28×10^{-3}
oxygen gas	32×10^{-3}

Work done by an expanding gas

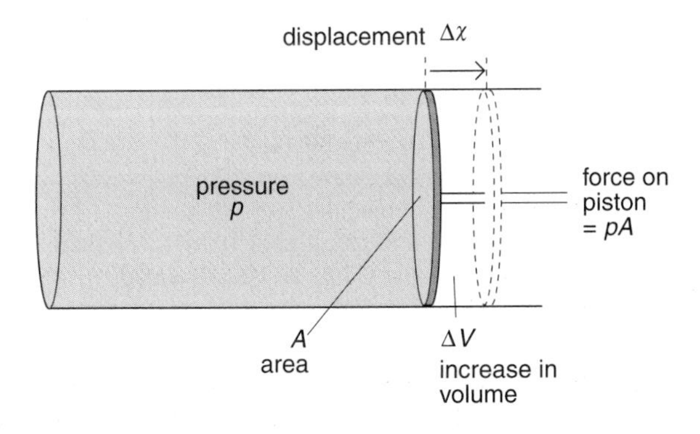

Above, a gas at pressure p exerts a force pA on the piston, and moves it a short distance Δx. If the expansion of the gas is so small that the pressure does not change:

work done by gas = force × displacement = $pA\Delta x$

But $A\Delta x = \Delta V$, the increase in volume.

So work done by gas = $p\Delta V$

Note:

- For convenience, p has been called the pressure. Really, it is the pressure *difference* across the piston (i.e. gas pressure minus atmospheric pressure).
- If the volume of the gas is *decreased* by ΔV, then $p\Delta V$ is the work done *on* the gas.

The graph below left shows the expansion of a gas at constant pressure. The area under the graph gives the work done by the gas ($p\Delta V$). The same principle applies when the pressure is not constant, as shown below right.

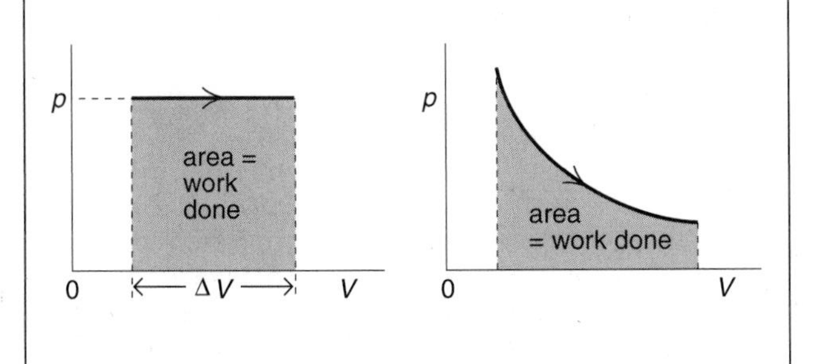

Adiabatic and isothermal expansion

According to the first law of thermodynamics, $\Delta U = Q + W$. The symbols are explained in B28. However, when dealing with an expanding gas, it is useful to know that:

Q = heat *taken in* by gas
$-\Delta U$ = *decrease* in internal energy
$-W$ = work done *by* gas

An ***adiabatic*** expansion is one in which no heat is taken in or given out, so $Q = 0$. If during an adiabatic expansion, a gas does work $-W$ it follows that $-W = -\Delta U$ (because $Q = 0$). So there is a decrease in internal energy equal to the work done. As a result, the temperature of the gas falls.

Note:

- Rapid expansions are adiabatic because the gas has negligible time to take in heat from its surroundings.
- Adiabatic *compression* produces a temperature *rise*.

An ***isothermal*** expansion is one in which the temperature is constant. There is no change in internal energy, so $\Delta U = 0$. As before, the gas does work $-W$. However, as $\Delta U = 0$, it follows that $-W = -Q$. So the gas takes in heat from it surroundings equal to the work done.

Note:

- For an isothermal expansion, a gas must stay in thermal equilibrium with its surroundings. In practice, this means a very slow expansion.
- During isothermal *compression*, a gas *gives out* heat.

Indicator diagrams

Pressure-volume graphs are called ***indicator diagrams***. They can be used to show the cycle of changes taking place in an engine. The diagram below shows, in simplified form, what happens in a cylinder of a petrol engine, where there is compression and expansion of a gas as a piston goes up and down.

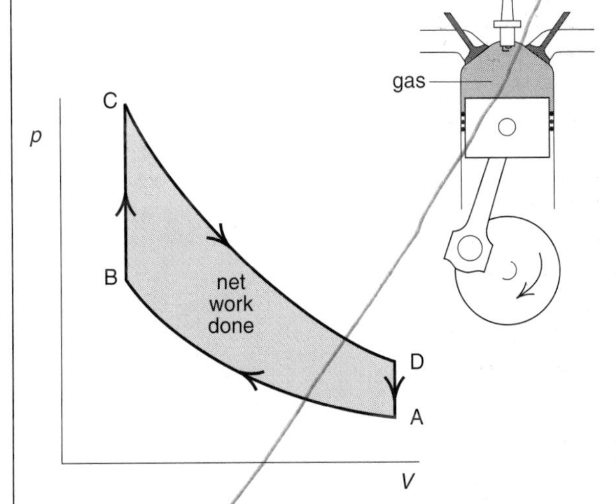

A to B Gas (air-petrol mixture) is compressed adiabatically by the rising piston. This causes a rise in temperature.

B to C Ignited by a spark, the mixture explodes. The further rise in temperature causes a further rise in pressure.

C to D The hot, high-pressure gas pushes down the piston as it expands adiabatically, and the temperature falls.

D to E The warm, waste gas is removed and replaced by cooler, fresh gas mixture, ready for the next cycle.

Note:

- From A to B, work is done *on* the gas. From C to D, work is done *by* the gas. The shaded area therefore represents the net work done during the cycle.

B30 Kinetic theory

Molecules in motion

According to the ***kinetic theory***, matter is made up of randomly-moving particles (e.g. molecules). The following effects provide evidence to support this theory for gases:

Brownian motion Smoke from a burning straw is mainly oil droplets which drift through the air. When illuminated, these oil droplets are just big enough to be seen as points of light, but small enough to be affected by collisions with molecules in the air. Observed through a microscope, the droplets wander in random, zig-zag paths as they are bombarded by the molecules of the air around them. These random wanderings are called ***Brownian motion***.

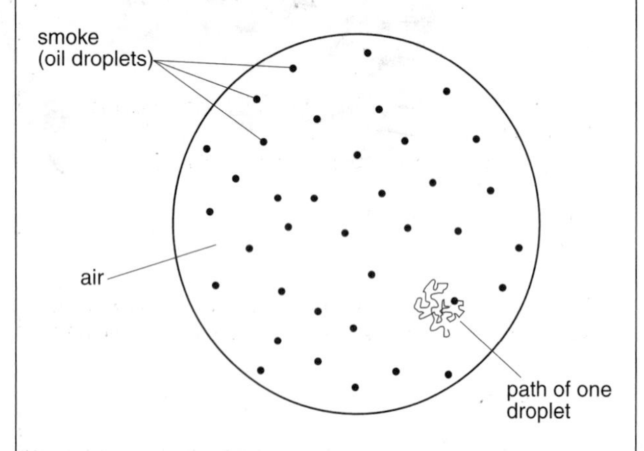

Diffusion If a phial of liquid bromine is broken in a tube of air (sealed for safety), brown bromine gas slowly spreads through the air. This spreading effect is called ***diffusion***. It happens because the bromine molecules keep colliding with the molecules of the air around them.

If there is no air in the tube (i.e. there is a vacuum), the bromine gas almost instantly fills the container when the phial is broken. This suggests that some bromine molecules travel at very high speeds.

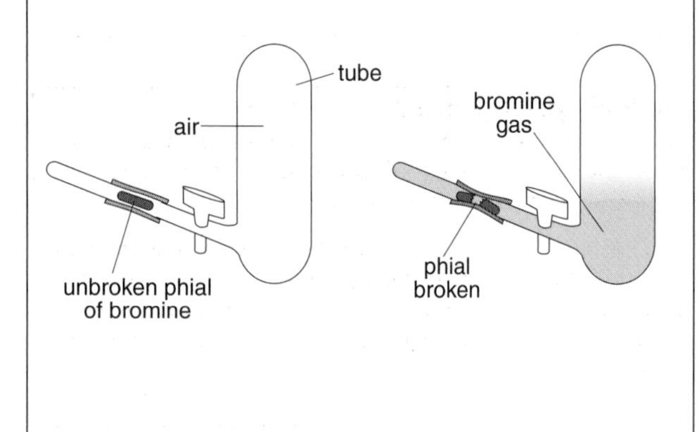

Size of a molecule

An estimate of molecular size can be obtained by putting a tiny drop of olive oil, of measured diameter, onto clean water, lightly covered with lycopodium powder. The oil spreads to form a very thin, circular film whose edge is made visible by the powder. Knowing the volume of oil, and the diameter of the film, the film's thickness can be calculated. Assuming that it is just one molecule thick, one molecule works out to be about 10^{-9} m. (Note: molecules vary considerably in size. Those in olive oil are relatively large.)

Kinetic theory for an ideal gas

The laws governing the behaviour of ideal gases can be deduced mathematically from the kinetic theory, as shown on the next page. In using the theory, the following assumptions are made:

- The motion of the molecules is completely random.
- The forces of attraction between the molecules are negligible.
- The molecules themselves have a negligible volume compared with the volume occupied by the gas.
- The molecules make perfectly elastic collisons (see B7) with each other and with the walls of their container.
- The number of molecules is so large that there are billions of collisions per second.
- Each collision takes a negligible time.
- Between collisions, each molecule has a steady speed.

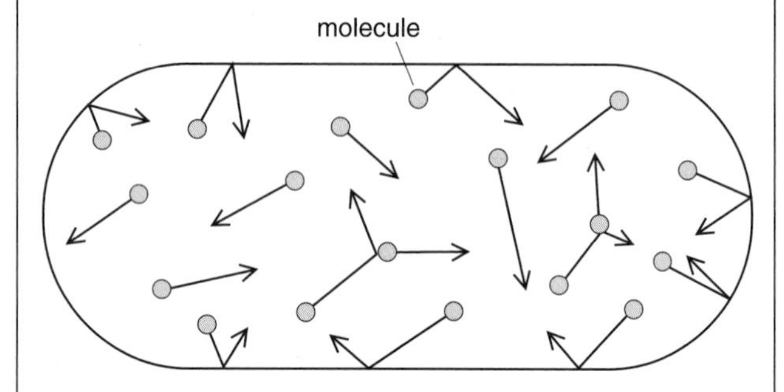

The diagram above shows a simple model of the moving molecules in a gas. The gas exerts a pressure on the walls of its container because its molecules are continually bombarding the surface and rebounding from it. The panel on the right shows how this pressure can be calculated.

Molecular speeds in a gas

In any gas, the molecules randomly collide with each other. In these collisions, some molecules gain energy (and therefore speed) while others lose it. As a result, at any instant, the molecules have a range of speeds, as shown in the distribution graph below.

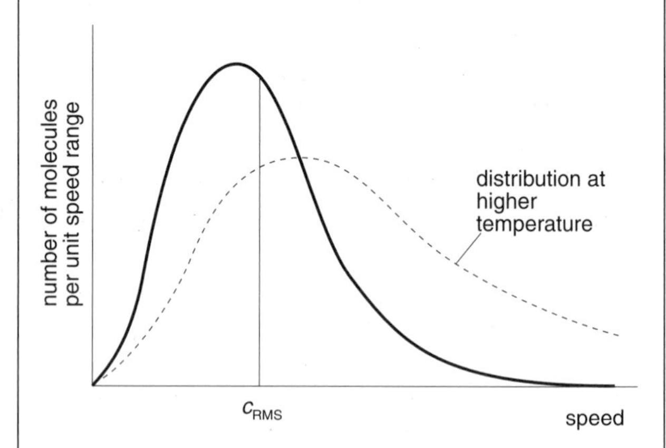

The temperature and the pressure of a gas depend, not on the average speed of the molecules, but on the average of (speed)^2, as explained on the next page. For this reason, it is useful to define the ***mean square speed*** of the molecules. This is the average of (speed)^2 for all the molecules. Its square root is called the ***root mean square speed***, or ***RMS speed***.

RMS speed is represented by the symbol c_{RMS}, or alternatively by $\sqrt{\overline{c^2}}$ or $\sqrt{<c^2>}$.

Pressure due to an ideal gas

The pressure of an ideal gas can calculated by considering the motion of its molecules. This has been done below for a gas in a spherical container, though the result applies for any shape. To begin with, it is assumed that all the molecules have the same speed, v.

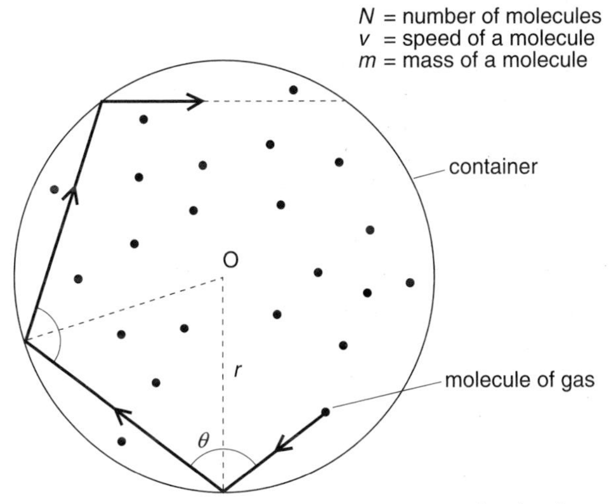

ρ = density of gas
V = volume of gas = $4\pi r^3/3$ (1)
surface area of container = $4\pi r^2$ (2)

Note: m has a different meaning from that used in B29.

The stages in the calculation are as follows:

- The labelled molecule above makes a series of collisions with the container, but always at the same angle θ. Just before each collison it has a component of momentum of $mv \cos \theta$ away from O. This is reversed by the collision. So, for each collision:

  change in momentum (away from O) = $2mv \cos \theta$ (3)

- For the labelled molecule, the distance between collisions is always $2r \cos \theta$. As time = distance/speed:

  time between collisions = $2r \cos \theta / v$ (4)

- The average force exerted by the molecule on the container can found by dividing the change in momentum (3) by the time (4) (see B6).

  This gives force due to one molecule = mv^2/r
  So total force due to all molecules = Nmv^2/r (5)

  The force does not depend on θ. A smaller angle gives a higher momentum change, but less frequent collisions.

- The pressure is found by dividing the force (5) by the area (2).

  This gives $p = Nmv^2/4\pi r^3$.
  Combining this with (1) gives $pV = Nmv^2/3$. (6)

- The pressure depends on v^2. But in reality molecules travel at a range of speeds, so v^2 should be replaced by the mean value of v^2 for all the molecules. This is c_{RMS}^2.
  So, equation (6) should be rewritten as follows:

  $$pV = \tfrac{1}{3} Nmc_{RMS}^2 \quad (7)$$

  For one mole of gas $$pV = \tfrac{1}{3} N_A mc_{RMS}^2 \quad (8)$$

  where N_A is the Avogadro constant (6.02×10^{23}) (see B1).

- Nm is the total mass of gas. So Nm/V is its density. Equation (7) can therefore be rewritten:

  $$p = \tfrac{1}{3} \rho\, c_{RMS}^2$$

Linking kinetic energy and temperature

In a gas, each molecule has kinetic energy because of its linear motion. This is called ***translational*** kinetic energy. Its average value depends on c_{RMS}. For simplicity, average translational kinetic energy will just be called KE.

So KE per molecule = $\tfrac{1}{2} mc_{RMS}^2$ (9)

This can be linked with the Kelvin temperature as follows:

- According to the ideal gas equation, for one mole of an ideal gas $pV = RT$ (see B29). This equation is used to define the ideal gas scale of temperature.
- Combining $pV = RT$ with (8) gives:

  $$\tfrac{1}{3} N_A mc_{RMS}^2 = RT \quad (10)$$

- Combining the above equation with (9) gives:

  $$\text{KE per molecule} = \frac{3}{2}\frac{R}{N_A} T$$

- R/N_A is the gas constant per molecule. Known as the ***Boltzmann constant***, k, its value is 1.38×10^{-23} J K^{-1}. Using k, the above equation can be rewritten:

  $$\text{KE per molecule} = \frac{3}{2} kT$$

Note:
- The KE per molecule is proportional to T. That is why the Kelvin thermodynamic scale (based on energy – see B27 and B29) coincides with the ideal gas scale.

Boltzmann Constant $\frac{KE}{3/2\,T} = k\ (JK^{-1})$
$KE = 3/2\, kT$

Deducing Boyle's law

According to equation (7) $pV = \tfrac{1}{3} Nmc_{RMS}^2$

On the right-hand side of this equation:
- If the mass of gas is fixed, N is constant.
- If the temperature is steady, the KE per molecule (9) is constant, so mc_{RMS}^2 is constant.

Therefore, it follows that, for a fixed mass of gas at steady temperature, pV is constant. This is Boyle's law (see B29).

Deducing Avogadro's law

According to ***Avogadro's law***, equal volumes of ideal gases under the same conditions of temperature and pressure contain equal numbers of molecules.

This law can be deduced from equation (7). If two gases are at the same temperature, then mc_{RMS}^2 is the same for each. If they are at the same pressure and volume, then pV is the same for each. So, from equation (7), N must also be the same for each.

Calculating c_{RMS}

$N_A m$ is the molar mass M of a gas (see B29). So equation (10) can be rewritten:

$$\tfrac{1}{3} Mc_{RMS}^2 = RT$$

Rearranged, this gives $c_{RMS} = \sqrt{3RT/M}$.

With R, T, and M known, c_{RMS} can be calculated. For example, for nitrogen (the main gas in air) at a room temperature of 300 K, c_{RMS} works out at 517 m s^{-1}.

B31 Heat transfer

Processes and particles

Heat (thermal energy) can be transferred by ***evaporation***, ***conduction***, ***convection***, and ***radiation***. Basic descriptions of these processes are given in A3. For simplicity, the explanations which follow refer to the motion of molecules. In reality, the particles of a substance may be molecules, atoms, or ions.

Evaporation

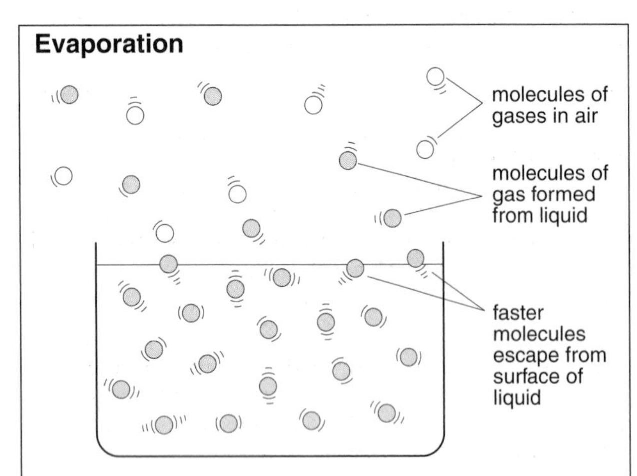

When a liquid evaporates, molecules escape from its surface and move about freely as a gas.

In a liquid, the vibrating molecules keep colliding with each other, some gaining kinetic energy and others losing it. At the surface, some of the faster, upward-moving molecules have enough kinetic energy to overcome the attractions from other molecules and escape from the liquid. With these faster molecules gone, the average KE of those left behind is reduced i.e. the temperature of the liquid falls. That is why evaporation has a cooling effect.

The rate of evaporation (and therefore the rate at which heat is lost from a liquid) is increased if:

- the surface area is increased (more of the faster molecules are near the surface),
- the temperature is increased (more of the molecules have enough kinetic energy to escape),
- the pressure is reduced (escaping molecules are less likely to rebound from other molecules back into the liquid),
- there is a draught across the surface (escaping molecules are removed before they can rebound),
- gas is bubbled through the liquid.

Thermal conduction: the processes

In gases Fast-moving molecules pass on kinetic energy to slower-moving ones when they collide with them. In this way, heat is slowly conducted through the gas.

In non-metal solids and liquids The molecules are ***coupled*** to each other by the forces between. So the molecules with most vibrational energy pass on some of this to those with less energy. However, this process of heat conduction is slow compared with that described next.

In metals Metals contain ***free electrons*** (see B15) which are in thermal equilibrium with the surrounding atoms. These electrons travel at high speeds, and transfer energy quickly from one part of the metal to another. That is why metals are such good conductors of heat. (They also conduct some heat by the transfer of vibrational energy.)

Thermal conductivity

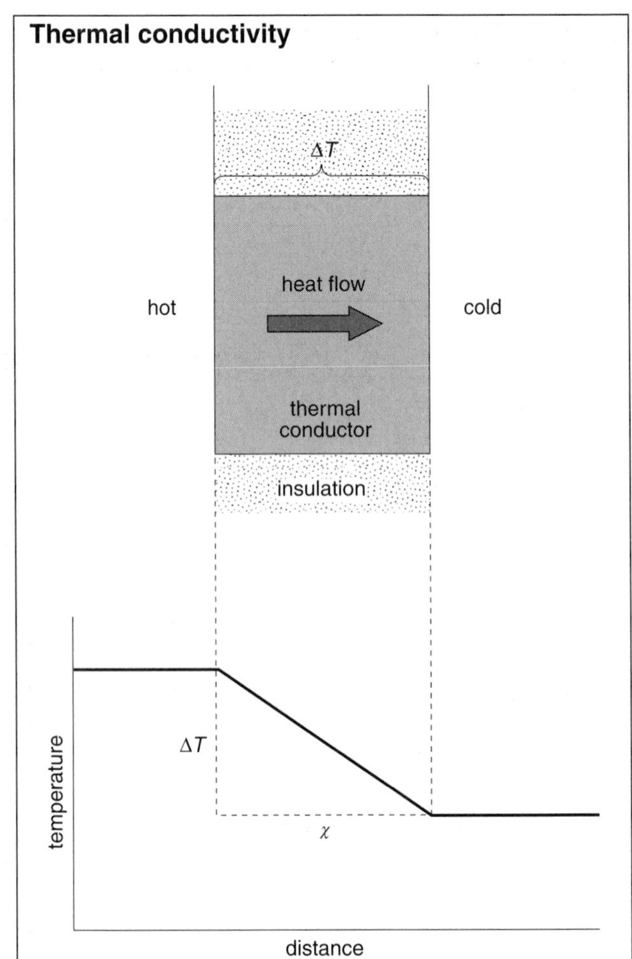

Above, there is a temperature difference ΔT across a block of material of thickness x. As a result, heat ΔQ flows through the material in time Δt. The flow is in the direction of *decreasing* temperature.

The graph shows how the temperature falls, through the block. $\Delta T/x$ is the temperature gradient. It is negative.

$\Delta Q/\Delta t$ is the rate of flow of heat. It is proportional to:

- the temperature gradient (a larger temperature difference or a thinner block give a greater heat flow),
- the cross-sectional area A (a larger area gives a greater heat flow).

The above principles can be expressed as an equation:

$$\text{rate of flow of heat} = -k \times \text{area} \times \text{temperature gradient} \qquad \frac{\Delta Q}{\Delta t} = -kA\frac{\Delta T}{x} \qquad (1)$$

k is called the ***thermal conductivity*** of the material. Some typical values of k are given below.

Note:

- In the above equations, the minus sign indicates that the heat flow is in the direction of *decreasing* temperature.
- Rate of flow of heat is the same as power. Its unit is the watt (W).
- As no heat escapes from the sides of the block, the rate of flow of heat is the same throughout.
- k is *defined* by the above equation. Good conductors have high k values. Good insulators have low k values.

Thermal conductivities, in W $m^{-1}K^{-1}$

copper	400
aluminium	238
air (at normal temperature and pressure)	0.03

Conductivity equations compared

The equations dealing with heat flow and charge flow are of a similar form (see also B15).

For a thermal conductor:

rate of flow of heat = constant × temperature difference

For an electrical conductor:

rate of flow of charge (current) = constant × potential difference

Thermal conduction through layers

On the right, a layer of brick is covered with insulating foam to reduce the heat flow. Knowing T_1 and T_2, x_1 and x_2, and k_1 and k_2, the temperature T at the boundary between the two materials can be found, and also the rate of flow of heat.

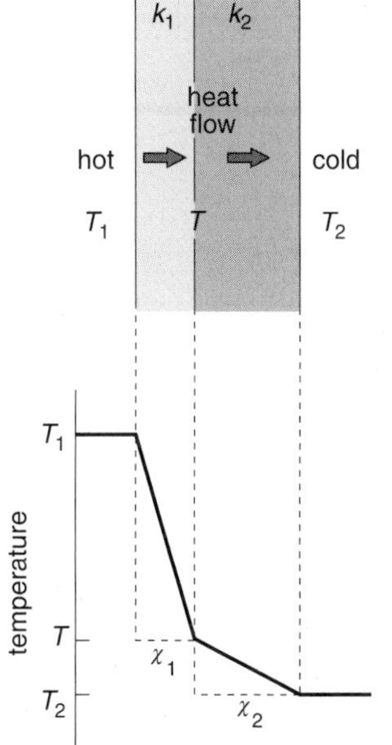

As no heat escapes from the sides, the rate of flow of heat, $\Delta Q / \Delta t$, must be the same through both layers. So, from (1):

$$\frac{\Delta Q}{\Delta t} = k_1 A \frac{(T_1 - T)}{x_1}$$

$$= k_2 A \frac{(T - T_2)}{x_2}$$

T can be found using the right-hand parts of the above equations, and rearranging. With T known, either of these parts gives the value of $\Delta Q / \Delta t$.

Note:

- In the above example $k_2 > k_1$. For the *same* rate of flow of heat, the material with the *lower* k must have the *higher* temperature gradient

U-values

Heating engineers use ***U-values***, rather than k values, when calculating heat losses through walls, windows, and roofs. A U-value is defined by the following equation:

rate of flow of heat = U-value × area × temperature difference

Using the symbols in the panel on the left:

$$\frac{\Delta Q}{\Delta t} = \text{U-value} \times A \, \Delta T \qquad (2)$$

From (1) and (2), it follows that, for a material of thermal conductivity k, the U-value = k/x. So, unlike k, the U-value depends on thickness. For good insulation, a low U-value is needed. The requirements for this are a low k and a high thickness. Here are some typical U-values:

U-values in W m^{-2} K^{-1}	
single brick wall	3.6
double brick wall with air space	1.7
window, single glass layer	5.7
double-glazed window	2.7

Convection

Rooms heaters (including so-called 'radiators') and refrigerators, lose most of their heat by convection. A hot surface heats the air next to it. The hot air rises, to be replaced by cooler air which then heats up, and so on. This is called ***natural convection***. The surface will lose heat more quickly of air is blown across it. This is known as ***forced convection***.

Convection is caused by an upthrust (see B26). A region of cold air just floats in the cold air around it because it displaces its own weight. However, when heated, it expands. It weighs the same as before, but now displaces more cold air, so the increased upthrust pushes it upwards. (The same principle applies to other gases and to liquids.)

Thermal radiation

Vibrating and spinning molecules in one object give off electromagnetic radiation whose energy can be absorbed by molecules in another object so that they speed up. This radiation is called ***thermal radiation***. From most warm or hot objects, it is mainly infrared (see A6).

Some surfaces are better absorbers of thermal radiation than others (see A3). A perfect absorber (i.e. one which reflects no radiation) is called a ***black body***. It is also the best possible emitter of thermal radiation. The Sun, odd though it may sound, is effectively a black body radiator.

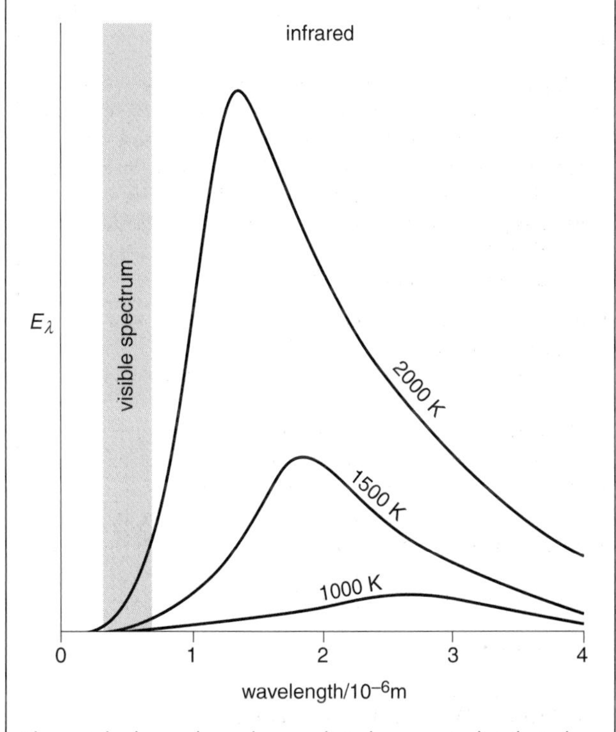

The graph above shows how radiated energy is distributed across different wavelengths for a black body radiator at various temperatures. The E_λ axis represents the relative energy output per second per unit range of wavelength.

Note:

- As the temperature increases, the total energy output per second increases (in proportion to T^4).
- As the temperature increases, the peak wavelength becomes less. By 1000 K some of the radiation has reached the red end of visible spectrum, so the object is glowing red hot. When the peak is within the visible spectrum, the object is glowing white hot.

For a radiator which is not a black body, the lines of the graph are of a similar form, but the peaks are lower.

B32 The nuclear atom

Evidence for a nucleus

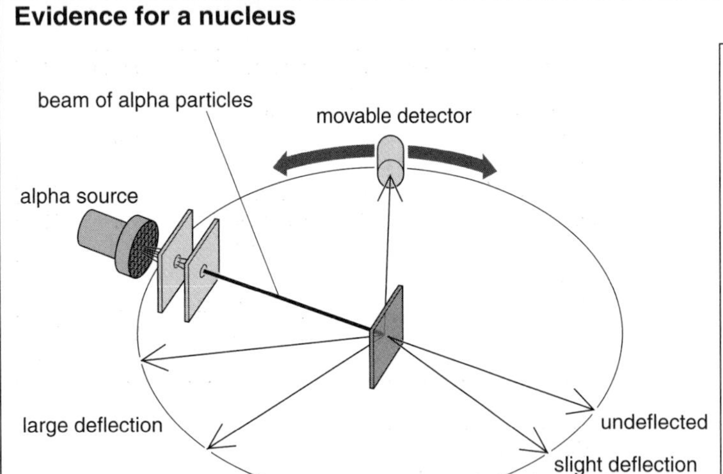

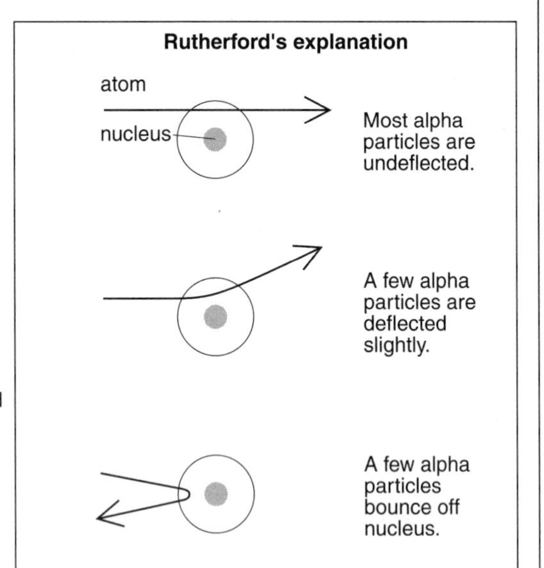

A neutral atom contains equal amounts of positive (+) and negative (–) charge (see A3). The above experiment, supervised by Ernest Rutherford in 1911, first provided evidence that an atom's positive charge and virtually all of its mass is concentrated in one small region of the atom.

A thin piece of gold foil was bombarded with alpha particles, which are positively charged (see next page). Most of the alpha particles passed straight through the gold atoms. But a few were repelled so strongly that they bounced back or were deflected through large angles. These results led Rutherford to propose this model of the atom: a heavy, positively charged ***nucleus*** at the centre, with much lighter, negatively charged electrons in orbit around it.

Atomic measurements

The ***unified atomic mass unit*** **(u)** is used for measuring the masses of atomic particles. It is very close to the mass of one proton (or neutron). However, for practical reasons, it is defined as follows:

$$1\ \text{u} = \frac{\text{mass of carbon-12 atom}}{12}$$

Converting into kg, 1 u = 1.66×10^{-27} kg.

mass of proton	1.007 28 u
mass of neutron	1.008 67 u
mass of electron	0.000 55 u
charge on proton	$+1.60 \times 10^{-19}$ C
charge on electron	-1.60×10^{-19} C
diameter of an atom	$\sim 10^{-10}$ m
diameter of a nucleus	$\sim 10^{-14}$ m

Note:
- The proton and neutron have approximately the same mass – about 1800 times that of the electron.
- ~ means 'of the order of' i.e. 'within a factor ten of'.
- The diameter of an atom is $\sim 10^4$ times that of its nucleus. (Atom size varies from element to element.)
- Confusingly, the symbol *e* may be used to represent the charge on an electron (–) or a proton (+). In this unit, the charge on an electron will be called –*e*.

Elements, nuclides, and isotopes

For most elements, a sample contains a mixture of different versions. These have the same number of protons (and electrons) but different numbers of neutrons (see A3).

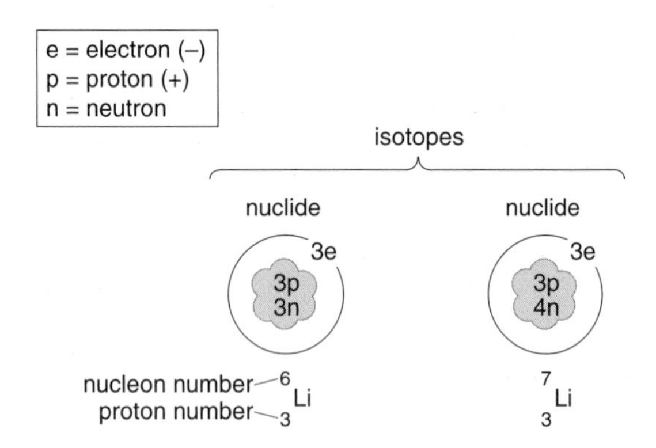

Nuclide This is any particular version of an atom. Above are simple models of the two naturally-occurring nuclides of lithium, along with the symbols used to represent them.

Nucleon number *A* As protons and neutrons are called ***nucleons***, this is the total number of protons plus neutrons in the nucleus. It was once called the ***mass number***.

Proton number *Z* This is the number of protons in the nucleus (and therefore the number of electrons in a neutral atom). It was once called the ***atomic number***.

Isotopes These are atoms with the same proton number but different nucleon numbers. They have the same electron arrangement and, therefore, the same chemical properties.

The following statements illustrate the meanings of the terms *element, nuclide,* and *isotope*.
- Lithium is an element.
- Lithium-6 is a nuclide; lithium-7 is a nuclide.
- Lithium-6 and lithium-7 are isotopes.

Note:
- A nuclide is commonly referred to as 'an isotope', though strictly speaking, this is incorrect.

Stability of the nucleus

If the number of neutrons ($A - Z$) in the nucleus is plotted against the number of protons (Z) for all known nuclides, the general form of the graph is like this:

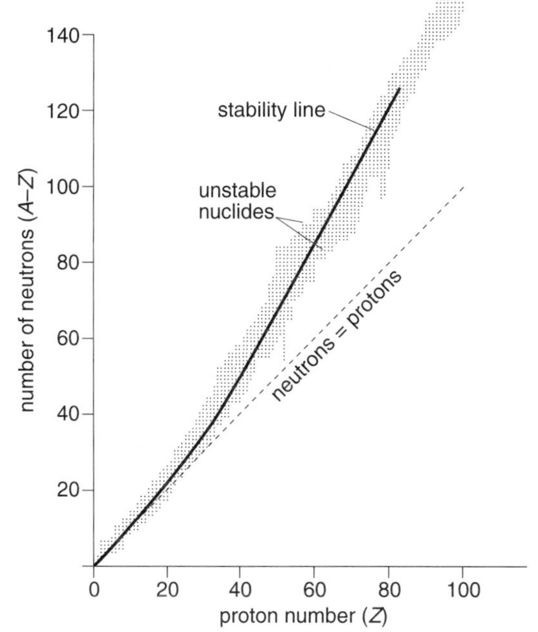

Element	Symbol	Z
hydrogen	H	1
helium	He	2
lithium	Li	3
beryllium	Be	4
boron	B	5
carbon	C	6
nitrogen	N	7
oxygen	O	8
fluorine	F	9

Element	Symbol	Z
neon	N	10
sodium	Na	11
iron	Fe	26
cobalt	Co	27
nickel	Ni	28
protactinium	Pa	91
uranium	U	92

Stable nuclides These have nuclei which are stable. They occur along the solid line.

- Light nuclides (those at the lower end of the graph) have about equal numbers of protons and neutrons.
- The heaviest nuclides have about 50% more neutrons than protons.
- The most stable nuclides tend to have an even number of protons and an even number of neutrons. This is because each group of 2 protons and 2 neutrons in the nucleus makes an especially stable combination.

Unstable nuclides These occur either side of the solid line. They have unstable nuclei which, in time, *disintegrate* (break up) – usually by emitting an ***alpha*** particle or ***beta*** particle and maybe ***gamma*** radiation as well (see also B33). The disintegration is called ***radioactive decay***.

Alpha (α) decay

An alpha (α) particle consists of 2 protons and 2 neutrons, so it has a charge of $+2e$. It is identical to a nucleus of helium-4 and may be represented by either of these symbols:

$${}^{4}_{2}\alpha \qquad {}^{4}_{2}\mathrm{He}$$

If an atom emits an α particle, its proton number is decreased, so it becomes the atom of a different element. For example, an atom of radium-226 emits an α particle to become an atom of radon-222, as shown by this equation:

$${}^{226}_{88}\mathrm{Ra} \rightarrow {}^{222}_{86}\mathrm{Rn} + {}^{4}_{2}\alpha$$

radium-226   radon-222   α particle

Note:

- Radon-222 and the α particle are the ***decay products***.
- The nucleon numbers on both sides of the equation balance (226 = 222 + 4) because the total number of protons and neutrons is conserved (unchanged).
- The proton numbers balance (88 = 86 + 2) because the total amount of positive charge is conserved.
- Alpha decay tends to occur in heavy nuclides which are below the stability line (see above graph) because it produces a nuclide which is closer to the line.

Beta (β) decay

β⁻ decay This is the most common form of beta decay. The main emitted particle is an electron. It has a charge of $-1e$ and may be represented by either of these symbols:

$${}^{0}_{-1}\beta \qquad {}^{0}_{-1}\mathrm{e}$$

Note:

- The beta particle is not a nucleon, so it is assigned a nucleon number of 0.
- The 'proton number' is –1 because the beta particle has an equal but opposite charge to that of a proton.

During β^- decay, a neutron is converted into a proton, an electron, and an almost undetectable particle with no charge and near-zero mass called an antineutrino. The electron is emitted, along with the antineutrino. For example, an atom of boron-12 emits a β^- particle to become an atom of carbon-12, as described by this equation:

$${}^{12}_{5}\mathrm{B} \rightarrow {}^{12}_{6}\mathrm{C} + {}^{0}_{-1}\mathrm{e} + {}^{0}_{0}\bar{\nu}$$

boron-12   carbon-12 β^- particle   antineutrino

Note:

- The nucleon numbers balance on both sides of the equation. So do the proton numbers.
- β^- decay tends to occur in nuclides above the stability line (see graph at top of page).

β⁺ decay Here, the main emitted particle is a ***positron***, with the same mass as an electron, but a charge of $+1e$. It is the ***antiparticle*** of an electron. For example, an atom of nitrogen-12 emits a β^+ particle to become an atom of carbon-12, as described by the following equation:

$${}^{12}_{7}\mathrm{N} \rightarrow {}^{12}_{6}\mathrm{C} + {}^{0}_{+1}\mathrm{e} + {}^{0}_{0}\nu$$

boron-12   carbon-12 β^+ particle   neutrino

Nuclear reactions

One element changing into another is called a ***transmutation***. It can occur when atoms are bombarded by other particles. For example, if a high-energy α particle strikes and is absorbed by a nucleus of nitrogen-14, the new nucleus immediately decays to form a nucleus of oxygen-17 and a proton. This is an example of a ***nuclear reaction***. It can be described by the following equation:

$${}^{14}_{7}\mathrm{N} + {}^{4}_{2}\alpha \rightarrow {}^{17}_{8}\mathrm{O} + {}^{1}_{1}\mathrm{p}$$

nitrogen-14   α particle   oxygen-17   proton

Note:

- The nucleon numbers balance on both sides of the equation. So do the proton numbers.

B33 Radiation and decay

Properties of alpha, beta, and gamma radiation

Type of radiation	α	β	γ
nature	2 p + 2 n	e	electromagnetic (see A6 and B22)
charge	+ 2*e*	− 1*e*	no charge
speed (typical) (c = speed of light)	0.1*c*	up to 0.9*c*	*c*
energy (typical)	10 MeV	0.03 to 3 MeV	1 MeV
ionizing effect: ion pairs per mm in air	~10^5	~10^3	~1
penetration (typical)	stopped by: 50 mm air 0.5 mm paper	stopped by: 5 mm aluminium	intensity halved by 100 mm lead
effect of magnetic field (B out of paper) *not to scale*	+	slow fast −	(undeflected)

Detecting alpha, beta, and gamma radiation

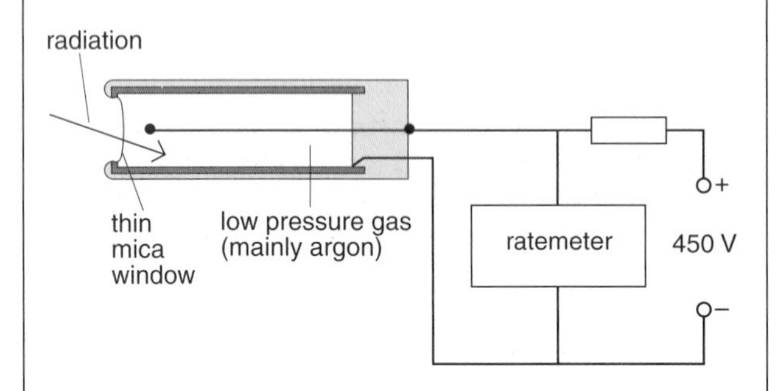

Detectors In the ***G-M tube*** (Geiger-Müller tube) above, a high voltage is maintained across the gas. When, say, a beta particle enters through the thin window, it ionizes the gas and makes it conduct. This causes a pulse of current in the circuit. The ***ratemeter*** registers the ***count rate*** (average number of pulses per second).

In a ***solid state detector***, incoming radiation ionizes the semiconductor material in a diode (see A4 and B15).

Telling the radiations apart To tell one type of radiation from another, absorbing materials of different thicknesses can be placed between the source and the detector. For example, a thick aluminium plate will stop α and β particles, but not γ radiation.

Background radiation In radioactivity experiments, allowance must be made for background radiation. This is low-level radiation whose sources include radioactive materials naturally present in rocks and soil, and cosmic radiation (high-energy particles from space).

Note:

- α, β, and γ radiations all cause ***ionization*** – they remove electrons from atoms (or molecules) in their path. The removed electron (–) and the charged atom or molecule (+) remaining are called an ***ion-pair***. The ionized material can conduct electricity.
- α particles interact the most with atoms in their path, so they are the most ionizing and the least penetrating.
- Unlike α particles, β particles are emitted from their source at a range of speeds.
- For γ radiation emitted from a point source in air, intensity $\propto$ 1/(distance from source)^2 (see B22).
- γ radiation is not stopped by an absorber, but its intensity is reduced.
- α and β particles are deflected by magnetic fields, as predicted by Fleming's left-hand rule (see A5 and B21). They are also deflected by electric fields.

Activity

The ***activity*** of a radioactive source is the number of disintegrations occurring within it per unit time.

The SI unit of activity is the ***becquerel*** (**Bq**):

1 becquerel = 1 disintegration s^{-1} (1 Bq = 1 s^{-1})

The activity of a typical laboratory source is ~ 10^4 Bq.

Each disintegration produces an α or β particle and, in many cases, γ radiation as well. The γ radiation is emitted as a 'packet' of wave energy called a ***photon*** (see B35). Particles and photons cause pulses in a detector, so the count rate is a measure of the activity of the source.

Note:

- The activity of a source is unaffected by chemical changes or physical conditions such as temperature. However, it does decrease with time (see next page).

The decay law

Unstable nuclei disintegrate spontaneously and at random. However, the more undecayed nuclei there are, the more frequently disintegrations are likely to occur. For any particular radioactive nuclide, on average:

activity $\propto$ number of undecayed nuclei

If N is the number of undecayed atoms after time t, then the activity is the rate of change of N with t. So, in calculus notation, the activity is $-dN/dt$. (The minus sign indicates that a *decrease* in N gives *positive* activity.)

With a suitable constant, λ, the above proportion can be rewritten as an equation:

$$-\frac{dN}{dt} = \lambda N \qquad (1)$$

λ is called the ***radioactive decay constant***. Each radioactive nuclide has its own characteristic value. (Note that the symbol λ is also used for wavelength.)

By applying calculus to equation (1), a link between N and t can be obtained:

$$N = N_0 e^{-\lambda t} \qquad (e = 2.718) \qquad (2)$$

where N_0 is the initial number of undecayed nuclei.

This is known as the ***radioactive decay law***.

A graph of N against t has the form shown above right. The graph is an *exponential* curve (see also B14).

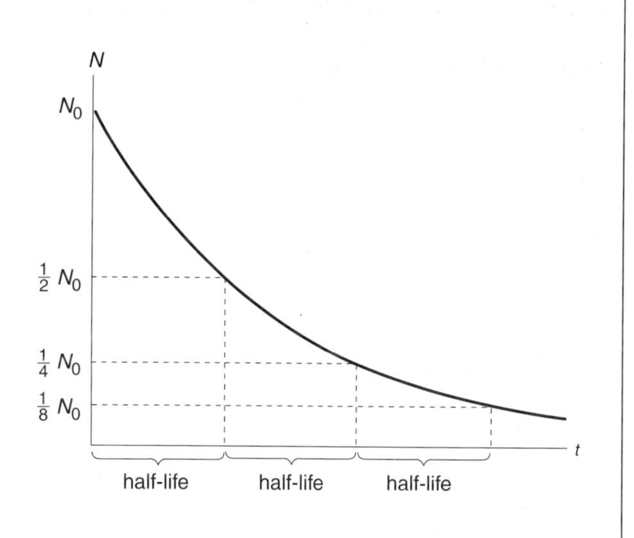

Half-life

There are two alternative definitions for this term.

The ***half-life*** of a radioactive nuclide is:

A the average time taken for the number of undecayed nuclei to halve in value,

B the average time taken for the activity to halve.

Version A is illustrated in the graph above. One feature of the exponential curve is that the half-life is the same from whichever point you start.

In equation (2), the half life, $t_{\frac{1}{2}}$, is the value of t for which $N = N_0/2$. Substituting this in the equation, taking logs, and rearranging gives:

$$t_{\frac{1}{2}} = \frac{0.693}{\lambda} \qquad (0.693 = \ln 2)$$

Combining equations (1) and (2) gives $-dN/dt = \lambda N_0 e^{-\lambda t}$. So the activity ($-dN/dt$) also decreases exponentially with time, and a graph of *activity* against *time* has the same general form as the graph above. Version B of the half-life definition follows from this.

Half-lives for some nuclides

Nuclide	Half-life
potassium-40	1.3×10^9 years
plutonium-239	24 400 years
carbon-14	5730 years
strontium-90	28 years
magnesium-28	21 hours
radon-224	55 seconds

Uses of radioisotopes

Elements are a mixture of isotopes. The radioactive ones are called ***radioisotopes***. Some can be produced artificially by transmutations in a nuclear reactor. They have many uses.

Tracers Radioisotopes can be detected in very small (and safe) quantities. This means that they can be used as tracers – their movements can be tracked. Examples include:

- tracking a plant's uptake of fertilizer from roots to leaves by adding a tracer to the soil water,
- detecting leaks in underground pipes by adding a tracer to the fluid in the pipe.

Testing for cracks γ rays have the same properties as short-wavelength X-rays, so they can be used to photograph metals to reveal cracks. A γ source is compact and does not need an electrical power source like an X-ray tube.

Cancer treatment γ rays can penetrate deep into the body and kill living cells. So a highly concentrated beam from a cobalt-60 source can be used to kill cancer cells in a tumour. Treatment like this is called ***radiotherapy***.

Carbon dating Living organisms are partly made from carbon which is recycled through their bodies and the atmosphere as they obtain food and respire. A tiny proportion is radioactive carbon-14 (half-life 5730 years). This is continually forming in the upper atmosphere as nitrogen-14 is bombarded by cosmic radiation. When an organism dies, no new carbon is taken in, so the proportion of carbon-14 is gradually reduced by radioactive decay. By measuring the activity, the age of the remains can be estimated to within 100 years. This method can be used to date organic materials such as wood and cloth.

Dating rocks When rocks are formed, some radioisotopes become trapped. As decay continues, the proportion of radioisotope (e.g. potassium-40) decreases, while that of its decay product (e.g. argon-40) increases. The age of the rock can be estimated from the proportions.

Smoke detectors These contain a tiny α source which ionizes the air in a small chamber so that it conducts a current. Smoke particles entering the chamber attract ions and reduce the current. This is sensed by a circuit which triggers the alarm.

B34 Nuclear energy

Energy and mass

One conclusion from Einstein's ***theory of relativity*** is that energy has mass. If an object gains energy, it gains mass. If it loses energy, it loses mass. The change of energy ΔE is linked to the change of mass Δm by this equation:

$$\Delta E = \Delta mc^2$$

where c is the speed of light: 3×10^8 m s^{-1}

c^2 is so high that energy gained or lost by everyday objects produces no detectable change in their mass. However, the energy changes in nuclear reactions produce mass changes which are measurable. For example, when a fast α particle is stopped, its mass decreases by about 0.2%. The mass of an object when it is at rest is called its ***rest mass***.

With nuclear particles, energy is often measured in MeV (the electronvolt, eV, is defined in B21):

$$1 \text{ MeV} = 1.60 \times 10^{-13} \text{ J}$$

From data on mass changes, scientists can calculate the energy changes taking place. With nuclear particles, mass is usually measured in u (see B32). By converting 1 u into kg and applying $\Delta E = \Delta mc^2$, it is possible to show that:

1 u	is equivalent to	931 MeV
change in mass		change in energy

Mass defect

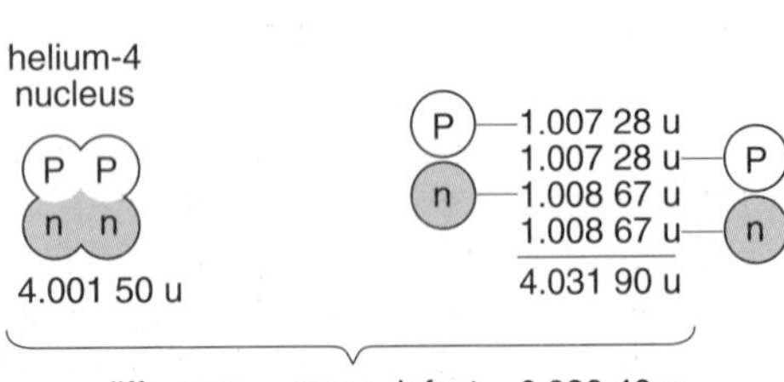

difference = mass defect = 0.030 40 u

$$\text{mass defect per nucleon} = \frac{0.030\ 40}{4} = 0.007\ 60 \text{ u}$$

A helium-4 nucleus is made up of 4 nucleons (2 protons and 2 neutrons). The calculation above shows that the nucleus has less mass than its four nucleons would have as free particles. The nucleus has a ***mass defect*** of 0.030 40 u.

The reason for the mass defect is as follows. In the nucleus, the nucleons are bound together by a strong nuclear force. As work must be done to separate them, they must have less potential energy when bound than they would have as free particles. Therefore, they must have less mass.

All nuclides have a mass defect (apart from hydrogen-1 whose nucleus is a single proton). For example:

	Mass defect	**Mass defect per nucleon**
hydrogen-2	0.002 40 u	0.001 20 u
iron-56	0.528 75 u	0.009 44 u
lead-208	1.757 84 u	0.008 45 u
uranium-238	1.935 38 u	0.008 13 u

Binding energy

The ***binding energy*** of a nucleus is the energy equivalent of its mass defect. So it is the energy needed to split the nucleus into separate nucleons. For example, a helium-4 nucleus has a mass defect of 0.030 40 u. As 1 u is equivalent to 931 MeV, 0.030 40 u is equivalent to 28.3 MeV. So the binding energy of the nucleus is 28.3 MeV.

Note:

- The term 'binding energy' is rather misleading. 'Unbinding energy' would be better. 28.3 MeV is the energy needed to 'unbind' the nucleons in helium-4.

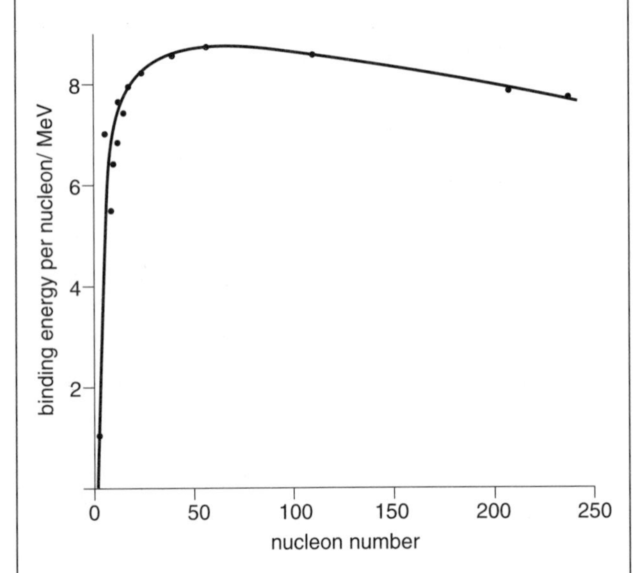

The stability of a nucleus depends on the ***binding energy per nucleon***. The graph above shows how this varies with nucleon number. The line gives the general trend; points for some individual nuclides have also been included.

Note:

- Nuclei near the 'hump' of the graph are the most stable, because they need most 'unbinding energy' per nucleon.
- A graph of *mass defect* against *nucleon number* has the same general form as the graph above.

If nucleons become rearranged so that they have a *higher* binding energy per nucleon, there is an *output* of energy:

Radioactive decay Unstable nuclei decay to form more more stable products, so energy is released. In α decay, for example, this is mostly as the kinetic energy of an α particle. When the α particle collides with atoms, it loses KE and they speed up. So radioactive decay produces heat.

Nuclear reactions The ***fission*** and ***fusion*** reactions on the next page give out energy. During fission, heavy nuclei split to form nuclei nearer the 'hump' of the graph. During fusion, light, nuclei *fuse* (join) to form heavier ones.

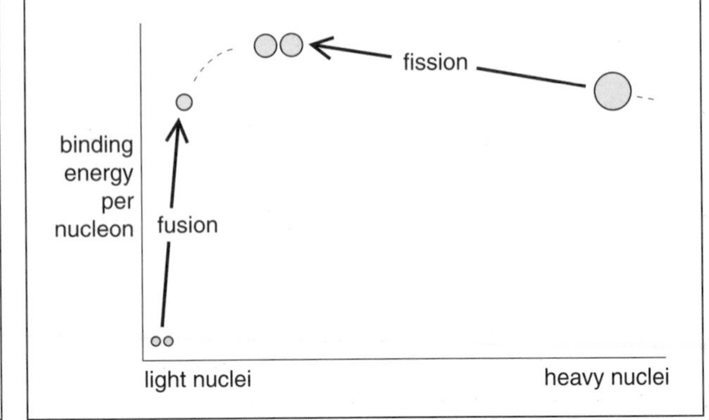

Nuclear fission

During ***nuclear fission***, a heavy nucleus (e.g. of uranium or plutonium) splits to form two nuclei of roughly the same mass, plus several neutrons. Rarely, fission happens spontaneously. More usually, it occurs when a neutron hits and is captured by the nucleus. For example, here is a typical fission reaction for uranium-235:

$$^{235}_{92}\mathrm{U} + ^{1}_{0}\mathrm{n} \rightarrow ^{144}_{56}\mathrm{Ba} + ^{90}_{36}\mathrm{Kr} + 2^{1}_{0}\mathrm{n}$$

The reaction releases energy, mostly as KE of the heavier decay products (see also B7). So fission is a source of heat.

Note:

- The energy released per atom by fission (about 200 MeV) is about 50 million times greater than that per atom from a chemical reaction such as burning.

Chain reaction The fission reaction above is started by one neutron. It gives off neutrons which may cause further fission and so on in a ***chain reaction***:

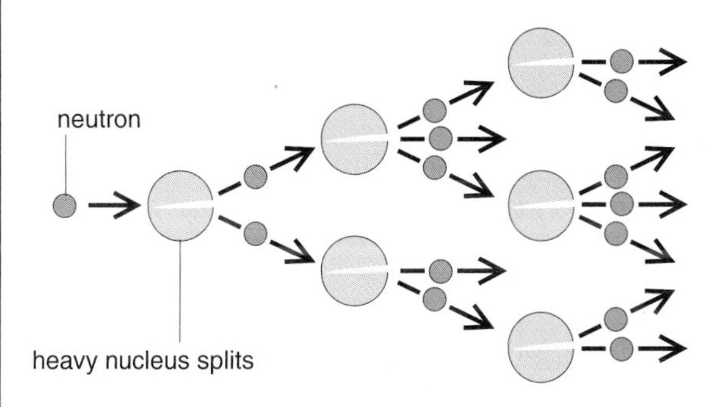

Uncontrolled chain reactions are used in nuclear weapons. Controlled chain reactions take place in ***nuclear reactors*** (see right) and release energy at a steady rate. The most commonly used fissionable material is uranium-235.

To maintain a chain reaction, a minimum of one neutron from each fission must cause further fission. However, to achieve this, these problems must be overcome:

- If the fission material is less than a certain ***critical size***, too many neutrons escape without hitting nuclei.
- The fission of uranium-235 produces medium-speed neutrons. But slow neutrons are better at causing fission.
- Less than 1% of natural uranium is uranium-235. Over 99% is uranium-238, which absorbs medium-speed neutrons without fission taking place.

Thermal reactors

In a nuclear power station, the heat source is usually a ***thermal reactor***. (Otherwise, the layout is as for a fuel-burning station – see B20.) In the reactor, there is a steady release of heat as fission of uranium-235 takes place. It is known as a *thermal* reactor because the neutrons are slowed to speeds associated with thermal motion.

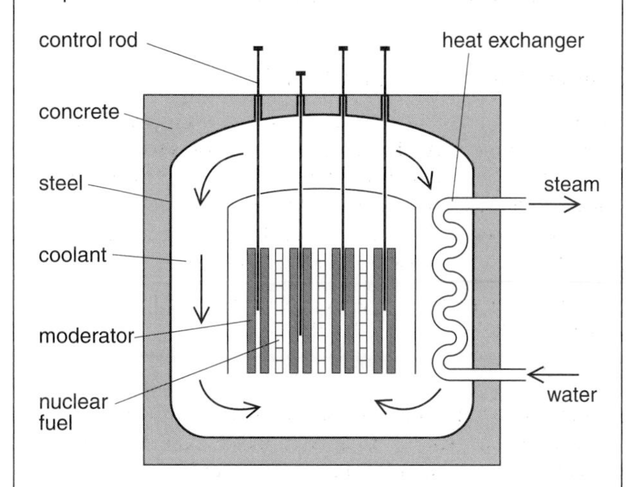

Nuclear fuel This is uranium dioxide in which the natural uranium has been enriched with extra uranium-235. 1 kg of this fuel gives as much energy as about 25 tonnes of coal.

Moderator This is a material which slows down the medium-speed neutrons produced by fission. Some reactors use graphite as a moderator. Others use water.

Control rods These are raised or lowered to control the rate of fission. They contain boron, which absorbs neutrons.

Coolant (e.g. water or carbon dioxide gas) This carries heat from the reactor to the heat exchanger.

Note:

- Many useful radioisotopes are made by bombarding stable isotopes with neutrons in the core of a reactor.

Safety issues Nuclear radiation can damage or kill living cells, so reactors have thick concrete shielding to absorb it. However, any radioactive gas or dust which escapes into the atmosphere is especially dangerous because it may be taken into the bodies of living things via food or water. 'Spent' fuel from reactors contains highly active decay products. Not all have short half-lives, and some will require safe, sealed storage for thousands of years.

Nuclear fusion

Reactors using ***nuclear fusion*** are many years away. Current research is based on the fusion of hydrogen-2 (called ***deuterium***) and hydrogen-3 (called ***tritium***):

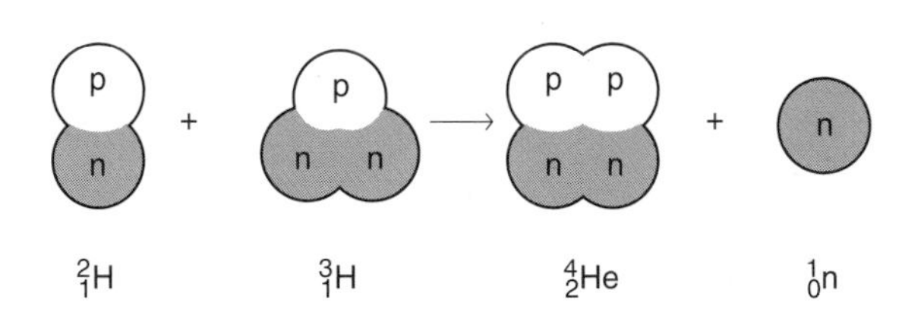

Although the energy release per fusion is less than 10% of that from a fission reaction, fusion is the better energy source if the processes are compared *per kg* of material.

Fusion is much more difficult to achieve than fission because the hydrogen nuclei repel each other.

- For the nuclei to collide at a high enough speed for fusion, the gas has to be heated to 10^8 K or more.
- No ordinary container can hold such a hot material and keep it compressed. Scientists are experimenting with magnetic fields to trap the nuclei.

The advantages of a fusion reactor will be:

- Fuels will be readily obtainable. For example, deuterium can be extracted from sea-water.
- The main waste product, helium, is not radioactive.
- Fusion reactors have built-in safety. If the system fails, fusion stops.

The Sun gets its energy from the fusion of hydrogen, though using a different reaction from that on the left. Its huge size and gravity maintain the conditions needed.

B35 Quantum theory

Quantum energy

To explain certain features of thermal radiation (see B31), Planck (in 1900) put forward the theory that energy cannot be divided into smaller and smaller amounts. It is only emitted in discrete 'packets', each called a ***quantum***. The energy E of a quantum depends on the frequency f of the radiating source, as given by this equation:

$$E = hf$$

where h is known as ***Planck's constant***. Its value, found by experiment, is 6.63×10^{-34} J s.

For electromagnetic radiation, $c = f\lambda$ (see B22), so the equation on the left can be rewritten as $E = hc/\lambda$,
where c is the speed of light and λ the wavelength.

Note:

- The shorter the wavelength (and therefore the higher the frequency), the greater the energy of each quantum.
- A quantum is an extremely small amount of energy.

quantum of red light: energy = 2 eV
quantum of violet light: energy = 4 eV
(1 eV = 1.60×10^{-19} J – see B21)

Photons

Some effects indicate that light is a wave motion. Examples include interference and diffraction (see B23). But there are others which suggest that light has particle-like properties. These include the ***photoelectric effect*** below. Einstein (in 1905) was able to explain this by assuming that light (or other electromagnetic radiation) is made up of 'packets' of wave energy, called ***photons***. Each photon is one quantum of energy.

The photoelectric effect

When some substances are illuminated by light (or shorter wavelengths), electrons are emitted from their surface. This is called the ***photoelectric effect***. The electrons are emitted with a range of kinetic energies, up to a maximum.

Experiments show that:

- Increasing the intensity of the light increases the number of electrons emitted per second.
- For light beneath a certain ***threshold frequency***, f_o, no electrons are emitted, even in very intense light.
- Above f_o, the maximum KE of the electrons increases with frequency, but is not affected by intensity. Even very dim light gives some electrons with high KE.

The wave theory cannot explain the threshold frequency, or how low-amplitude waves can cause high-KE electrons.

Einstein's quantum explanation Each photon delivers a quantum of energy, hf, which is absorbed by an electron. Energy Φ is needed to free the electron from the surface. If hf is more than this, the remainder is available to the electron as KE (though most electrons lose some KE before emission because they interact with other atoms). So:

hf	=	Φ	+	$\frac{1}{2}m_e v_{max}^2$	(1)
energy delivered by photon		energy needed to free electron from surface		KE of electron (with no further energy losses)	

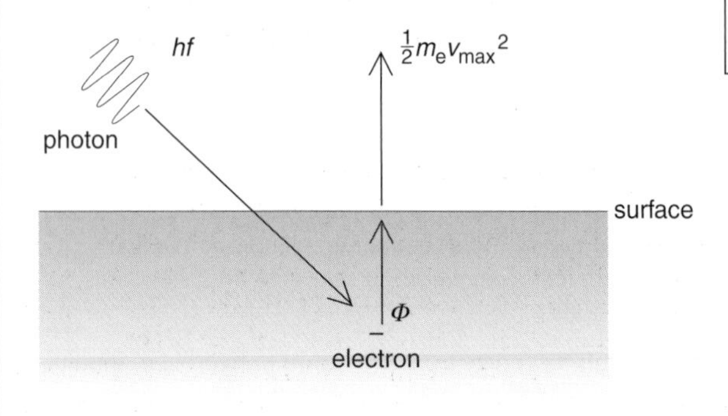

Investigating the photoelectric effect

galvanometer
light
A
V
DC supply (variable)
vacuum
plate (e.g. zinc)

The principle of an experiment to investigate the photo electric effect is shown above. The material being investigated (e.g. zinc) is illuminated with light of known frequency f. Emitted electrons reach plate A, so the galvanometer detects a current in the circuit. The maximum KE of the emitted electrons is found by applying just enough *opposing* voltage, V_s, to *stop* them reaching A, so that the galvanometer reading falls to zero.

V_s is called the ***stopping voltage***. At this voltage:

$eV_s = \frac{1}{2}m_e v_{max}^2$ (see B21)

So, if equation (2) below is correct:

$eV_s = hf - hf_o$

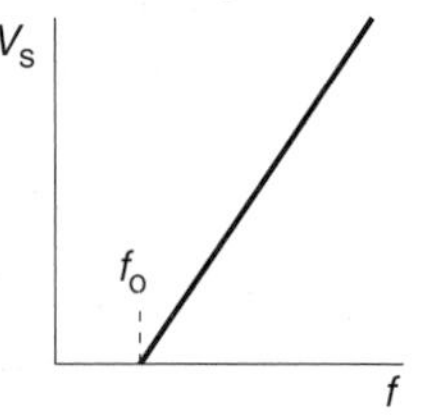

Therefore, if V_s is measured for light of different frequencies, a graph of V_s against f should be of the form shown above.

Note:

- The number of electrons emitted is proportional to the number of photons absorbed.
- Φ is called the ***work function***. Materials with a low Φ emit electrons in visible light. Those with a higher Φ require the higher-energy photons of ultraviolet.
- If $hf < \Phi$, no electrons are emitted.
- The energy of a photon at the threshold frequency = hf_o = Φ. So, equation (1) can be rearranged and rewritten:

$$\tfrac{1}{2}m_e v_{max}^2 = hf - hf_o \quad (2)$$

Spectral lines

A ***spectrum*** (see A6) contains a mixture of wavelengths, but not always in a continuous range. For example, if there is an electric discharge through hydrogen at low pressure, the gas emits particular wavelengths only, so the spectrum is made up of lines (visible colours, ultraviolet and infrared), some of which are shown below:

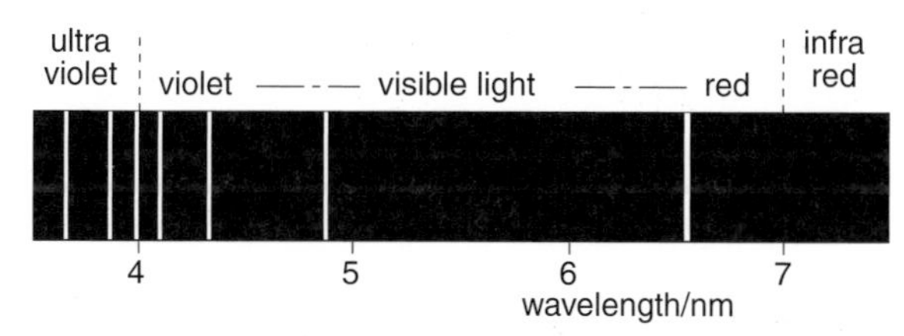

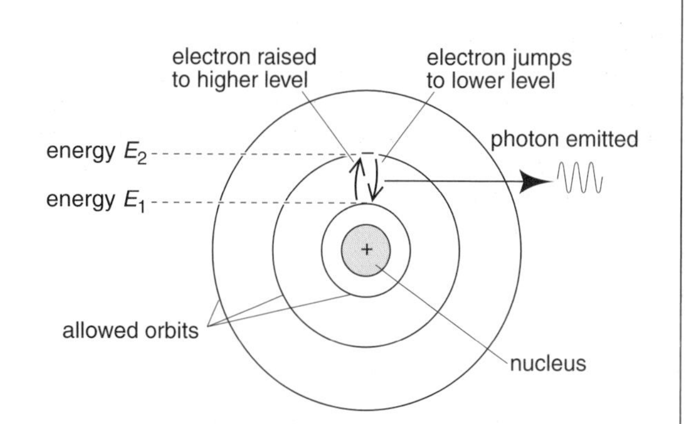

Bohr's quantum explanation (1913) In an atom, the electrons can move around the nucleus in certain allowed orbits only (top right). An electron has a different amount of energy (KE + PE) in each orbit. It may be raised to a higher orbit, for example, by colliding with an electron from another atom. When it jumps back to a lower orbit, it loses energy ($E_2 - E_1$) which is emitted as a photon. So:

$$hf = E_2 - E_1$$

An electron jump is called a ***transition***.

- The greater the energy change ($E_2 - E_1$) of the transition, the higher the frequency f of the photon.
- Each possible transition gives a different spectral line.

Bohr's allowed-orbit analysis only works for the simplest atom, hydrogen. It has now been replaced by a mathematical, ***wave mechanics*** model of the atom in which allowed orbits are replaced by allowed ***energy levels***. However, the above equation still applies.

A line spectrum is a feature of any gas in which individual atoms do not interact. If atoms exert forces on each other, many more energy levels are created. Tightly-packed atoms or molecules which are vibrating, rotating, or colliding with each other have so many possible energy states that the spectrum is a continuous range of colours.

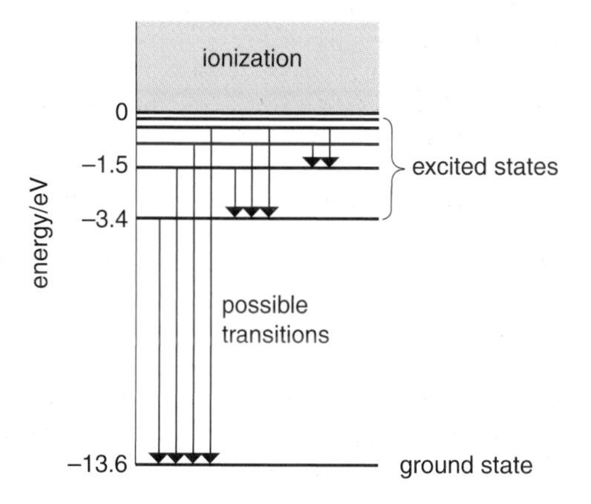

The main energy levels and transitions for hydrogen (with isolated atoms) are shown above.

Note:

- If an atom is in its ***ground state***, no electron has an unoccupied energy level beneath it.
- If an atom is in an ***excited state***, an electron has been raised to a higher energy level, so there is an unoccupied level beneath it.
- If an atom is in an ***ionized state***, an electron has been raised above the highest energy level (i.e. it has escaped). From the energy scale on the above chart, the minimum energy required to ionize a hydrogen atom is 13.6 eV.

Emission and absorption spectra

If light is radiated directly from its source, its spectrum is called an ***emission spectrum***. Examples include the line spectrum above and the continuous spectrum of the Sun.

The Sun's emission spectrum is crossed by many faint, dark lines. These are an ***absorption spectrum***. They occur because some wavelengths emitted by the Sun's core are absorbed by cooler gases (e.g. hydrogen) in its outer layers.

Some of the lines in the absorption spectrum of hydrogen are shown below. When the Sun's radiation passes through the gas, the atoms *absorb* photons whose energies match those in their emission spectrum. They then re-emit photons of these energies, but in all directions, so the intensity in the forward direction is reduced for those wavelengths.

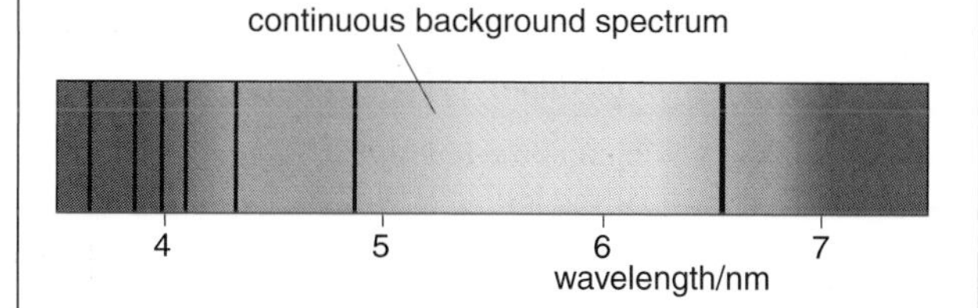

Wave-particle duality

Light waves have particle-like properties. De Broglie (in 1922) suggested that the converse might also be true: matter particles, such as electrons, might have wave-like properties. There might be ***wave-particle duality***.

According to de Broglie, if a particle of momentum p is associated with a ***matter wave*** of wavelength λ, then:

$$\lambda = \frac{h}{p}$$

Electron diffraction If a beam of electrons is passed through a thin layer of graphite, the electrons form a diffraction pattern. This suggests that the rows of atoms are acting rather like a diffraction grating (see B23). Measurements indicate that the electron wavelength is ~10^{-10} m, as predicted by the de Broglie equation. This is much shorter than light wavelengths. That is why an ***electron microscope***, which uses a beam of electrons, has a much greater resolving power (see B24) than an optical one.

C1 Particle physics – 1

Probing the nucleus

To investigate the nucleus, scientists have broken it into bits using beams of high-energy particles (such as protons), from ***particle accelerators*** (see next page).

Protons must be accelerated to very high speeds to penetrate the nucleus. They have to overcome the electric repulsion of the protons there. This is called a ***Coulomb repulsion*** (from Coulomb's inverse square law: see B13).

Being uncharged, neutrons can penetrate the nucleus more easily. But they cannot be directed and controlled by electric and magnetic fields.

Ordinary matter is made up of protons, neutrons, and electrons. But collision experiments with accelerators have produced hundreds of other 'elementary' particles as well. These are described in the next unit, C2.

Relativistic effects

The mass of a particle when at rest to an observer is its ***rest mass***, m_o. As the particle gains speed (and therefore energy), its mass increases (see B34). Its total observed mass is called its ***relativistic mass***, m. For a particle at a speed v relative to the observer (c is the speed of light):

$$m = \frac{m_o}{\sqrt{1 - v^2/c^2}} \qquad (1)$$

At the speeds achieved in accelerators, the mass increase can be significant. For example, for an electron travelling at 90% of c, m is more than twice m_o.

Energy and mass According to Einstein (see B34), a mass m has an ***energy equivalent*** E as given by this equation:

$$E = mc^2 \qquad (2)$$

For a particle at rest, $E_o = m_o c^2$. This is its ***rest energy***.

Energy and momentum If a particle's momentum is p, then $p = mv$. So, from equation (2), it follows that:

$$p = Ev/c^2 \qquad (3)$$

Using equations (1), (2), and (3), it can be shown that:

$$E^2 = m_o^2 c^4 + p^2 c^2$$

Note:
- If E is much greater than E_o, then $E \approx pc$.

Units The energies of particles from accelerators are often measured in GeV: 1 GeV = 1000 MeV = 10^9 eV.

As energy, mass, and momentum are linked, the masses and momenta of particles can be expressed in energy-related units. For example:

Mass can be measured in GeV/c^2. (from equation 2)

Momentum can be measured in GeV/c. (from equation 3)

The strong nuclear force

In the nucleus, the nucleons (neutrons and protons) are bound together by the strong nuclear force. The strong force:
- is strong enough to overcome the Coulomb repulsion between protons, otherwise they would fly apart,
- has a short range, ~10^{-15}m, and does not extend beyond neighbouring nucleons,
- becomes a repulsion at very short range, otherwise the nucleus would collapse.

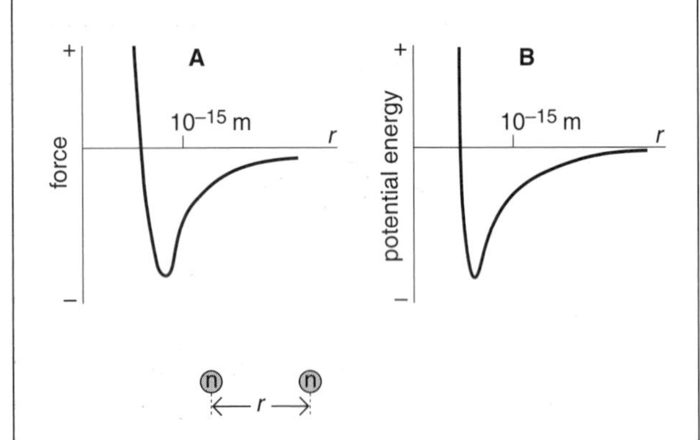

Graph A shows how the strong force varies with separation, for two neutrons. (An *attractive* force is *negative*.)

Graph B shows how the potential energy of the neutrons varies with separation. Minimum potential energy corresponds with the position of zero force in graph A.

Escaping from the nucleus: α decay

The graph below shows how the potential energy of an α particle varies along a line through the centre of a nucleus. Outside the nucleus, there is Coulomb repulsion (giving positive PE). Inside the nucleus, this is overcome by the strong force (giving negative PE). The result is a potential energy 'well' with a ***Coulomb barrier*** around it. Within this well, there are different energy levels.

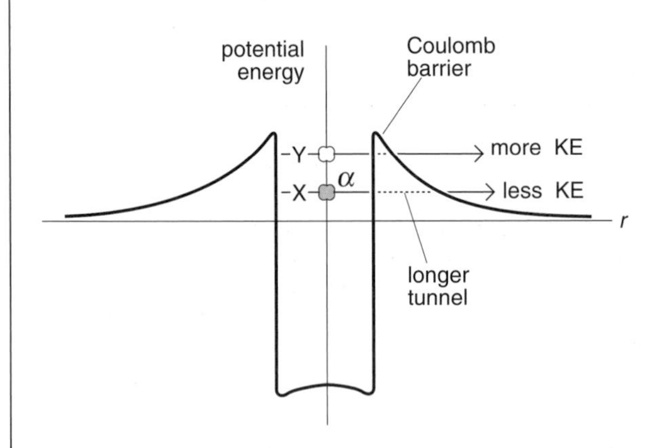

Above, an α particle has formed at X. It seems to be trapped by the Coulomb barrier. But because of the ***uncertainty principle*** (see C2) there is a chance that it may briefly 'borrow' enough energy to tunnel through the barrier and escape. This is called ***quantum mechanical tunnelling***.

An α particle at Y will escape with more KE – and is likely to escape sooner because the tunnel is shorter and easier to pass through. That is why α particles with the *highest* KEs come from nuclides with the *shortest* half-lives.

Particles and antiparticles

Most types of particle have a corresponding ***antiparticle*** (see also B32). This has the same rest mass, but at least one property which is opposite to that of the particle. Here are some examples.

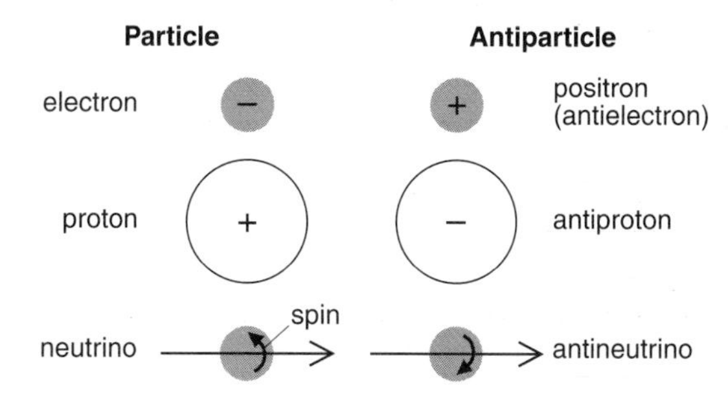

When a particle and its antiparticle meet, in most cases, they ***annihilate*** each other and their mass is converted into energy as given by $E = mc^2$. For example, the annihilation of an electron and positron may produce a pair of gamma photons.

Note:

- There are far more particles than antiparticles in the Universe, so annihilation is extremely rare.

Creating matter Energy can also be converted into mass. For example, if a gamma photon has at least 1.02 MeV of energy, it may, when passing close to a nucleus, convert into an electron-positron pair (total rest mass 1.02 MeV/c^2). In high-energy collisions, heavier particles (and antiparticles) may materialize from the energy supplied.

Particle accelerators

Accelerators can supply charged particles with the energy needed to create new matter in collisions.

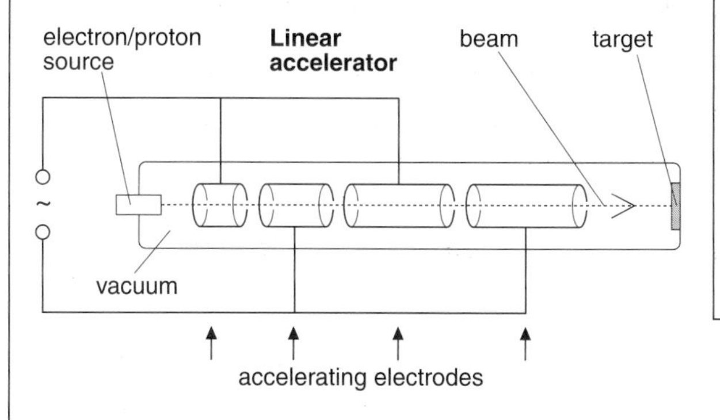

Linear accelerator (up to 20 GeV) Charged particles (e.g. electrons or protons) in a vacuum pipe are accelerated through a series of electrodes by an alternating voltage. The frequency is carefully chosen so that, as each electrode goes alternately + and –, particles leaving one electrode are always pulled towards the next. The beam of particles is directed at a target or into a ***synchrotron***.

Synchrotron (1000 GeV or more) In effect, this is a linear accelerator, bent into a ring (see right) so that the charged particles can be given more energy each time they go round. Electromagnets keep the particles in a curved path. As the speed increases, the magnetic field strength is increased to compensate for the extra mass.

Some synchrotrons are ***beam colliders***. They have two loops which overlap at one point so that particles (e.g. protons), in one loop can collide head on with antiparticles (e.g. antiprotons) in the other. This means that much more of the collision energy is converted into mass as new particles.

Detectors

In experiments using accelerators, detectors are needed to reveal the paths of the particles produced.

Bubble chamber This is filled with liquid hydrogen whose pressure is suddenly reduced so that it is ready to vaporize. Charged particles entering the chamber ionize the hydrogen. This triggers vaporization, so that a trail of bubbles is formed along the track of each particle.

Drift chamber This is a gas-filled chamber containing, typically, thousands of parallel wires. Incoming particles cause a trail of ionization in the gas. Their track is worked out electronically by timing how long it takes ionization electrons to drift to the nearest sense wires. A computer processes the signals and displays the tracks graphically.

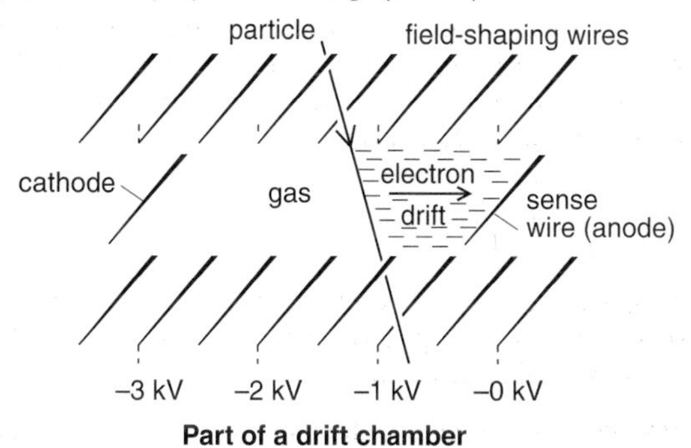

Part of a drift chamber

Identifying particles Charged particles can be identified by their paths in a magnetic field (see B33). Uncharged particles, which leave no tracks, must be identified by the tracks of charged particles they interact with.

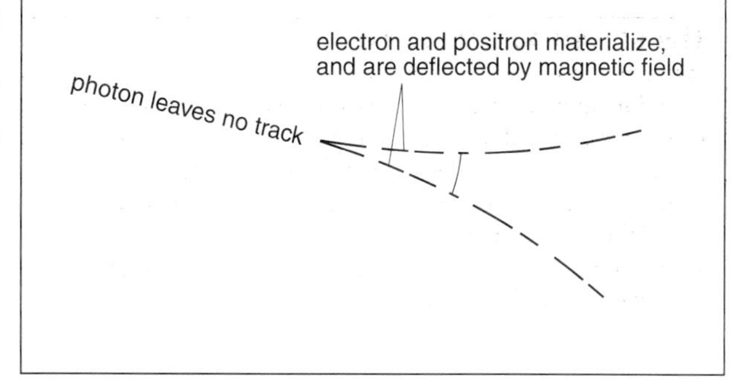

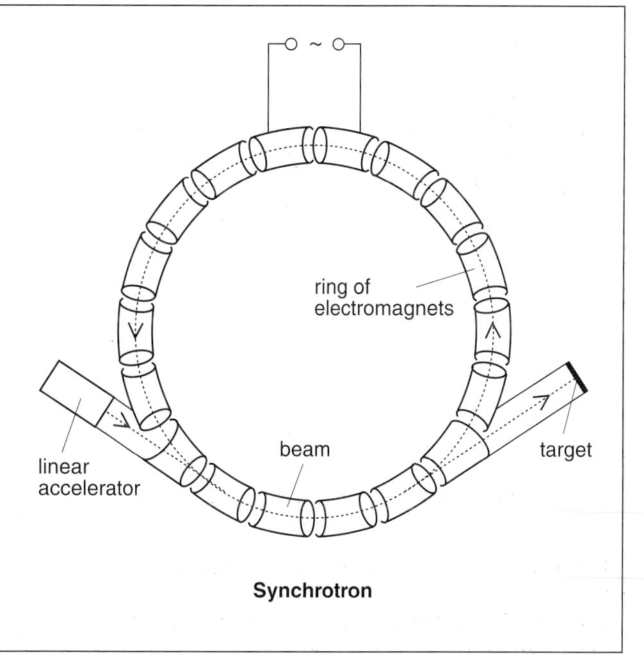

Synchrotron

C2 Particle physics – 2

Fundamental forces

Force	Range /m	Relative strength	Effects e.g.
strong	$\sim10^{-15}$	1	Holding nucleons in nucleus
electro-magnetic	∞	$\sim10^{-2}$	Holding electrons in atoms; holding atoms together
weak	$\sim10^{-17}$	$\sim10^{-5}$	ß decay; decay of unstable hadrons
gravitational	∞	$\sim10^{-39}$	Holding matter in planets, stars, and galaxies

Particles *interact* by exerting forces on each other. There are four known types of force in the Universe (see chart above). As electric and magnetic forces are closely related, they are regarded as different varieties of one force, the electromagnetic. ***Grand unified theories (GUTs)*** seek to link the strong, weak, and electromagnetic forces. Gravitational force has yet to be linked with the others. It is insignificant on an atomic scale.

Conservation laws

There are conservation laws for *momentum* and *total energy.* However, as mass and energy are equivalent, the total energy must include the rest energy (see C1).

Particles have various ***quantum numbers*** assigned to them. These are needed to represent other quantities which may be conserved during interactions. For example:

Charge In any interaction, this is conserved: it balances on both sides of the equation (see B32 for examples).

Lepton number This is +1 for a lepton, –1 for an antilepton, and 0 for any other particle. For example, a 'free' neutron decays, after about 15 minutes, like this:

neutron	→	proton	+	electron	+	antineutrino
(0)		(0)		(+1)		(–1)

The numbers (in brackets) have the same total, 0, on both sides of the equation, so lepton number is conserved. This applies in any type of interaction.

Baryon number This is +1 for a baryon, –1 for an antibaryon, and 0 for any other particle. It is conserved in all interactions.

Strangeness This is needed to account for the particular combinations of 'strange particles' (certain hadrons) produced in some collisons. It is conserved in strong and electromagnetic interactions, but not in all weak ones.

Charm relates to the likelihood of certain hadron decays.
Spin relates to a particle's angular momentum.
Topness and **bottomness** are further quantum numbers.

Classifying particles

Ordinary matter is made up of protons, neutrons, and electrons. However, in high-energy collisions, many other particles can be created. Most are very short-lived.

Matter particles can be divided into two main groups:

Hadrons (see right) These feel the strong force. They can be subdivided into ***baryons*** (which include protons, neutrons, and heavier particles that these), and ***mesons*** (which are generally lighter than protons).

Leptons (see below) These do not feel the strong force. They have no size and, in most cases, low or no mass. There are three generations of leptons, but only the first (the electron and its neutrino) occurs in ordinary matter.

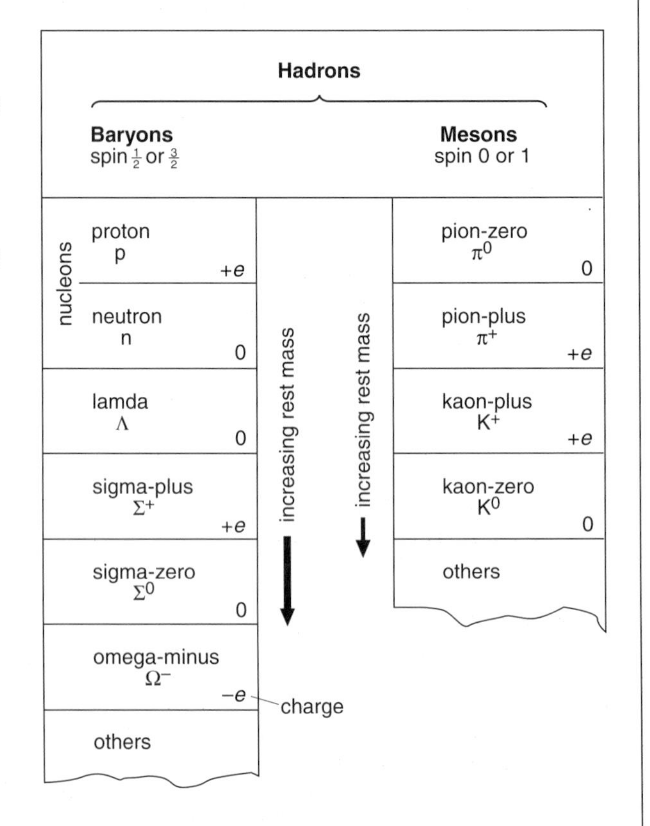

Generation	Leptons spin ½			
1	electron e^-	$-e$	electron-neutrino ν_e	0
2	muon μ^-	$-e$	muon-neutrino ν_μ	0
3	tau τ^-	$-e$	tau-neutrino ν_τ	0

charge

- All leptons and most hadrons have corresponding antiparticles.
- The neutrino, ν, produced by beta decay (see B32), is the electron-neutrino ν_e in the chart above.

Quarks

The properties and quantum numbers of hadrons can be accounted for by assuming that each particle is a combination of others, called ***quarks***. These have a fractional charge of $+\frac{2}{3}e$ or $-\frac{1}{3}e$. ***Symmetry theory*** predicts that there should be three generations of quarks to match the three generations of leptons. (For each type of quark, there is also a corresponding antiquark.)

Generation	Quarks spin $\frac{1}{2}$		Charge	Baryon number	Strangeness	Charm	Topness	Bottomness
1	up	u	$+\frac{2}{3}e$	$\frac{1}{3}$	0	0	0	0
	down	d	$-\frac{1}{3}e$	$\frac{1}{3}$	0	0	0	0
2	strange	s	$-\frac{1}{3}e$	$\frac{1}{3}$	–1	0	0	0
	charmed	c	$+\frac{2}{3}e$	$\frac{1}{3}$	0	1	0	0
3	top	t	$+\frac{2}{3}e$	$\frac{1}{3}$	0	0	1	0
	bottom	b	$-\frac{1}{3}e$	$\frac{1}{3}$	0	0	0	–1

Note:
- Ordinary matter contains only the first generation of quarks. Very high energies are needed to make hadrons of other quark generations. These hadrons quickly decay into first generation particles.
- Individual quarks have never been detected.

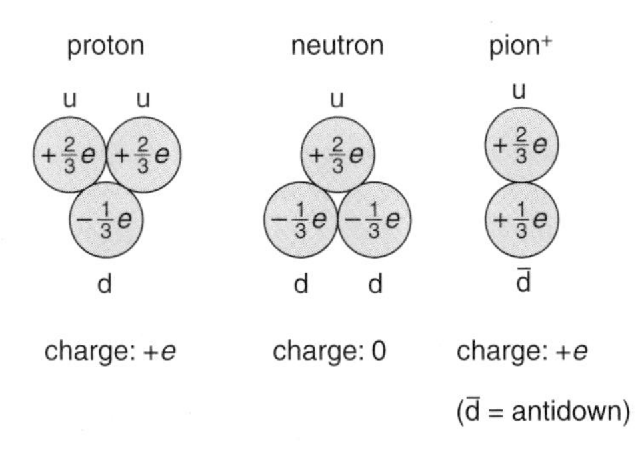

All known hadrons can be constructed from different quark (and antiquark) combinations. Examples are given above.
- Baryons are each made up of three quarks.
- Mesons are each made up of a quark and an antiquark.

Energy and the uncertainty principle

According to the ***uncertainty principle***, a particle's momentum and position cannot both have precise values. There is a level of uncertainty about them. One consequence of this is that the law of conservation of energy can, briefly, be *violated* (disobeyed). A particle can have more energy than it 'ought' to, by an amount ΔE, provided that this is paid back in a time Δt, where $\Delta E.\Delta t \approx h$. This has important consequences for the behaviour of particles, including quantum mechanical tunnelling in C1.

Force carriers

Like other particles, nucleons need not be in contact to exert forces on each other. To explain how the strong force is 'carried' from one nucleon (e.g. neutron) to another, the idea of ***exchange particles*** is used:

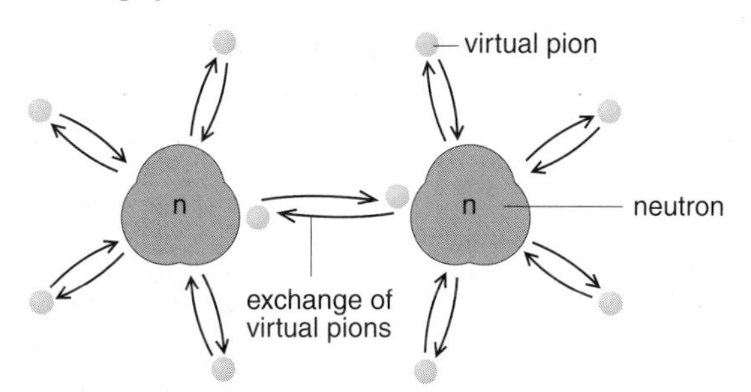

Each nucleon is continually emitting and reabsorbing ***virtual pions***, which surround it in a swarm. When close, two nucleons may exchange a pion. The momentum transfer produces the effect of a force (attractive or repulsive).

Note:
- The emitting nucleons lose no mass, so virtual pions are only allowed their brief existence by the uncertainty principle. To create 'real' pions, the missing mass must be supplied by the energy of a collision.

All the fundamental forces are believed to be carried by exchange particles. For example, electrons repel each other by exchanging ***virtual photons***. This process can be represented by a ***Feynmann diagram*** as below. For 'real' photons to exist, energy must be supplied.

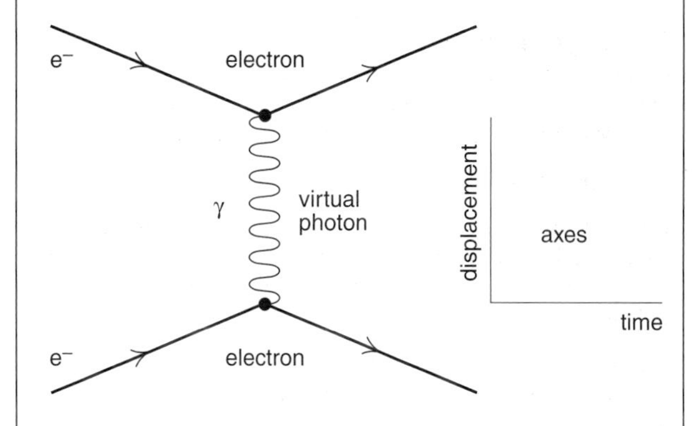

The particles that carry the fundamental forces are known as ***gauge bosons***. They are listed in the chart below.

Note:
- Quarks are bound together by ***gluons***. As nucleons and pions are made of quarks, the gluon would seem to be the basic force carrier for all strong interactions.
- The existence of the graviton is speculation only.

Force	Gauge bosons		
strong	gluon		
electromagnetic	photon		
weak	W^+	W^-	Z^0
gravitational	graviton		

C3 Astrophysics – 1

Solar System, stars, and galaxies

The Earth is one of many ***planets*** in orbit around the Sun. The Sun, planets, and other objects in orbit, are together known as the ***Solar System***.

Most of the planets move in near-circular orbits. Many have smaller ***moons*** orbiting them (see B10 for orbital equations and laws). ***Comets*** are small, icy objects in highly elliptical orbits around the Sun. Planets, moons, and comets are only visible because they reflect the Sun's light.

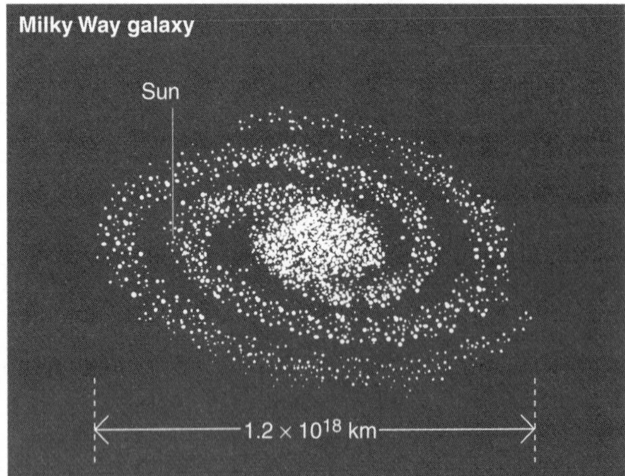

The Sun is one star in a huge star system called a ***galaxy***. Our galaxy contains about 10^{11} stars, as well as interstellar matter (thinly-spread gas and dust between the stars). Our galaxy, called the ***Milky Way***, is slowly rotating, with a period of more than 10^8 years. It is held together by gravitational attraction. It is just one of many billions of galaxies in the known ***Universe*** (see C5).

Normal galaxies emit mostly light. However, about 10% of galaxies have active centres which emit strongly in other parts of the electromagnetic spectrum as well.

Distance units

In astrophysics, the following distance units are used.

Light-year (ly) This is the distance travelled (in a vacuum) by light in one year. 1 light-year = 9.47×10^{15} m.

Astronomical unit (AU) This is the mean radius of the Earth's orbit around the Sun. 1 AU = 1.50×10^{11} m.

Parsec (pc) This is the distance at which the mean radius of the Earth's orbit has an angular displacement of one arc second (1/3600 degree). (See also *Parallax* in C4).

1pc = 3.26 ly = 2.06×10^5 AU = 3.09×10^{16} m

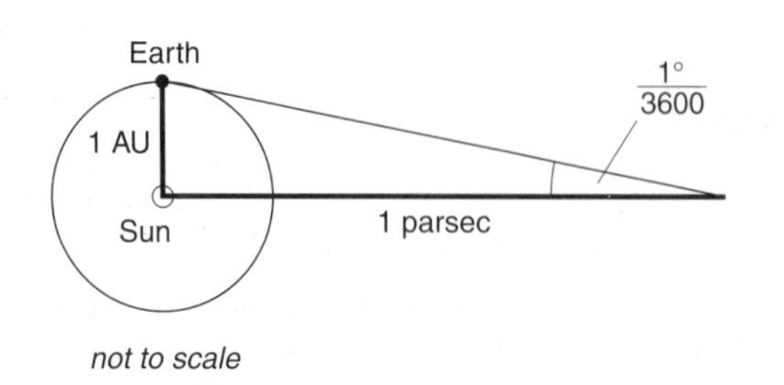

Diameter of Earth = 1.3×10^4 km
Diameter of Sun = 1.4×10^6 km
Radius of Earth's orbit = 1.5×10^8 km = 1 AU

Diameter of Solar System = 50 AU
Distance to nearest star (*Proxima Centauri*) = 2.7×10^5 AU = 4.2 ly = 1.3 pc

Diameter of galaxy (*Milky Way*) = 1.3×10^5 ly = 40 kpc
Distance to neighbouring galaxy (*Andromeda*) = 2.2×10^6 ly = 0.7 Mpc

Collectors and detecting radiation

Information about planets, stars, and galaxies is obtained by analysing the electromagnetic radiation they emit. Depending on the source, this can range from radio waves to γ radiation. Some form of telescope is used as the ***collector***. This is linked to a ***detector***.

Electromagnetic radiation	Telescope: collector e.g.	detector e.g.
radio	concave metal dish	antenna
infrared	concave mirror	solid state detector
light ultraviolet	concave mirror (see B24)	photographic plate or CCD
X-rays γ rays	concave metal dish	solid state detector

Charge-coupled device (CCD) This is used in many optical (e.g. light) telescopes instead of a photographic plate. It is more sensitive, and the image on it can be processed electronically. It consists of an array of tiny photodiodes, each contributing one piece *(a **pixel**)* to the whole picture. Signals from the photodiodes are amplified and processed by a computer for display on a screen.

Siting telescopes Most incoming radiation is blocked by the Earth's atmosphere. That which does pass through includes light, parts of the radio spectrum, and some infrared and ultraviolet. Radio waves can pass through interstellar dust, which blocks light from galactic centres.

Telescopes are sited as follows:

- Radio telescopes are usually ground-based.
- Optical telescopes are mounted as high in the atmosphere as possible (e.g. on mountain tops) or above it. This is to reduce image quality problems caused by atmospheric refraction and 'light pollution' from cities.
- Infrared, ultraviolet, X and γ radiation telescopes are placed in high-altitude balloons or orbiting satellites. Satellite-based instruments include:
  HST The Hubble Space Telescope (optical),
  COBE The Cosmic Background Explorer (microwave),
  IRAS The Infrared Astronomical Satellite.

Stefann Boltzmann Law

Lumin = kT^4
$= kT^4 A (A = 4\pi r^2)$
= Watts m²

Telescope design

Optical telescopes These are described in B24.

Radio telescopes Most have a large concave dish to reflect incoming radio waves towards the antenna. Microwaves need a smooth metal reflector. With longer wavelengths, wire mesh can be used, provided the mesh size is less than about $\lambda/20$. A computer-generated 'radio image' is built up by ***scanning*** the source line by line.

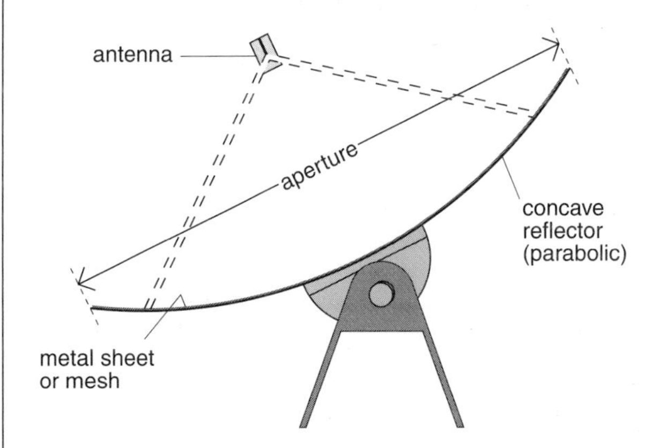

Radio telescopes have to deal with much longer wavelengths than optical instruments, so they need much wider apertures to give the same resolving power (see B24). Effective apertures of many kilometres can be achieved by linking several telescopes electronically.

Luminosity and magnitude

The ***luminosity*** of a star is the rate at which it radiates energy. The unit of luminosity is the watt (W).

The observed brightness of a star depends on its luminosity *and* on its distance from Earth. A very luminous star can appear dim if it is far enough away, because the intensity of its radiation obeys an inverse square law (B22).

The ***apparent magnitude***, m, of a star is a measure of its observed brightness. On the scale of m values, 0, 1, 2, 3 etc represents an order of *decreasing* observed brightness.

- By definition, a star for which $m = 1$ appears 100 times brighter than a star for which $m = 6$.
- The brightest stars in the sky have negative values of m.
- A star's apparent magnitude can be deduced by analysing its image on a photographic plate or CCD.

The ***absolute magnitude***, M, of a star is the apparent magnitude it would have if it were 10 parsecs away.

- Absolute magnitude is directly related to luminosity and does not depend on the star's distance from the Earth.

Using the inverse square law for intensity (see B22), it can be shown that a star's distance d (in pc), apparent magnitude m, and absolute magnitude M are linked like this:

$$m - M = 5 \log \frac{d}{10} \qquad (1)$$

For methods of estimating distances to stars, see C4.

Star	Apparent magnitude (m)	Absolute magnitude (M)	Distance/ pc
Sirius	−1.5	1.4	2.7
Rigel	0.1	−7.2	290
Deneb	1.3	−7.2	490
Proxima C	11.1	15.5	1.3

Spectral analysis

Information about a star's temperature, composition, and motion can be found by analysing its spectrum.

Thermal radiation in B31 includes a graph which shows how the peak wavelength changes with temperature for a black body radiator (e.g. a star). According to ***Wien's law***:

$$\lambda_{max} T = 2.90 \times 10^{-3} \text{ m K}$$

If λ_{max} is found from a star's spectrum, the surface temperature T can be calculated.

Emission and absorption spectra in B35 explains how the composition of the Sun's outer layers can be deduced from its absorption spectrum. This also applies to other stars. For more on stellar (star) spectra, see C4.

The Doppler effect

wavelength lengthened

wavelength shortened

detector

moving source

If a wave source is receding (moving away) from a detector, the waves reaching the detector are more spaced out, so their measured wavelength is increased and their frequency reduced. This is an example of the ***Doppler effect***. It causes the change of pitch which you hear when an ambulance rushes past with its siren sounding.

Star motion can be fast enough to cause a detectable Doppler shift in light waves. If a star is moving *away* from the Earth, its spectral lines are shifted towards the *red* end of the spectrum. If v is the relative velocity of recession, and v is small compared with the speed of light, c:

$$\frac{\Delta f}{f} = -\frac{v}{c} \quad \text{and} \quad \frac{\Delta \lambda}{\lambda} = \frac{v}{c}$$

f and λ are the emitted frequency and wavelength. Δf and $\Delta\lambda$ are the observed changes – both defined as *increases*.

- The Sun's rotation causes a broadening of its spectral lines, because light from the receding side is red-shifted while that from the approaching side is blue-shifted. This effect can be used to work out the speed of rotation.

Radar astronomy

The distance of a planet (or moon), and its speed of rotation, can be found by directing radar (microwave) pulses at its surface and analysing the pulses reflected back.

The distance is found by measuring the time interval between the outgoing and returning pulses.

The speed of rotation is found by measuring the Doppler shifts which occur when pulses are reflected from the receding and approaching sides of the planet.

C4 Astrophysics – 2

Classifying stars

Stars can be classified according to their spectra. The main spectral classes are: O, B, A, F, G, K, M. This represents an order from high to low temperature (see diagram below).

Here are details of some of the spectral classes:

- O-type stars are the hottest and appear blue-white. Helium lines are prominent in their absorption spectra.
- A-type stars appear white. Hydrogen lines are prominent in their absorption spectra.
- G-type stars, like the Sun, appear yellow-white. There are many metallic lines in their absorption spectra.
- M-type stars are the coolest, and appear red. Banding in their absorption spectra indicates the presence of molecules.

The Hertzsprung-Russell (H-R) diagram

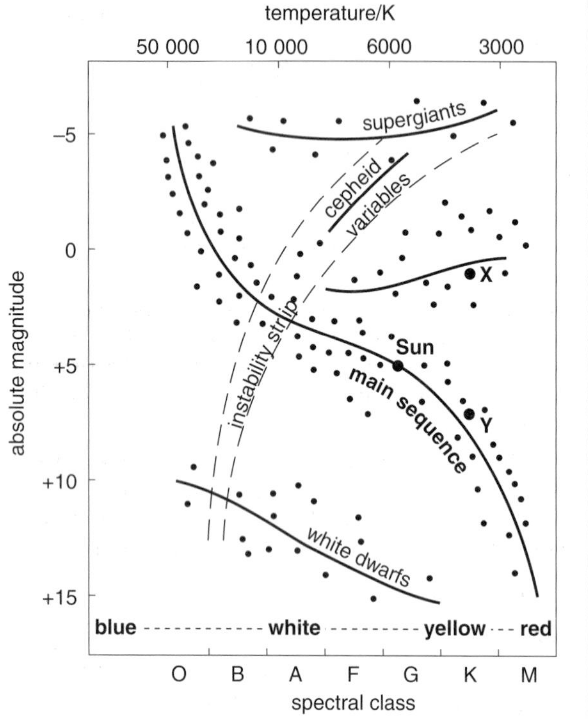

This is a diagram in which the absolute magnitudes of stars are plotted against their spectral classes. A simplified version is shown above.

Note:

- Star X is the same spectral class as star Y, but higher up the diagram, i.e. X is at the same temperature as Y, but radiates more light. So X is larger than Y.
- Terms such as ***giant*** and ***dwarf*** indicate star size.
- The points on an H-R diagram occur in zones. Most stars, including the Sun, belong to the ***main sequence***.

Estimating distances to stars and galaxies

These are the main methods used:

Parallax As the Earth orbits the Sun, neaby stars appear to move agains the background of very distant stars. The nearer the star, the greater its apparent movement. This effect is called ***parallax***.

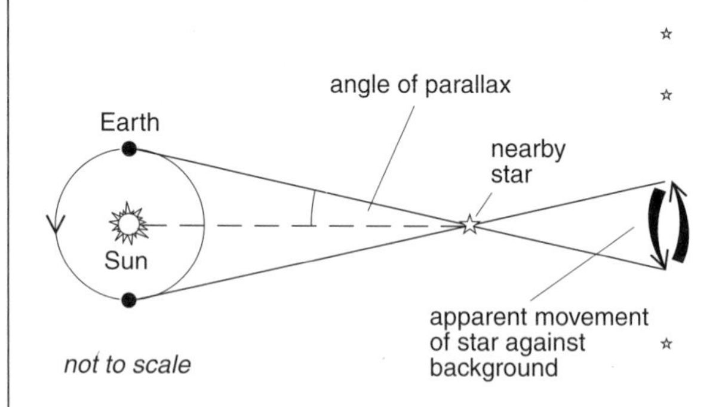

By measuring the angle of parallax, the distance can be calculated using trigonometry. The method is suitable for distances up to ~ 100 pc. (The pc - parsec, see C3 - was defined to aid calculations involving parallax.)

Inverse square law The distance of a star or galaxy is worked out by comparing its apparent and absolute magnitudes, and using equation (1) in C3. The method is suitable for very distant objects. However, it requires 'standard' sources, of known absolute magnitude, e.g:

- stars whose positions on the H-R diagram can be worked out by spectral analysis
- cepheid variables (see below). These can be observed in other galaxies as well as our own.

The Hubble law Galaxies have a red shift which is proportional to their distance from the Earth (see C5). This can be used to estimate the distance.

Birth of a star

Stars form in huge clouds of gas (mainly hydrogen) and dust called ***nebulae.*** The Sun formed in a nebula about 5×10^9 years ago. The process took about 5×10^7 years:

Gravity pulled more and more nebular matter into a concentrated clump called a ***protostar***. The loss of gravitational PE caused a rise in core temperature which triggered the fusion of hydrogen and the release of energy (see B34). Thermal activity stopped further gravitational collapse. The Sun had become a main sequence star. (Its planets had formed in an orbiting disc of nebular matter.)

Cepheid variables

Most of the stars in the ***instability strip*** (see the H-R diagram above) are ***cepheid variables***. These show a regular variation in brightness, as in the example in the graph on the right.

The period (of brightness variation) of a cepheid variable is directly related to its absolute magnitude. The more luminous the star, the longer the period. By measuring the period, the absolute magnitude can be found and, from this the distance, using equation (1) in C3.

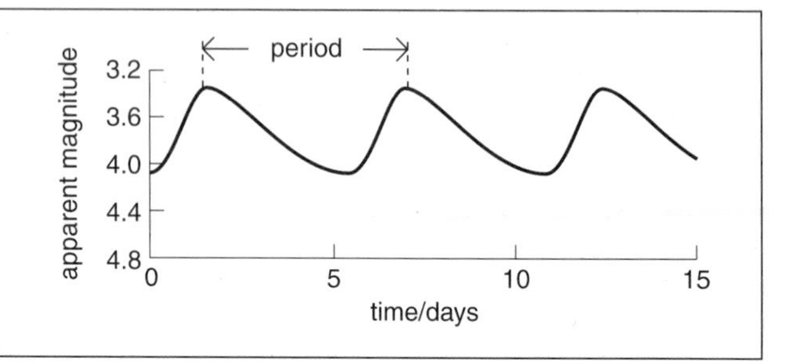

Life and death of a star

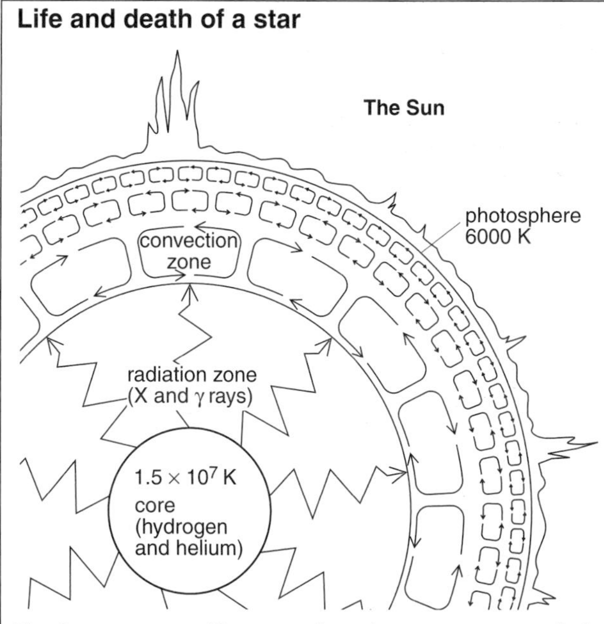

The Sun gets most of its energy from the ***proton-proton chain***, a multi-stage fusion process which converts hydrogen-1 into helium-4. Hotter, more massive stars use the ***CNO cycle***. This also changes hydrogen-1 into helium-4, but involves carbon, nitrogen, and oxygen nuclei.

The Sun is about half way through its life on the main sequence (about 10^{10} years). Hotter, more massive stars consume hydrogen more quickly and have shorter main sequence lives.

When all its hydrogen has been converted into helium, the Sun will take the path shown on the H-R diagram below.

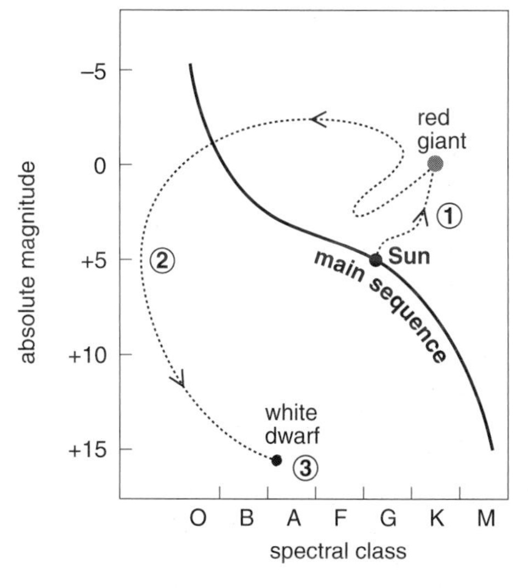

1. The core collapses. The Sun becomes a ***red giant*** as its outer layers expand and cool (and engulf the Earth). With the core temperature rising to over 10^8 K, energy is released by the fusion of helium into carbon.
2. After further changes, the outer layers expand and drift off into space. The core and inner layers become a ***white dwarf*** whose core is so dense that the normal atomic structure breaks down. The electrons form a ***degenerate electron gas*** whose pressure stops further collapse.
3. Fusion ceases. The white dwarf cools and fades for ever.

Note:

- Stars less massive than the Sun end up as white dwarfs, without going through the giant stages.
- Massive stars become giants or supergiants, then end up as ***neutron stars*** or ***black holes*** (see right).

More stellar objects

Supernovae When a massive star enters its giant phase, its core becomes so hot that carbon is fused into heavier elements. If the star exceeds about 8 solar (Sun's) masses, iron is produced. As this is at the top of the binding energy curve (see B34), fusion no longer supplies energy. The core collapses, causing a shock wave which blows away the star's outer layers in a huge explosion called a ***supernova***. For a few days, this is millions of times brighter than a star. Elements ejected from supernovae eventually 'seed' the nebulae in which new stars and planets will form.

Neutron stars If the core of a supernova exceeds about 1.4 solar masses, the degenerate electron gas cannot resist gravitational collapse. Electrons and protons are pushed together to form neutrons. The result is a neutron star – essentially a giant nucleus about 10–30 km across.

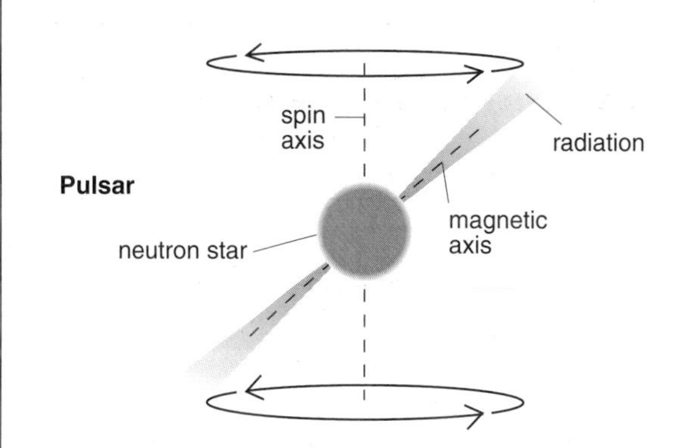

Pulsars These emit radio, light, or X-ray pulses at up to 500 times per second. They are believed to be rapidly spinning neutron stars. Pulses are detected because the star sends out two narrow radiation beams which rotate with it, rather like the beams of light from a lighthouse.

Black holes If the core of a supernova exceeds about 2.5 solar masses, even the neutrons formed cannot resist gravitational collapse. The core shrinks to become a black hole from which no particles or radiation can escape.

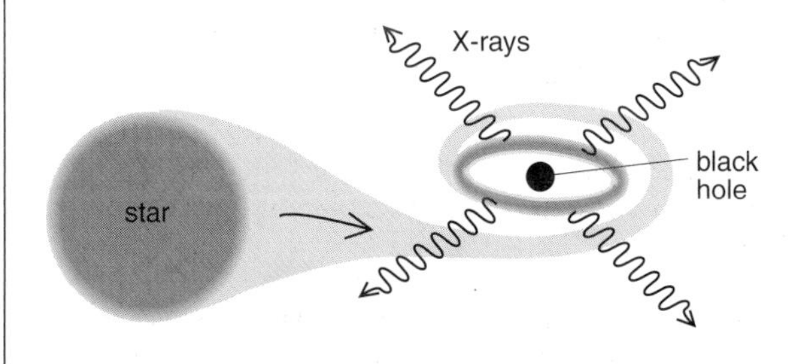

X-ray binary system

Binary stars These are two stars which rotate about a common centre of mass. If they are close, gravity may pull material from one to the other. If one is a neutron star or black hole, material falling into it will give off X-rays.

Quasars These have red shifts which suggest that they are the most distant objects in the Universe (see *Hubble's law* in C5). If they really are distant, they radiate as much energy as some galaxies, but have only the volume of a solar system. Each may be the active centre of a galaxy where nebular matter surrounds a supermassive black hole.

Note:
Some scientists argue that quasars are closer, less luminous objects whose red shifts have some other cause.

C5 Cosmology

The structure of the Universe

The study of the Universe, its origins, and evolution is called ***cosmology***.

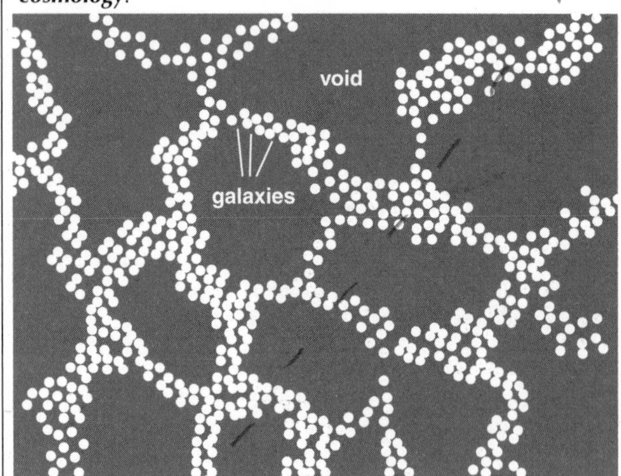

The Universe contains billions of galaxies. Their average separation is ~ 10^6 light-years. Together, they form a network of long, clumpy filaments with huge voids (spaces) in between. Despite their local irregularities, the galaxies are, on a large scale, evenly distributed in all directions.

The motion of galaxies indicates that they are surrounded by massive amounts of thinly-spread, invisible material. This is called ***dark matter***. Its nature is not yet known.

Hubble's law

Measurements of Doppler red shifts (see C3) indicate that, in general, the galaxies are receding from each other. The further away the galaxy, the greater is its red shift and, therefore, the greater its recession velocity.

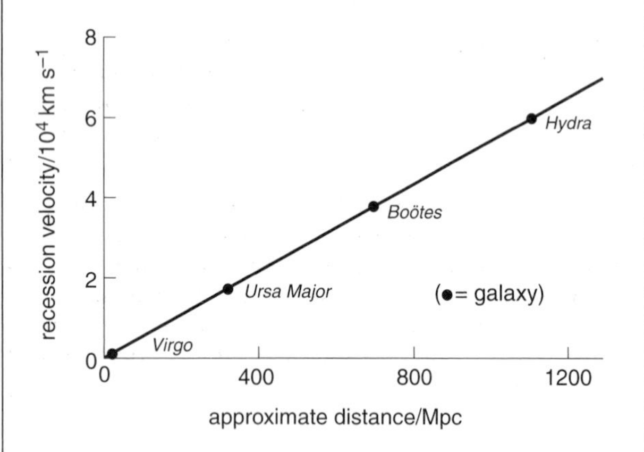

According to ***Hubble's law***, the distance d of a galaxy and its recession velocity v are linked by this equation:

$$v = H_0 d \qquad (1)$$

H_0 is called the ***Hubble constant***. Large distances are difficult to estimate accurately, so the value of H_0 has a high uncertainty. However, it is thought to lie in the range 50–100 km s^{-1} Mpc^{-1} (1.6–3.2×10^{-18} s^{-1}). Its value is important for several reasons:

- It enables the distances of the most remote galaxies to be estimated from their red shifts.
- The age of the Universe can be estimated from it (see above right). (H_0 has dimensions of 1/time.)
- The fate of the Universe depends on it (see next page).

The expanding Universe

The most generally accepted explanation of galactic red shifts is that the Universe is expanding. At zero time, all its matter and energy was together in a highly concentrated state.

Estimating the age of the Universe If a galaxy is d from our own, and has a steady recession velocity v, then separation of the galaxies must have occurred at a time d/v ago. This represents the approximate age of the Universe. From equation (1) $d/v = 1/H_0$, so:

The age of the Universe $\approx 1/H_0$

This gives an age in the range 1–2×10^{10} years (10–20 billion years).

Note:

- The above calculation assumes constant v. In reality, v is thought to have decreased with time (see next page). This gives a reduced age estimate.

Olber's paradox In the 17th century, it was pointed out that, if the stars continued out to infinity, the night sky should be white, not dark – because light must be coming from every possible direction in the sky. This became known as Olber's paradox.

Two reasons for the dark night sky have been suggested:

- In an expanding Universe, red-shifted wavelengths mean reduced photon energies (see B35), so the intensity of the light from distant stars is reduced.
- There is a limit to our observable Universe. If, say, the Universe is 15 billion years old, then we have yet to receive light from stars more than 15 billion light-years away. So everything beyond that distance looks dark.

The cosmological principle This says that, apart from small-scale irregularities, the Universe should appear the same from all points within it (i.e. the distribution of galaxies and their recession velocities should appear the same from all points).

The hot big bang theory

According to this theory, sometimes called the ***standard model***, the Universe (and time) began about 10–20 billion years ago when a single, hot 'superatom' erupted in a burst of energy called the ***big bang***. As expansion and cooling took place, particles and antiparticles formed. Further cooling meant that combinations were possible, so nuclei and then atoms formed – and eventually galaxies (see next page).

Fundamental forces In the instant after the big bang, the fundamental forces (see C2) existed as one superforce. But within 10^{-11}s, they had separated from each other.

Cosmic background There is a steady background radiation which comes from every direction in space. It peaks in the microwave region, and corresponds to the radiation from a black body (see B31) at 2.7 K. It is thought to be the red-shifted remnant of radiation from the big bang. Its presence is predicted by the big bang theory.

Inflation The standard model cannot satisfactorily explain why, on a large scale, the Universe and its microwave background radiation are so uniform. Mathematically, it is possible to overcome this difficulty by assuming that the early Universe went through a brief period of very rapid inflation, when its volume increased by a factor 10^{50}.

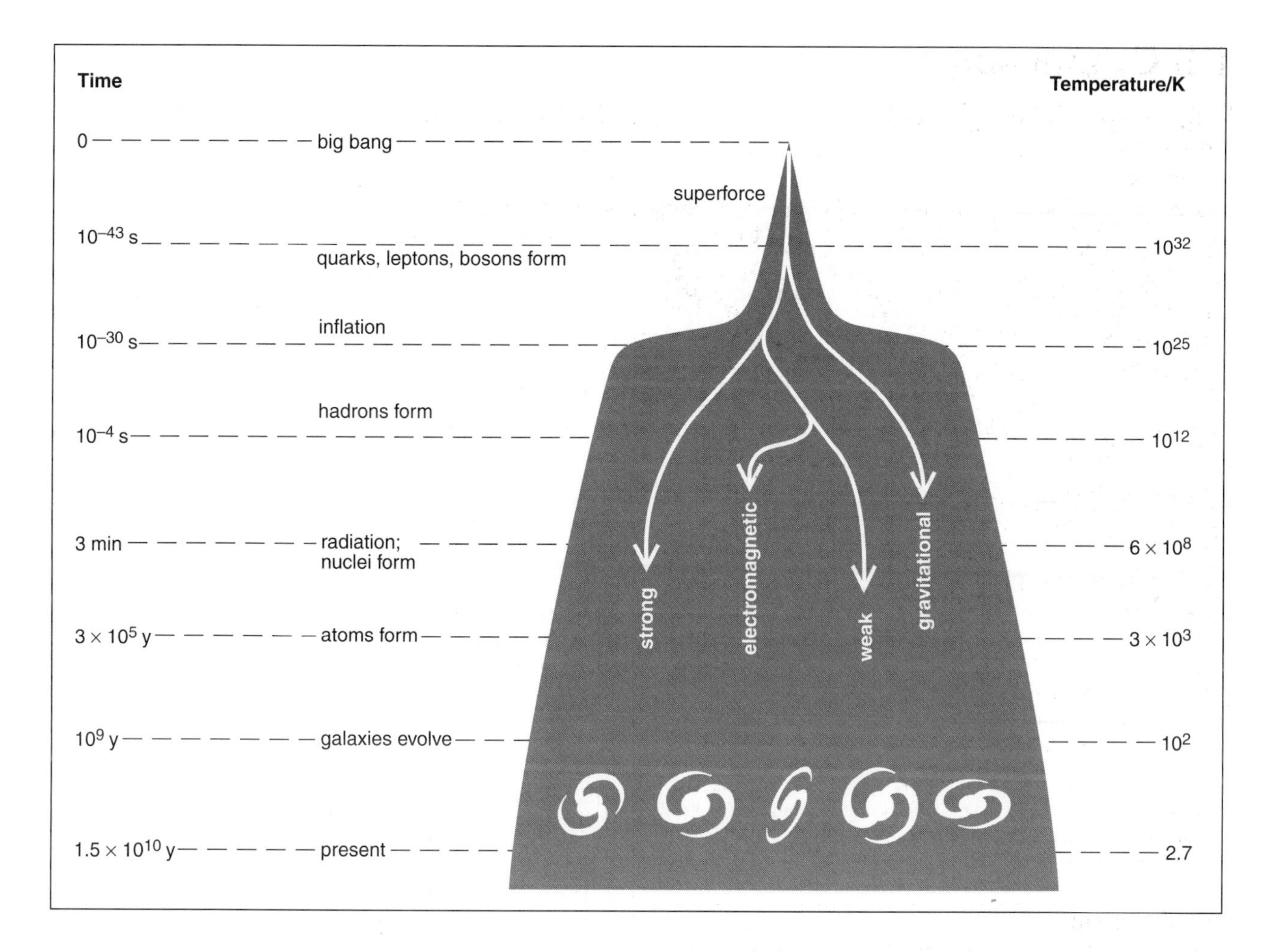

The fate of the Universe

Gravity is slowing the expansion of the Universe. The fate of the Universe depends on how its average density ρ compares with a certain **critical density** ρ_0:

- If $\rho < \rho_0$ the expansion continues indefinitely.
- If $\rho = \rho_0$ the expansion continues, but the rate falls to zero after infinite time.
- If $\rho > \rho_0$ the expansion reaches a maximum, and is followed by contraction.

The average density of the Universe is thought to be close to the critical density.

Linking ρ_0 and H_0 The critical density depends on the value of the Hubble constant. A higher H_0 means a higher recession velocity per unit separation. So a higher density is needed to stop the expansion. It can be shown that:

$$\rho_0 = \frac{3H_0^2}{8\pi G}$$

where G is the gravitational constant (see B9)

This gives ρ_0 in the range 5–20 × 10^{-27} kg m^{-3}.

Models of the Universe

The big bang was not an explosion into existing space. Space itself started to expand. The galaxies are separating because the space between them is increasing.

Space has three dimensions of distance (represented by x, y, and z co-ordinates) and one of time. According to Einstein's theory of general relativity, gravity causes a curvature of space-time. If gravity is sufficiently strong, it may produce a 'closed' Universe, as shown below.

To visualize the expansion of the Universe, it is simpler to use models with only two of the distance dimensions. Imagine that the Universe is on an expanding, elastic surface. Three possible models are shown below. In each case, the galaxies move apart as the surface stretches. From any position on the surface, each galaxy recedes at a velocity that is proportional to its distance away.

Note:

- It is the value of the critical density, and therefore of the Hubble constant, which decides whether we live in an open, flat, or closed Universe.

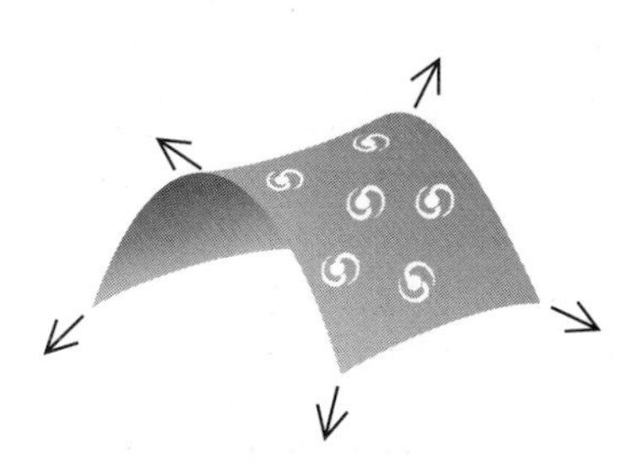

Open Universe ($\rho<\rho_0$) The surface is infinite and unbounded.

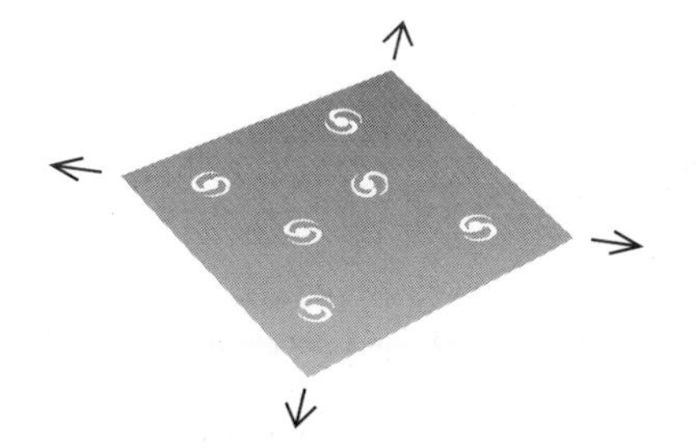

Flat Universe ($\rho = \rho_0$) The surface is infinite and unbounded.

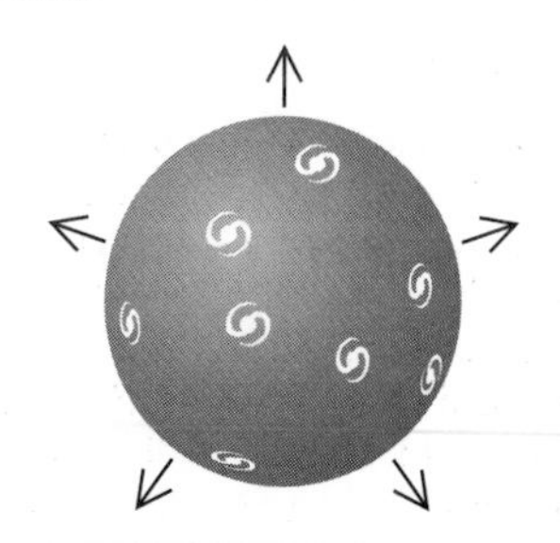

Closed Universe ($\rho>\rho_0$) The surface is finite and bounded.

C6 Materials – 1

Read B25 before studying this unit and the next one.

Bonds

The electric forces that make atoms stick together are called ***bonds***. Some different types of bonds are described below.

Ionic bonds These are strong bonds, formed by the *transfer* of electrons between atoms.

For example, a crystal of sodium chloride consists of a lattice of negative (–) ions and positive (+) ions. The ions are formed by the transfer of electrons from sodium to chlorine. The attractions between opposite ions are the bonds.

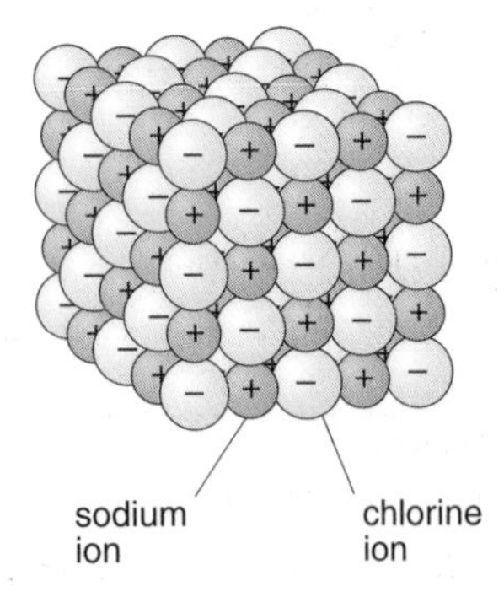

Metallic bonds In metals, some electrons are loosely held, and not tied to particular atoms. So a metal is effectively made up of positive (+) ions in a 'sea' of free electrons (–) which bind them together strongly.

Covalent bonds These are the bonds that hold atoms together in molecules. They are strong, but highly directional. They are formed by the *sharing* of electrons. For example, in a water molecule, two hydrogen atoms each share their electron with an oxygen atom as shown below.

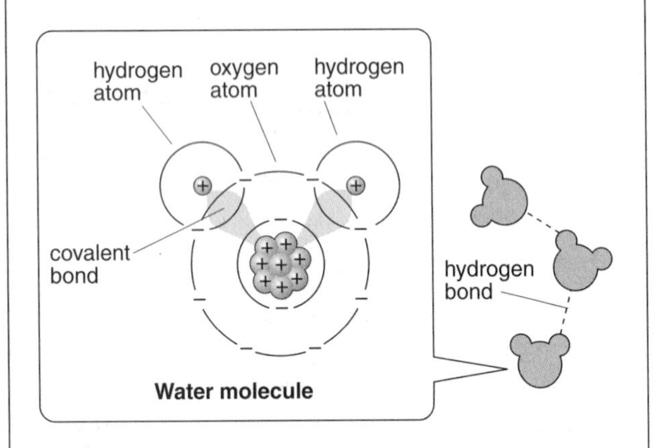

Hydrogen bonds These are the weak bonds which pull water molecules together. Although the molecules are electrically neutral, their electrons are unevenly distributed, giving them positive and negative parts which pull on other molecules.

A molecule with + and – ends is a ***polar*** molecule: it is ***polarized***. The separated charges are an ***electric dipole***. Dipoles tend to turn so that they attract each other.

Van der Waals bonds These are weak bonds existing between all neighbouring molecules (or atoms) because of dipole attractions. Polar molecules temporarily *induce* (see B13) dipoles in nearby non-polar ones. And even non-polar molecules can have instantaneous dipoles because of the random motion of their electrons.

Forces, energy, and separation

The physical properties of materials depend on how their atoms or molecules are stuck together.

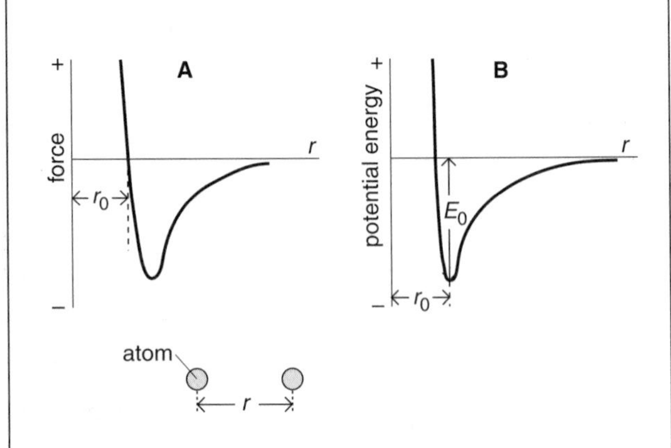

Graph A above shows how the force between two atoms varies with separation (an *attractive* force is *negative*). When very close, the outer electrons cause repulsion. At greater separations, the bonding force is dominant, but decreases with distance. n_0 is the ***equilibrium separation*** (~10^{-10} m).

Graph B shows how the potential energy of the atoms varies with separation. Minimum PE corresponds with the position for zero force in graph A. E_0 is the ***bonding energy***. It is the energy needed for complete separation. The specific latent heat of vaporization (see B28) depends on it.

Hooke's law Imagine that atoms r_0 apart are to be further separated by a force. As graph A is straight in this region, the increase in separation is proportional to the force. For a wire containing rows of billions of atoms, Hooke's law (strain ∝ stress) follows directly from this.

Energy density, and strain

A material stores energy when stretched or compressed elastically. The area under a stress-strain graph gives the ***energy density*** i.e. the energy stored *per unit volume*.

Apart from the tensile and compressive strain, other forms of strain include those below.

Bulk strain The deformation is caused by an increase in external pressure.

Shear strain The deformation is as on the right. (Twisting also causes shear strain in a material).

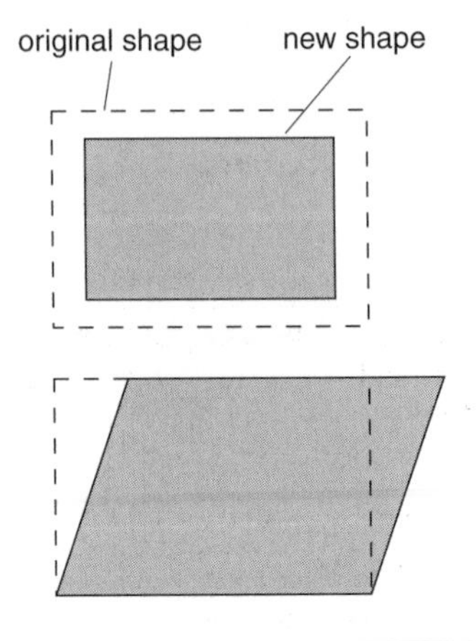

Crystal structures

Many solids are crystalline: their atoms (or other particles) are stacked in a regular pattern. Crystal structures include those on the right. The basic pattern repeats throughout the crystal.

FCC and HCP give the closest packing. The two structures are very similar. Both have layers A and B, as shown below. However, in HCP, the next layer is a repeat of A. In FCC, it is in a third site, C. (You need to study a model to visualize this.)

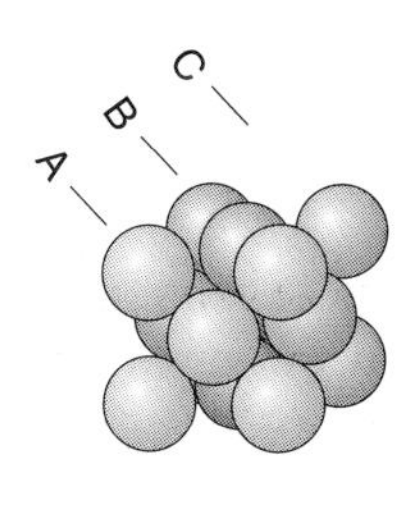

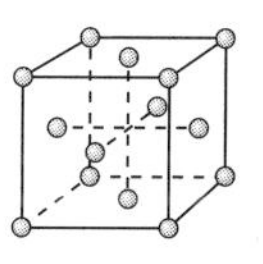

Face-centred cubic (FCC) e.g. aluminium, cobalt

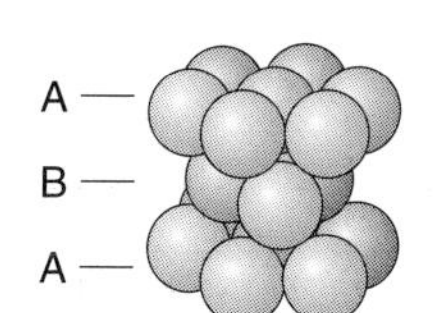

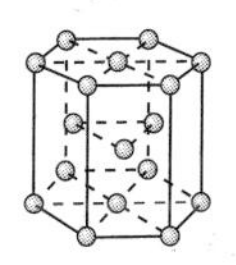

Hexagonal close-packing (HCP) e.g. magnesium, zinc

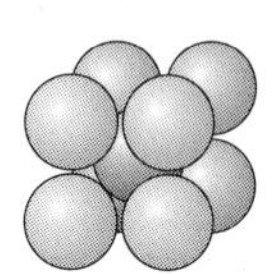

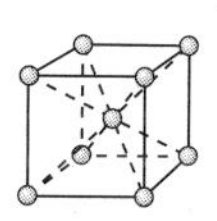

Body-centred cubic (BCC) e.g. iron, sodium

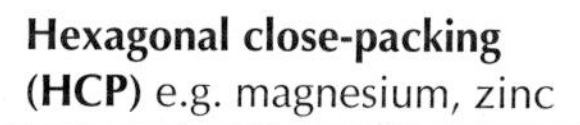

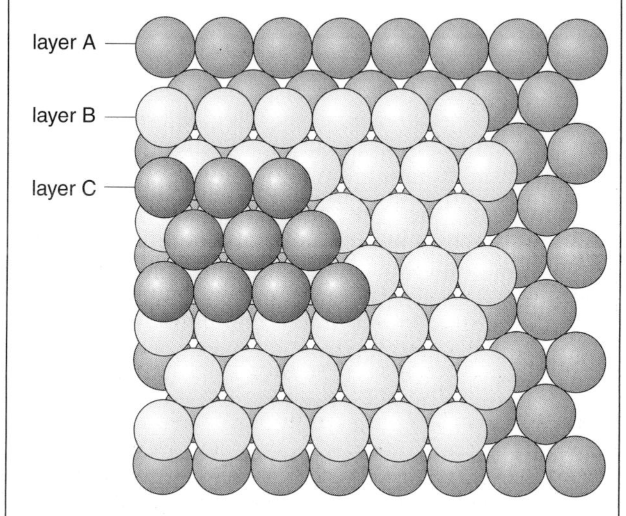

Stacking ABAB etc gives the HCP structure.
Stacking ABCABC etc gives the FCC structure.

Some substances can have more than one structure. For example, carbon can exist as *diamond* or *graphite*, as below. Diamond is very hard because of its strong bonds and rigid ***tetrahedral*** structure. Graphite is soft, slippery, and easy to break. It has layers that can slip over each other because the bonds between them are weak.

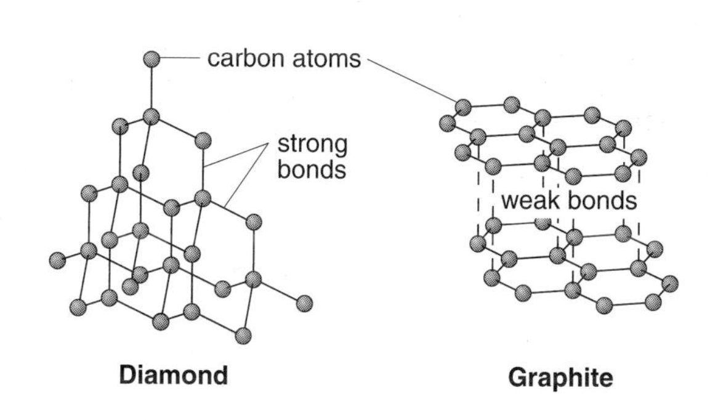

Defects

Defects occur in virtually all crystals (e.g. grains).

Line defects These are the ***dislocations*** described in B25. They are associated with ***stacking faults***: for example, layers of atoms like those on the left slipping so that they stack ABCACABC instead of ABCABCABC.

When a wire is stretched plastically, layers of atoms slip over each other. With dislocations present, much less force is needed to cause slipping. This diagram shows why.

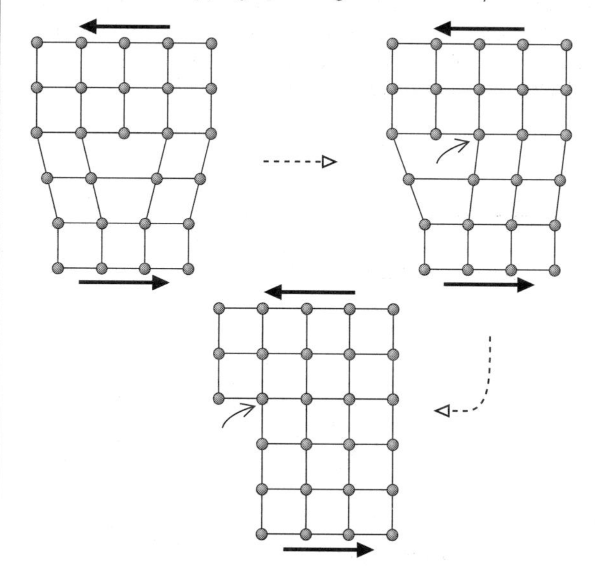

When the bottom part of the crystal is moved to the right, bonds are broken one at a time before rejoining with the next atom along. Without the dislocation, the bonds would all have to be broken at once, which takes more force.

Point defects These can be ***vacancies*** (missing atoms) or ***interstitials*** (extra atoms) in the structure. Some can move through a crystal by diffusion (see also B30).

Mechanical properties

These describe how a material behaves when forces are applied. They depend on its structure, the strength of the bonds, and the type and number of defects present.

Strength A *strong* material has a high ultimate tensile stress i.e. a high stress is needed to break it.

Ductility A *ductile* material can be drawn into wires.

Malleability A *malleable* material can be hammered into different shapes.

Stiffness A *stiff* material has a high Young's modulus, i.e. a high stress produces little strain.

Toughness A *tough* material will deform plastically before it breaks. It is not brittle, i.e. cracks do not easily spread.

C7 Materials – 2

Making metals stronger

Pure metals with large crystals are neither very stiff nor very strong. Dislocations can spread through them easily, allowing slip to take place. To improve the mechanical properties, the spread of dislocations must be reduced.

Smaller grains The smaller the grains, the more difficult it is for dislocations to spread. Smaller grains are produced if a molten metal is cooled and solidified rapidly. Grain size is also affected by later heating or mechanical treatment.

Forming alloys Alloys are mixtures of metals (or of metals and non-metals). For example, steel is an alloy of iron (about 99%) and carbon, and sometimes other elements as well. It is stronger, stiffer, and tougher than iron.

In an alloy, the 'foreign' atoms block the spread of dislocations and make slipping more difficult.

Work hardening This occurs when a metal is hammered, stretched, or bent. It produces *more* dislocations, but these become so jumbled that they block the spread of the others.

Note:

- In some applications, metals *need* to be softer and more flexible. Reducing the number of dislocations has this effect. It can be achieved by ***annealing***, a processs in which the metal is heated and cooled very slowly.

Plastics

Plastics are polymers. They are made up of long-chain molecules whose atoms are linked by strong covalent bonds. There are two main classes of plastics.

Thermoplastics These soften when heated and harden on cooling. Resoftening is possible because thermal activity can overcome the weak bonds between the polymer chains. Thermoplastics creep under stress: they are ***viscoelastic***.

Amorphous thermoplastics have tangled chains. They are *glassy* when cold, but *rubbery* (soft and flexible) above their ***glass transition temperature*** (e.g. 100 °C for Perspex).

Semicrystalline thermoplastics have regions where the chains are parallel and close, so the bonds between the chains are stronger. This produces stiffness and good tensile strength. Amorphous regions add flexibility.

Note:

- Stretching a thermoplastic makes it more crystalline, i.e. its chains uncoil and become less tangled.

Thermosets These do not soften when warmed, so they cannot be remoulded. During manufacture, they develop strong and permanent cross-links (bonds) between their chains.

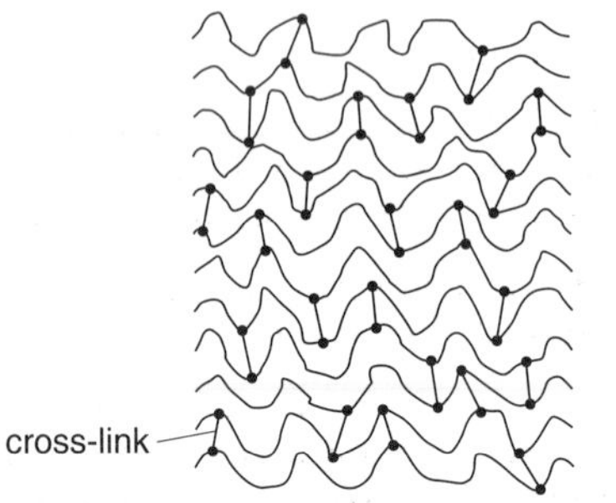

Composites

These are combinations of materials, produced to make use of the best properties of each.

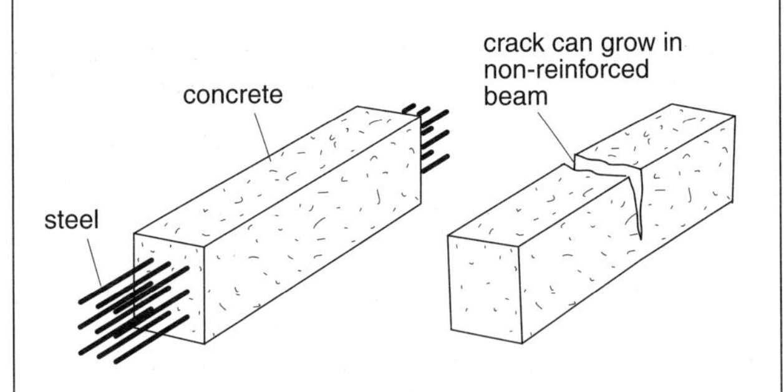

Reinforced concrete Concrete has high compressive strength but is brittle and weak in tension, so will crack and break if bent (see B25). To prevent this, it can be reinforced with steel rods. In ***pre-stressed concrete***, the rods are stretched elastically before the concrete sets. This gives even greater strength and stiffness. (Concrete is itself a composite of sand, chippings, and cement.)

Glass-reinforced plastic (GRP) ('fibre glass') Glass fibres are embedded in plastic resin. The fibres provide tensile strength. The resin gives stiffness, by bonding the fibres together, and toughness, by stopping crack growth.

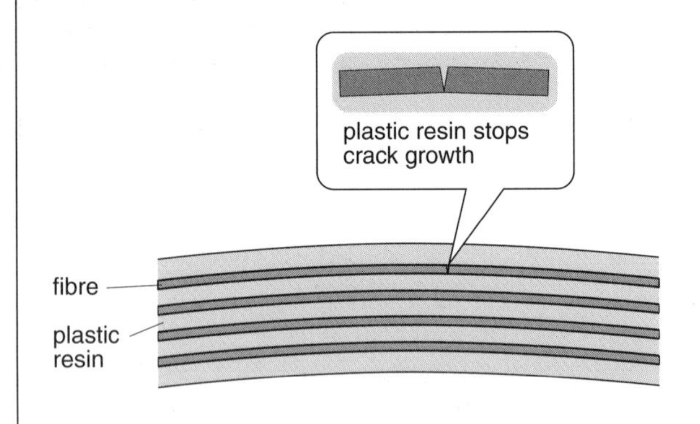

Carbon-fibre-reinforced plastic (CFRP) ('carbonfibre') This is similar to GRP, but with stronger, stiffer carbon fibres instead of glass.

	Plastics			
	Thermoplastics		**Thermosets**	
Property	resoften on warming		permanent set	
Type	amorphous	semi-crystalline	elastomer	rigid
Structure	tangled chains	many chains parallel	some cross links	many cross links
Examples	Perspex	polythene nylon	artificial rubber	epoxy resins Melamine

Magnetic properties

Read A5 and B17 first.

If a material is placed in a field B_o, its atoms change the flux density to a new value, B. The ratio B/B_o is the relative permeability, μ_r. Depending on the material, B may be slightly less, slightly more or much more than B_o.

Diamagnetism ($B < B_o$) This very weak effect occurs in all materials. Orbiting electrons oppose the applied field.

Paramagnetism ($B > B_o$) This occurs in materials where the electron orbits make the atoms (or molecules) behave as tiny electromagnets. These align with the applied field and strengthen it. The diamagnetic effect is overcome.

Ferromagnetism ($B >> B_o$) This occurs in strongly magnetic materials, such as iron, nickel, and cobalt. The atoms are grouped into tiny ***domains***, each containing magnetically aligned atoms. An applied field magnetizes the material by aligning the magnetic axes of the domains.

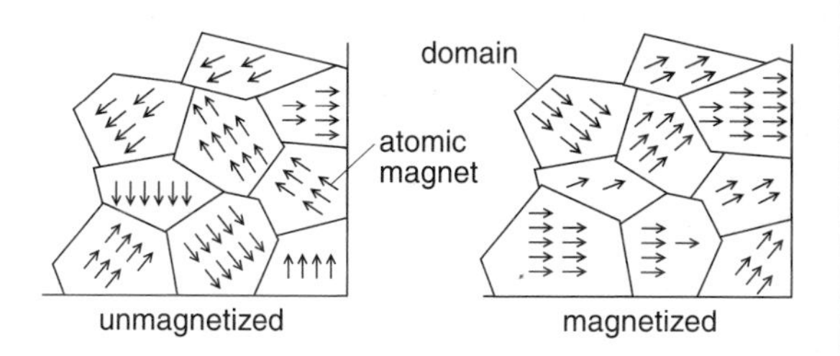

The graph below is for a ferromagnetic material. It shows how B changes when B_o is increased from zero, reduced to zero, applied in the opposite direction, reduced, and so on. The outer loop is called a ***hysteresis*** loop.

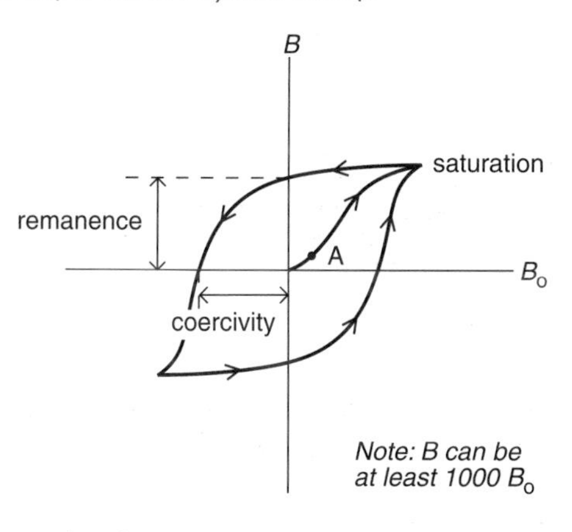

- Beyond A, the material stays magnetized when the applied field is removed.
- The ***remanence*** is the flux density remaining in the material when a strong magnetizing field is removed.
- The ***coercivity*** is the flux density needed to reduce the field from the magnetized material to zero. *Soft* magnetic materials (e.g. iron) have a low coercivity and demagnetize easily. *Hard* magnetic materials (e.g. steel) have a high coercivity and become permanent magnets.
- Above their ***Curie temperature*** (≈1000 K for iron), ferromagnetic materials become paramagnetic.

Piezoelectric effect Compressing or stretching some crystals (e.g. quartz and ferroelectrics) sets up a PD across them. The effect is used in gas lighters and in some microphones. The *reverse* effect is used to keep time in watches. A quartz crystal is made to oscillate by applying an alternating voltage across it.

Electrical conduction

Read B15 and B35 first.

When atoms are close (e.g. in a solid), their energy levels broaden into ***bands***, i.e. lots of levels close together. To take part in conduction, electrons must be able to move between atoms. This requires an energy transfer, so it can only happen if there are unoccupied levels for electrons to go to.

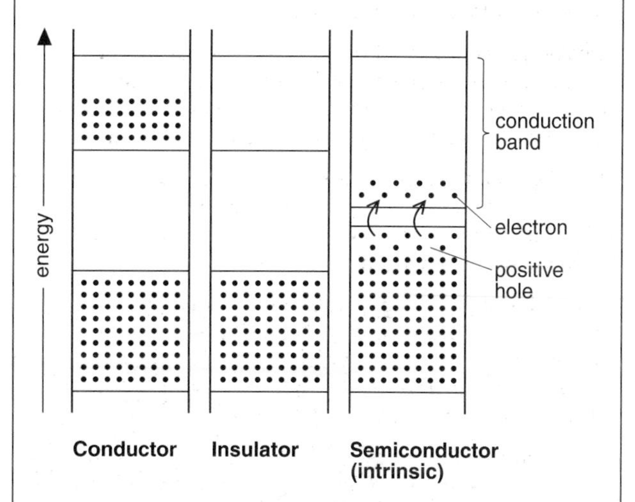

Conductors (e.g. copper) The outer band (the ***conduction band***) is only partly filled. It has unoccupied energy levels, so its electrons are free to move between atoms. (In many metals, the conduction band overlaps with the band below).

Insulators (e.g. nylon) All the electrons are in full bands, so they are unable to change energy and move between atoms.

Semiconductors (e.g. silicon) When cold, these are insulators because the conduction band is empty. However, it is so close to the band below that a temperature rise can give electrons enough energy to jump the gap. Conduction can then take place both by electron movement in the conduction band and by movement of the 'gaps' (called ***positive holes***) created in the band below.

The conductivity of an ***intrinsic*** (pure) semiconductor can be improved by ***doping*** it with small amounts of impurity. It is then an ***extrinsic*** semiconductor.

- ***n-type*** semiconductors have extra conduction electrons.
- ***p-type*** semiconductors have extra positive holes.

Polarization in insulators

Read B14 and B15 first.

Dielectrics These become polarized in an electric field, i.e. electrons and nuclei are displaced slightly in opposite directions. In a capacitor, this means that each plate has opposite charge near it. So less work is needed to put charge on the plates (for any given PD) and the capacitance is increased.

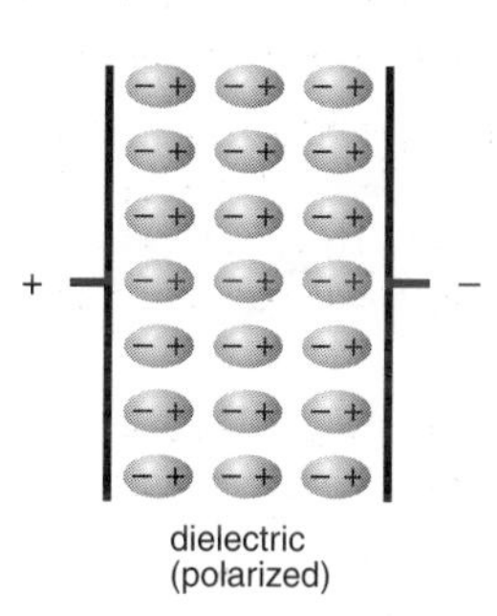

Dielectric loss is the energy transformation which occurs in a dielectric in an alternating electric field. The alternating displacement causes thermal motion: it has a heating effect.

Dielectric strength is the value of E above which a dielectric breaks down and conducts.

Ferroelectric crystals (e.g. barium titanate) These have a naturally-occurring, uneven distribution of charge. Though neutral, the whole crystal has an electric dipole.

C8 Fluid flow

Read B26 before studying this unit.

Viscosity

A fluid is flowing smoothly through a wide pipe. The diagram below shows part of the flow near the surface of the pipe. The arrows called ***streamlines***, represent the direction and velocity of each layer. The smooth flow is called ***laminar*** (layered) or ***streamline*** flow.

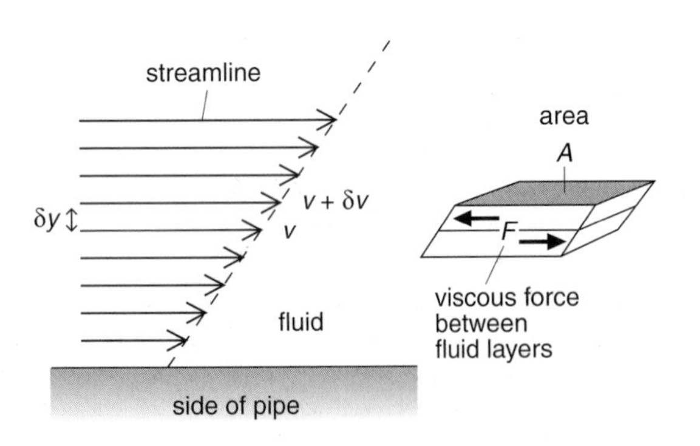

Molecules next to the pipe stick to it and have zero velocity. Molecules in the next layer slide over these, and so on. The fluid is *sheared* (see also C6), and there is a ***velocity gradient*** $\delta v/\delta y$ across it. The sliding between layers is a form of friction known as ***viscosity***. The fluid is ***viscous***.

Because of viscosity, a force is needed to maintain the flow. If F is the viscous force between layers of area A, then the coefficient of viscosity η is defined by this equation:

$$\eta = \frac{\text{shear stress}}{\text{velocity gradient}} = \frac{F/A}{\delta v/\delta y}$$

At any given temperature, most fluids have a constant η, whatever shear stress is applied. Fluids of this type (e.g. water) are called ***Newtonian fluids***. However, some liquids are ***thixotropic***: when the shear stress is increased, η decreases. Some paints and glues are like this. They are very viscous (i.e. semi-solid) until stirred.

Liquid flow through a pipe

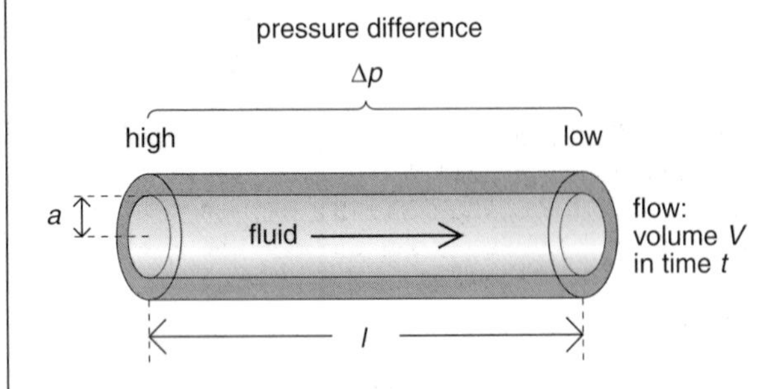

The viscosity of a liquid affects how it can flow through a pipe. If quantities are defined as in the diagram above, and there is streamline flow:

$$\frac{V}{t} = \frac{\pi a^4 \Delta p}{8\eta l}$$

This is called ***Poiseuille's equation***.

- As $V/t \propto a^4$, halving the radius of a pipe reduces the rate of flow to 1/16th for the same pressure difference.

Stokes' law

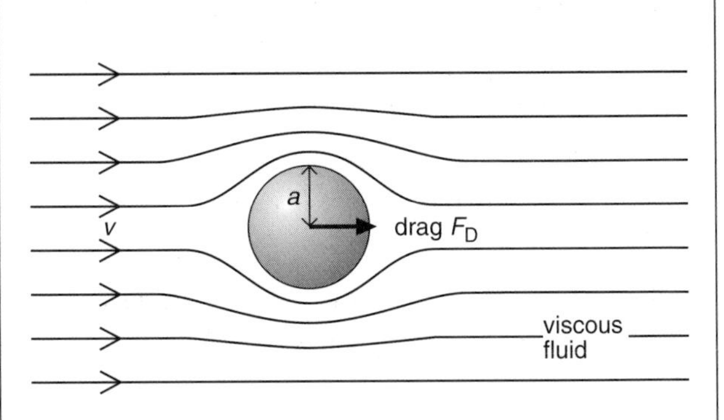

Above a sphere is moving through a fluid at a speed v (for simplicity, in this and later diagrams, the air is shown moving, rather than the object). If the flow is streamline, as shown, then the ***drag*** F_D (resisting force from the fluid) is given by this equation, called ***Stokes' law***:

$$F_D = 6\pi\eta a v$$

Note (in this case):

- drag $\propto$ speed

A falling sphere will reach its ***terminal velocity*** when the forces on it balance (see right, and also B12). i.e:

weight = drag + upthrust

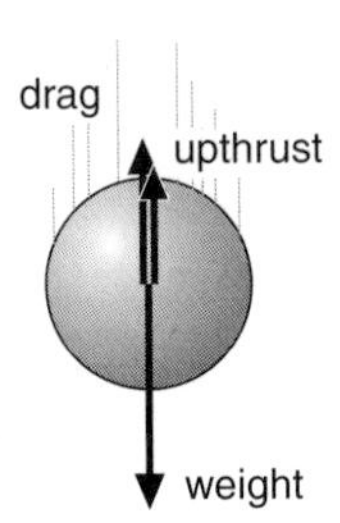

Turbulent flow

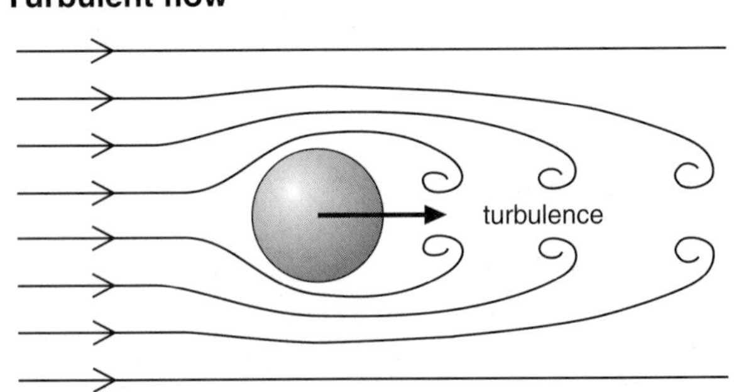

When a sphere (or other object) moves through a fluid, or a fluid flows through a pipe, the flow is only streamline beneath a certain ***critical speed***. Beyond this speed, it becomes *turbulent*, as shown above. Turbulence arises in most practical situations involving fluid flow.

Note:

- Poiseuille's equation and Stokes' law only apply at low speeds, where the flow is non-turbulent.

Reynolds' number (*Re*) This is defined as $\rho v l/\eta$, where ρ is the density of the fluid, v its speed (or that of an object moving through it), and l is a characteristic length (e.g. $2r$ for a sphere).

If the Reynolds' number at the critical speed v_c is $(Re)_c$:

$$v_c = \frac{(Re)_c \eta}{\rho l}$$

Note:

- A dimensions check on this equation shows that Reynolds' number is dimensionless, i.e. it has no units.
- For a fluid flowing through a pipe, the flow usually becomes turbulent if the Reynolds' number > 2500.

Drag from turbulent flow

Above the critical velocity, when the flow is turbulent, the drag F_D becomes dependent on the momentum changes in the fluid, rather than on the viscosity. It therefore depends on the density ρ of the fluid. For a sphere of radius r:

$$F_D = Br^2\rho v^2$$

where B is a number related to the Reynolds' number.
Note:

- In this case, drag $\propto$ (speed)^2.
- Vehicles and aircraft are 'streamlined' in order to increase the critical speed and reduce drag (see C14).

Drag coefficient The drag F_D on the moving vehicle (e.g. a car) can be worked out using its drag coefficient C_D. This is defined by the following equation:

$$F_D = \frac{1}{2}AC_D\rho v^2$$

where A is the cross-sectional (i.e. frontal) area of the vehicle, v its speed, and the ρ is the density of the air.

Car designers try to achieve as low a drag coefficient as possible (see C14). A low value for C_D would be 0.30.

The equation of continuity

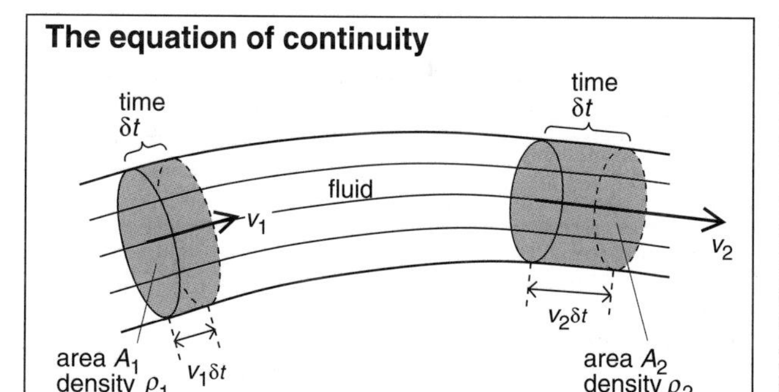

Above, in time δt, the same mass of fluid must pass through A_2 as through A_1, otherwise mass would not be conserved. But mass = density × volume. So:

$$\rho_1 A_1 v_1 \delta t = \rho_2 A_2 v_2 \delta t$$

So $\rho_1 A_1 v_1 = \rho_2 A_2 v_2$

This is called the ***equation of continuity***.

If the fluid is *incompressible* (e.g. a liquid), then $\rho_1 = \rho_2$.

So $A_1 v_1 = A_2 v_2$ (1)

Bernoulli's equation

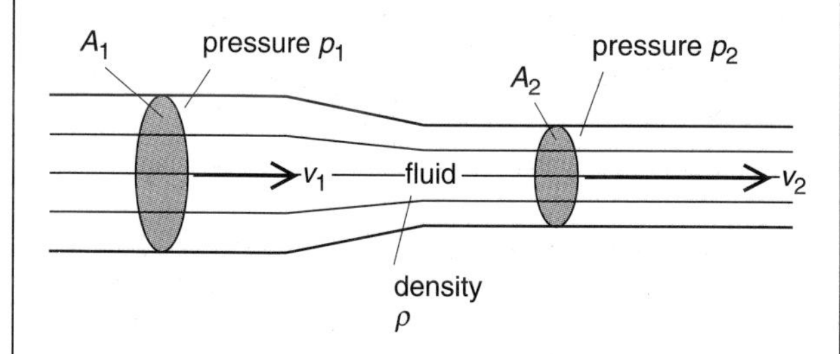

The fluid in the pipe above is incompressible. It is also non-viscous, i.e. in pushing the fluid through the pipe, there are no viscous forces to overcome, so no energy losses.

As $A_2 < A_1$, it follows from equation (1), that $v_2 > v_1$, i.e. the narrowing of the pipe makes the fluid speed up. As the fluid gains speed, work must be done to give it extra KE. And as this requires a resultant force, p_2 must be less than p_1. So the *increase* in velocity is accompanied by a *reduction* in pressure. This is called the ***Bernoulli effect***.

Working through the above steps mathematically, and assuming that no energy is wasted, gives the following:

$$p_1 + \frac{1}{2}\rho v_1^2 = p_2 + \frac{1}{2}\rho v_2^2 \quad (2)$$

This is one form of ***Bernoulli's equation***.
Note:

- Bernoulli's equation follows directly from the law of conservation of energy.

Using the Bernoulli effect

Equation (2) is only valid for a non-viscous, incompressible fluid in a horizontal pipe. However the Bernoulli effect applies in situations where the fluid is both viscous and compressible. Examples include the following.

Aerofoil (wing) This is shaped so that the airflow speeds up across its top surface, causing a pressure drop above the wing and, therefore, a pressure difference across it. The result is an upward force which contributes to the total ***lift***. (Most of the lift is due to the ***angle of attack***: see C14.)

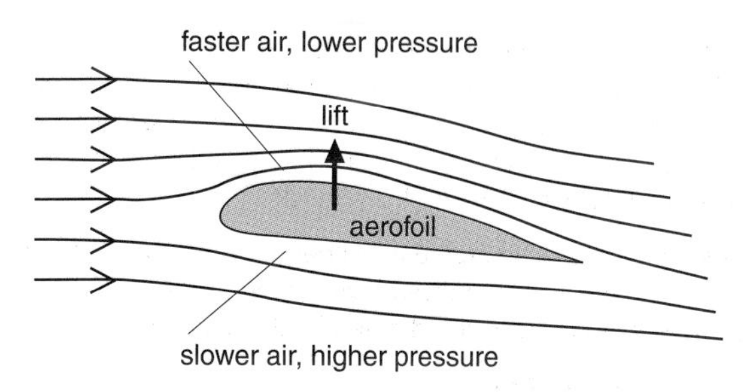

Venturi meter This can be used to find the rate of flow of a fluid. The faster the flow, the greater the pressure difference between X and Y (see right) and, therefore, the greater the height difference h on the manometer.

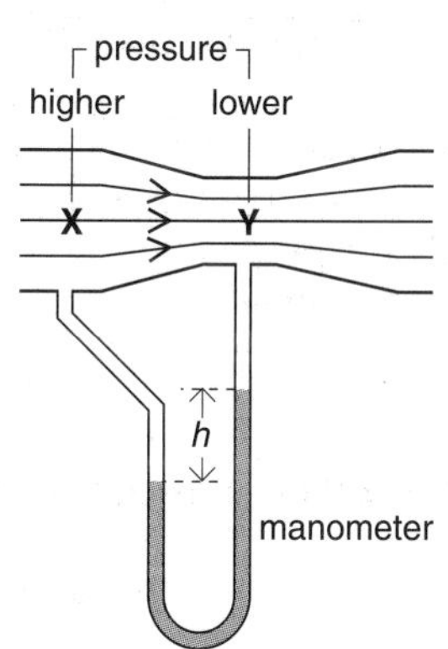

Spinning ball In some sports, 'spin' is used to make the ball 'swing'. Below, a spinning ball is moving through the air. Being viscous, air is dragged around by the surface of the ball, so the airflow is speeded up on side X and slowed down on side Y. This causes a pressure difference which produces a force.

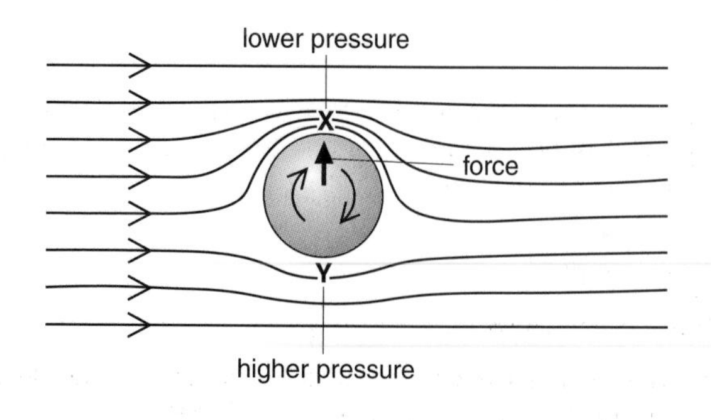

C9 Medical physics – 1

Body mechanics

The human body is supported by a framework of bones called a ***skeleton***. The bones, which are light, stiff, and strong, are connected at ***joints***. Most joints are flexible, the bones being held together by bands of tissue called ***ligaments***. These are elastic, with similar properties to nylon.

The joints of the skeleton are moved by ***muscles***. These are the body's 'engines' where transformation of chemical energy into kinetic energy takes place. They are attached to bones by ***tendons***, which are similar to ligaments.

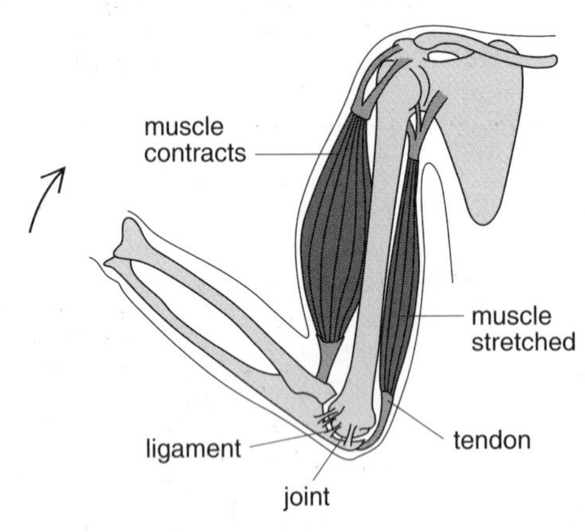

Jointed bones act as levers, with muscles providing the forces. Muscles can only contract, so they are arranged in pairs, with one muscle pulling the joint one way and its partner pulling it back again. The attachment points are close to the pivot (the joint), so high muscle forces are needed (see B5).

Spinal stresses The bones of the vertebral column (spine) are separated and cushioned by cartilage ***discs***. The lowest discs are subject to high compressive stress and also shear stress (see C6). In time, damage may occur. The situation is made worse by poor posture (body position), or by lifting heavy loads while leaning forward.

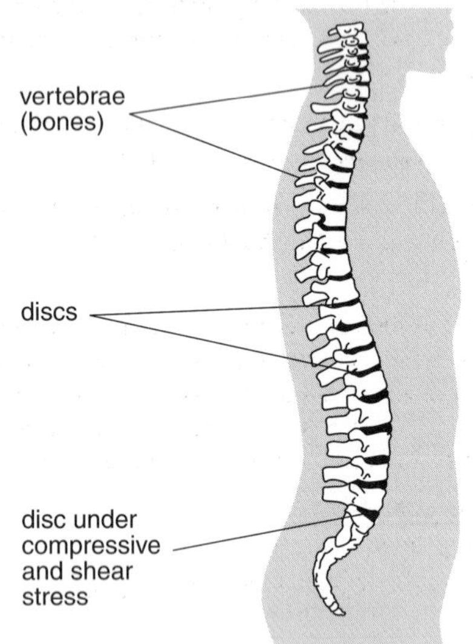

Walking This is only possible because of frictional forces between the feet (or shoes) and the ground.

Walking action tends to make the body's centre of gravity move up and down. This wastes energy, so the knees and ankles flex to reduce the vertical displacement. Also, when each foot strikes the ground, tendons and ligaments in the ankle and foot absorb strain energy, then return some of it as the leg is pushed back. This too reduces energy 'wastage'.

Body energy

Energy release The body gets most of its energy from chemical reactions in which food is combined with oxygen. The process is called ***respiration***. (Confusingly, the word 'respiration' is also commonly used for 'breathing'.)

Even when resting, the body still needs a supply of energy. The ***basal metabolic rate*** **(*BMR*)** is the minimum rate of energy release required to maintain basic life processes. As this energy is ultimately transferred from the body as heat, the BMR is normally expressed as the heat output per hour per square metre of body surface. Typical values are:

young adult female 150 kJ h^{-1} m^{-2}

young adult male 165 kJ h^{-1} m^{-2}

When the body is doing work (by moving muscles), the rate of energy transformation must rise. However, the second law of thermodynamics (see B28) limits the body's efficiency as an 'engine' to about 10%. So most of the energy results in heating the environment.

Temperature control For life processes to be maintained, the temperature of the body's ***core*** must be kept close to 37 °C. This requires a balance between the rates of heat gain and heat loss. The diagram below shows that main processes involved. Adjustments to the balance are made automatically by sweating, shivering, and control of the blood flow (and therefore the heat flow) to the skin. Clothing provides extra insulation to reduce energy transfer.

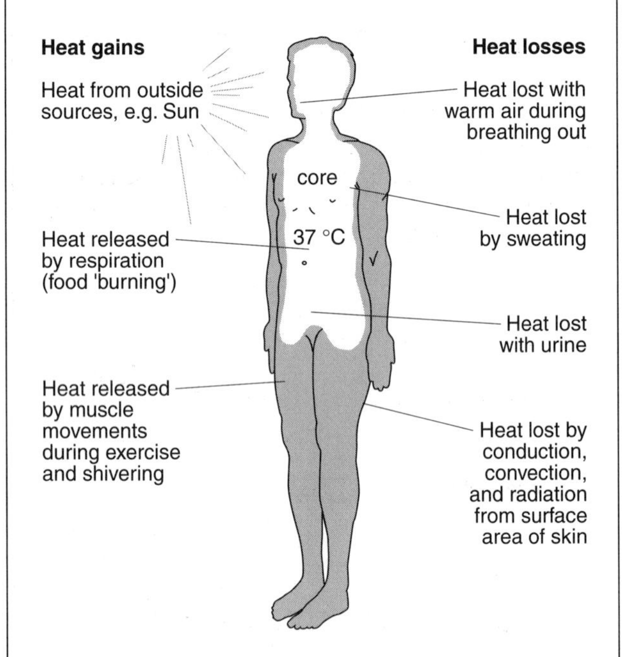

Note:

- At room temperature, an inactive body mainly transfers heat by conduction, convection, and radiation from the skin.
- In hot conditions, or when active, the body transfers most of its excess energy by sweating. The evaporation of sweat from the skin has a cooling effect (see A3 and B28).

Hypothermia This means a dangerously low body temperature. It occurs in cold conditions, when the body transfers more energy to the environment than it can replace. Babies are more at risk than adults. Being smaller, they have higher surface area per kg of body mass, so cool more quickly. Outdoors, ***windchill*** can cause hypothermia: the wind increases the energy transfer by convection – and by evaporation if the clothes are damp.

The human eye

Read B24 first.

In the eye, the cornea and lens form a real image on the ***retina***. The focus is adjusted by changing the shape of the lens – a process called ***accommodation***. This enables a normal eye to form a clear image of any object between its ***near point*** (about 25 cm away) and infinity. The amount of light reaching the retina is controlled by the ***iris***.

The retina contains millions of light-sensitive cells which send signals to the brain. ***Rods*** are the most sensitive, but do not respond to colour. Different ***cones*** respond to the *red, green,* and *blue* regions of the spectrum.

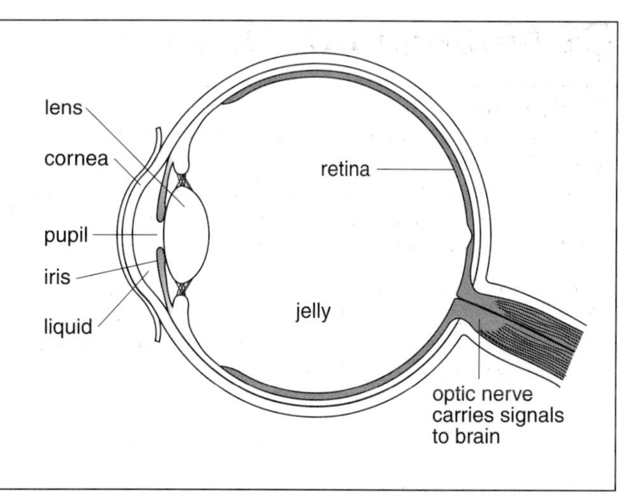

Myopia (short sight) A short-sighted eye cannot accommodate for distant objects. The rays are brought to a focus before they reach the retina. The defect is corrected by a *concave* spectacle lens.

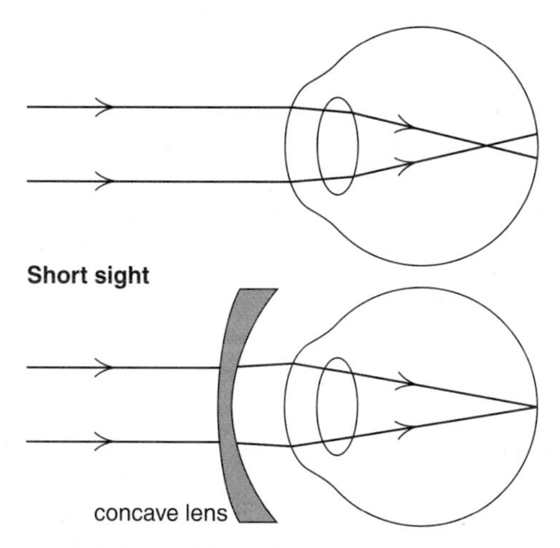

Hypermetropia (long sight) A long-sighted eye cannot accommodate for close objects. The rays are still not focused by the time they reach the retina. The defect is corrected by a *convex* spectacle lens.

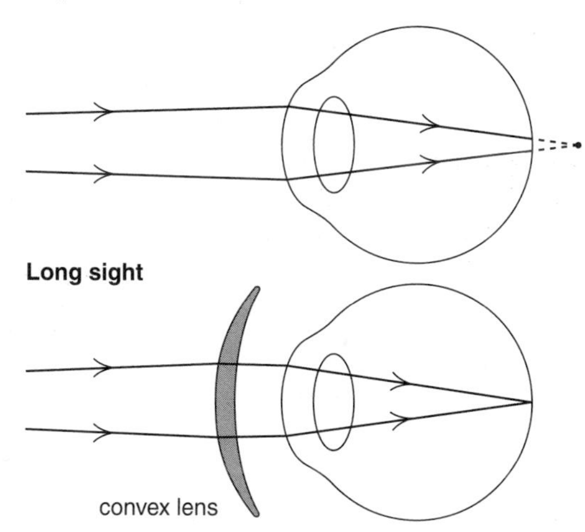

Lens power This is defined as $1/f$. With f in metres, the unit is the ***dioptre*** (D). (Note: *diverging* lenses have *negative* powers). The power of the eye's lens system varies. It is lowest when distant objects are being viewed.

The powers of close lenses can be added algebraically. For example, if a normal eye must reduce its power to 50 D to see distant objects, but a short-sighted eye cannot get beneath 54 D, then the defect is corrected by a lens of power –4D, i.e. a concave lens with $f = \frac{1}{4} = -0.25$ m.

Astigmatism This effect occurs when the curve of the cornea is not perfectly spherical. So, for example, vertical lines might be seen in clearer focus than horizontal ones.

Human hearing

Read B22 first.

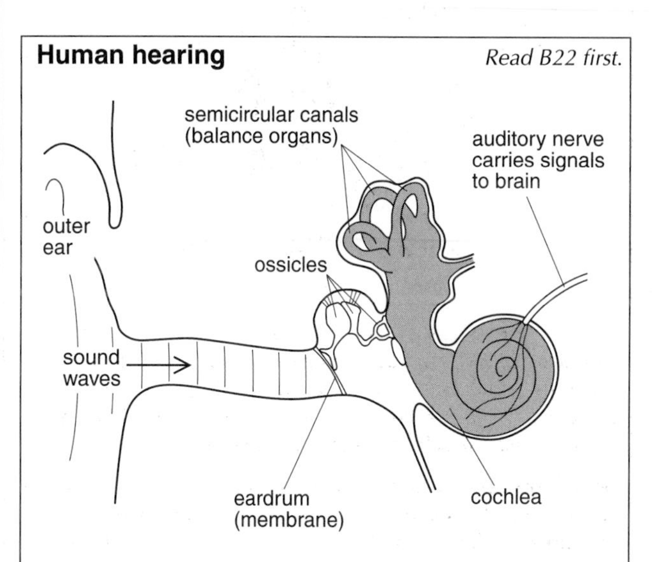

Sound waves entering the ear set up vibrations in the ***ear drum***. These are transmitted to the ***cochlea*** by ***ossicles*** (small bones) which act as levers and magnify the pressure changes. In the cochlea, sensory cells respond to different frequencies and send signals to the brain.

Frequency response The ear detects frequencies in the range 10 Hz to 20 kHz. It is most sensitive around 2 kHz.

Intensity levels The lowest intensity of sound which the ear can detect is known as the ***threshold intensity***, I_0. It is taken as 10^{-12} W m^{-2}.

The ear responds to sounds according to the *ratio* of their intensities. For example, each doubling of intensity gives the same sensation of increased loudness. For this reason, the ***intensity level*** of a sound is defined as below, where dB stands for ***decibel***, and I is the intensity of the sound:

$$\text{intensity level in dB} = 10 \log_{10}(I/I_0)$$

For two sounds of intensities I_1 and I_2:

$$\text{difference in intensity level in dB} = 10 \log_{10}(I_2/I_1)$$

Note:

- Any two sounds with the same intensity ratio I_2/I_1 have the same difference in intensity level.

dBA scale This is a dB scale, adjusted to allow for the ear's different sensitivity to different frequencies. It is used to measure noise levels. Typical values are:

hearing threshold	0 dBA	legal noise limit	90 dBA
conversation	50 dBA	near disco speakers	120 dBA
busy street	70 dBA	pain threshold	140 dBA

C10 Medical physics – 2

X-rays

Read B21 and B35 first.

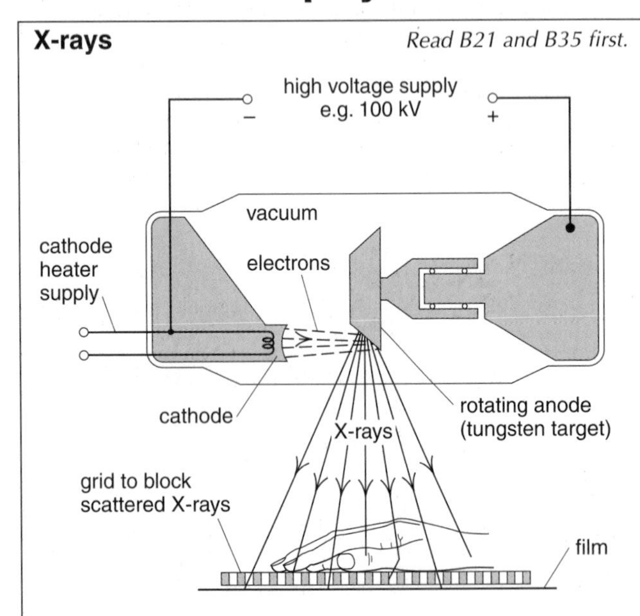

In the X-ray tube above, electrons gain high KE before striking a metal target. About 1% of the KE is converted into X-ray photons; the rest is released as heat. The anode is rotated rapidly to prevent 'hot spots'.

Quality The X-ray beam contains a range of wavelengths. The spectral spread is known as the ***quality***. The longer, least penetrating wavelengths are called *soft* X-rays; the shorter, more penetrating ones are *hard*. The beam can be hardened by using filters to absorb the longer wavelengths.

Tube current and voltage Increasing the current increases the intensity of the beam. Increasing the voltage increases the intensity *and* reduces the peak wavelength, i.e. it produces more photons, which are more penetrating.

Attenuation As X-rays pass through a material, their energy is gradually absorbed and their intensity reduced. This is called ***attenuation***. It is in addition to any reduction in intensity due to beam divergence.

If I_0 is the intensity of the incident beam (do not confuse with I_0 as used in C9), and I is the intensity at a distance x into the material, then, for a non-diverging beam:

$$I = I_0 e^{-\mu x} \qquad (1)$$

μ is the ***total linear attenuation coefficient***. Its value depends on the absorbing material and on the photon energy. X-rays are more attenuated by bone than by soft tissue. The difference is greatest for photons of around 30 keV energy.

The half-thickness $x_{\frac{1}{2}}$ of an absorber is the value of x for which $I/I_0 = \frac{1}{2}$. From equation (1): $x_{\frac{1}{2}} = \log_e 2/\mu$

X-ray photographs X-rays affect photographic film, but cannot be focused, so the photos are 'shadow' pictures of the absorbing areas. For a sharp image, the X-rays need to be emitted as if from a point source. To reduce the risk of cell damage, exposure times are normally less than 0.2 s.

CAT scanning (computed axial tomography) A cross-section of the body is scanned by rotating an X-ray beam around it. The intensity reduction caused by each 'slice' is measured by a detector. Then a computer carries out a mathematical analysis on the total data and uses it to construct an image of the cross-section on the screen.

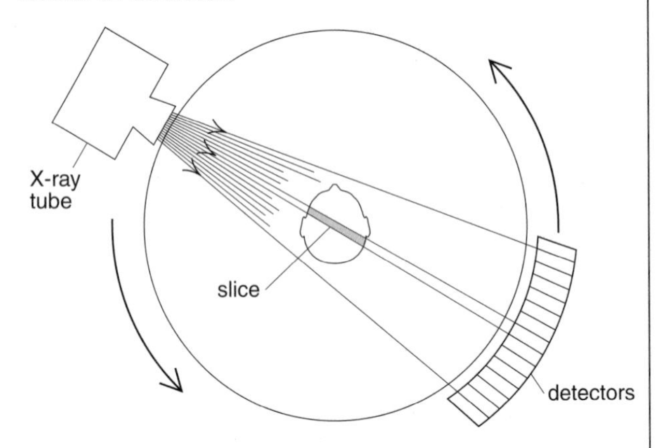

Radiotherapy Very hard X-rays (photon energies around 10 MeV) can be used to destroy cancer cells deep in the body. However, to reduce damage to the surrounding tissue, the beam is rotated around the patient so that only the target area stays in the beam all the time. (Note: gamma rays from a cobalt-60 source can be used instead of X-rays).

MRI (magnetic resonance imaging)

This produces images of the body by scanning, but without the risks of X-rays. It uses the fact that different tissues contain different concentrations of hydrogen atoms. In a magnetic field, the spinning motions of the hydrogen nuclei are disturbed by pulses of radio waves of suitable frequency. As a result, the nuclei emit radio-frequency signals which can be detected and located electronically. The very strong magnetic fields needed for MRI come from high-current electromagnets whose superconducting coils (see B15) are cooled by liquid helium.

Using light

Read B22 first.

Endoscope This is a flexible tube used for looking inside the body. Light from objects at the far end is carried to the viewing end by a *coherent* bundle of optical fibres, i.e. fibres whose positions alongside each other are the same throughout their length, so an accurate image is formed.

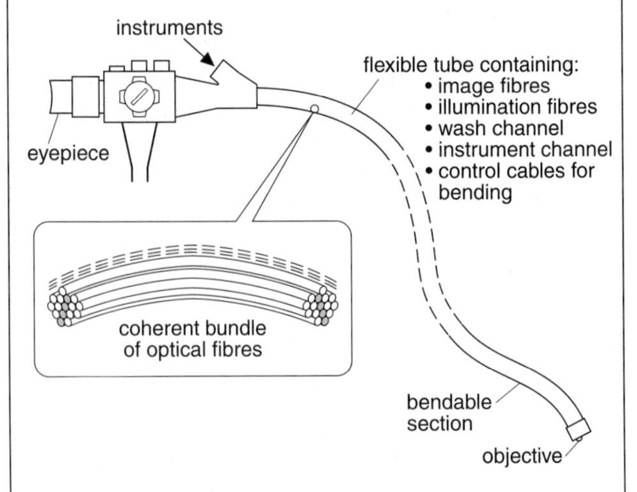

Laser This gives a fine beam of high-intensity light. It can be used like a scalpel to cut tissue, but its heating effect also seals small blood vessels at the same time. The type of laser chosen depends on the tissue – the aim being to select a wavelength which gives maximum energy absorption. In some cases, the light can be carried to the required point by an optical fibre, i.e. through an endoscope.

Using tracers

Read B33 first.

Tracers used in medical diagnosis include the γ-emitting radioisotopes iodine-123 (half-life 13 h) and technetium-99^m (half-life 6 h). Small amounts can be carried in the bloodstream to various sites in the body.

Gamma camera γ photons from the tracer strike the sodium iodide disc, causing flashes of light whose intensity is amplified by the photomultiplier tubes. Signals from these are processed electronically, and an image built up on a CRO screen. The collimator improves image quality by only letting through γ rays travelling at right angles to the disc.

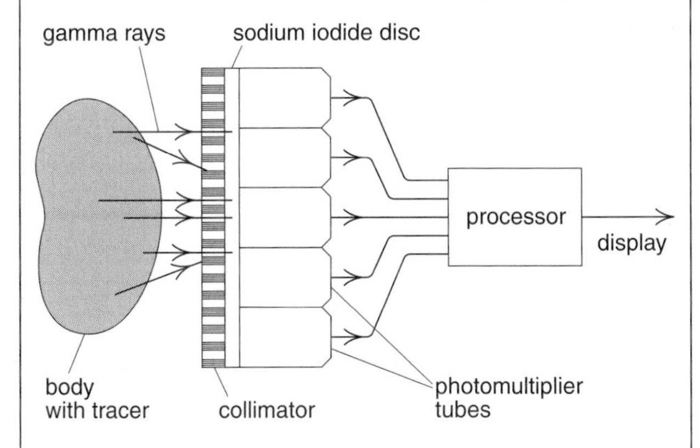

Checking blood flow in the lungs With technetium-99^m tracer present in the bloodstream, a gamma camera will reveal which parts of the lungs do not contain the tracer and, therefore, have blocked blood vessels.

Checking thyroid function The thyroid has a natural uptake of iodine. With iodine-123 tracer present in the bloodstream, the uptake can be checked by measuring the activity in the thyroid.

Radiation risks

Read B33 first.

Ionizing radiations such as X and γ rays can cause cell damage which may lead to cancer or genetic changes in sex cells. The amount of damage depends on the amount of energy absorbed. This rises with increased exposure time.

Absorbed dose This is the energy absorbed per unit mass of tissue. The SI unit is the J kg^{-1}, called the ***gray*** (Gy).

Dose equivalent For the same amount of energy delivered, α particles cause more biological damage than X or γ rays. To allow for this, the ***dose equivalent*** is defined as the absorbed dose × *Q*, where *Q* is a ***quality factor*** (e.g. 1 for X and γ rays, 20 for α particles). The SI unit of dose equivalent is the J kg^{-1}, known in this case as the ***sievert*** (Sv).

UK average dose equivalent per person per year	2.5 mSv	**Sources:**	
		natural (e.g. rocks)	87%
		medical (e.g. X-rays)	12%
		other	1%

Note:
- At low levels, radiation is ***stochastic*** (random) in its effects. There is no minimum safe level. The risk of damage increases with the dose equivalent absorbed.

Half-lives When a radioisotope is in the body, its *effective* half-life T_E is less than its *physical* ('real') half-life T_P because biological processes gradually remove it from the body. If T_B is the *biological* half-life, i.e. the time for half the original radioactive material to be removed:

$$1/T_E = 1/T_P + 1/T_B \qquad (T_P = T_{\frac{1}{2}} \text{ in B33})$$

Ultrasound

Ultrasonic sound, or ***ultrasound***, has frequencies above the upper limit of human hearing, i.e. above 20 kHz. If a pulse of ultrasound is sent into the body, it is partially reflected at the boundaries between different layers of tissue, so their positions can be worked out from the time delays of the echoes received. The frequency used (in the 2–10 MHz range) depends on the depth of tissue. Increasing the frequency gives better resolution but poorer penetration.

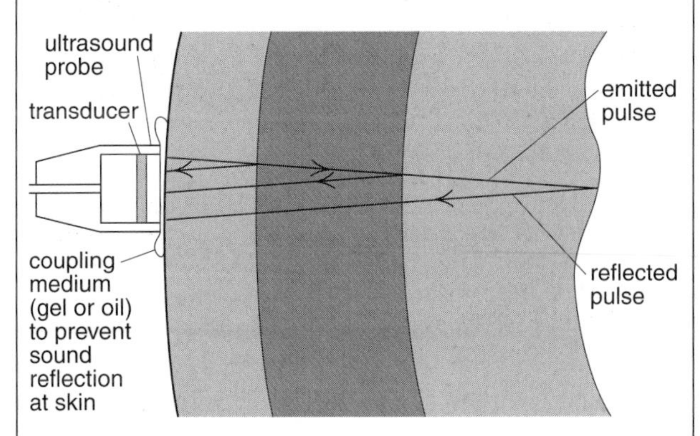

Probe This contains a ***transducer*** (see C15) which sends and receives the ultrasound pulses. The ultrasound is produced using the ***piezoelectric effect*** (see C7): a high frequency alternating voltage is applied across a slice of crystalline ceramic so that it vibrates at its resonant frequency and emits sound waves. When the reflected waves return, they cause vibrations in the slice, which generates a small alternating voltage. Signals from the probe can be displayed on a CRO or processed by a computer.

A-scan The reflected pulses are displayed as peaks on a CRO, i.e. as **A**mplitude changes. Positions along the time axis are a measure of distances into the body.

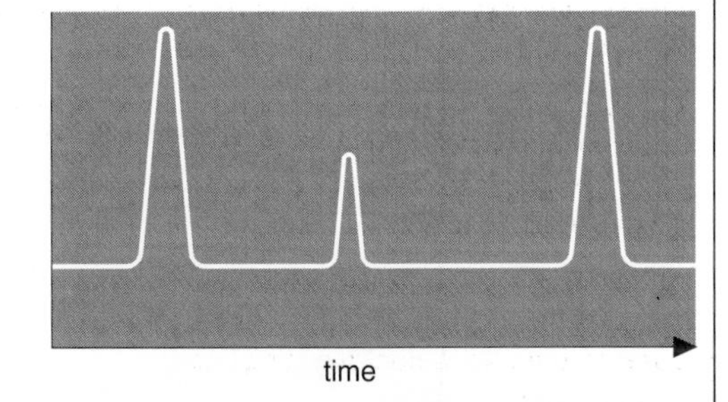

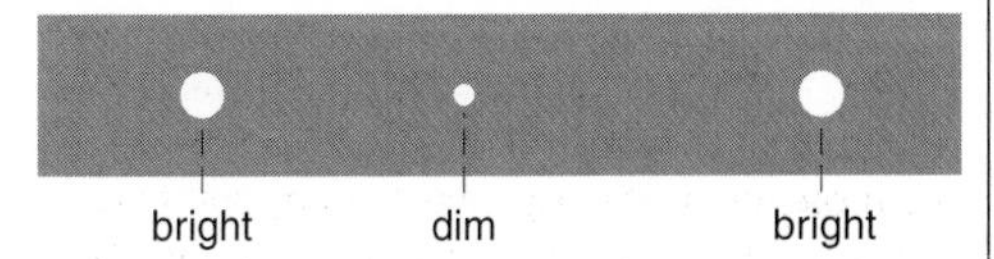

B-scan The reflected pulses are displayed as spots whose **B**rightness is a measure of their amplitude. In a ***two-dimensional B-scan***, the probe is moved around the body in order to build up a complete cross-sectional image.
- Though its resolution is poorer, ultrasound imaging is safer than X-ray imaging and cheaper than MRI.

Using the Doppler effect Any motion within the body causes a Doppler shift (see C3) in the reflected ultrasound. This can be used to check the heart beat or blood flow in an unborn baby. Continuous, rather than pulsed, ultrasound is used. Any difference between the outgoing and returning frequencies is heard as a tone or displayed on a screen.

Destructive ultrasound Focused ultrasound, at an intensity above 10^7 W m^{-2}, can be used to break up kidney stones and gallstones, so surgery is not required.

C11 Earth and atmosphere

Age of the Earth

Read B33 first.

The Earth is believed to have formed, along with the other planets, about 4.6×10^9 years ago (see C4). Its oldest rocks are around 3.8×10^9 years old. Age estimates like this come from ***radiometric*** data, i.e. data from radioactive decay measurements (see B33). Methods include:

- Comparing the proportions of uranium-235 and uranium-238 now found in natural uranium with those which would have existed when the Earth was formed
- Finding the ratio of uranium-238 to trapped helium (formed from emitted α particles) in rock samples.

Variations in *g*

Read B9 first.

Across the Earth's surface, the measured value of *g* varies slightly, though by less than 1%. It is lowest at the equator 1) mainly because of the effects of the Earth's rotation 2) also because the Earth has a slightly greater radius towards the equator than towards the poles. *g* is also less where the crust is thick, because crust is less dense than mantle.

Variations in *g* can be detected using a ***gravimeter*** – a very sensitive spring balance with a mass attached. Local anomalies (unusual variations) in *g* can give clues about the presence of mineral deposits.

Structure of the Earth

The Earth's probable structure and internal conditions are shown in the diagram. The main sources of data are:

- analysis of ***seismic waves*** (see next page)
- gravitational measurements (see also B9)
- measurement of the heat flow out of the Earth.

Radioactive decay provides the energy which maintains the high temperatures within the Earth.

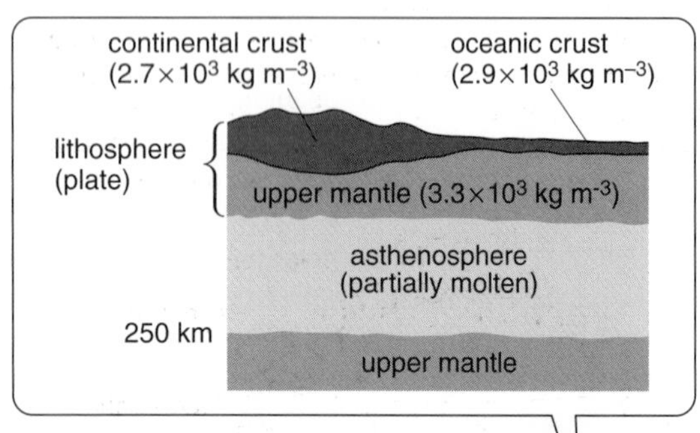

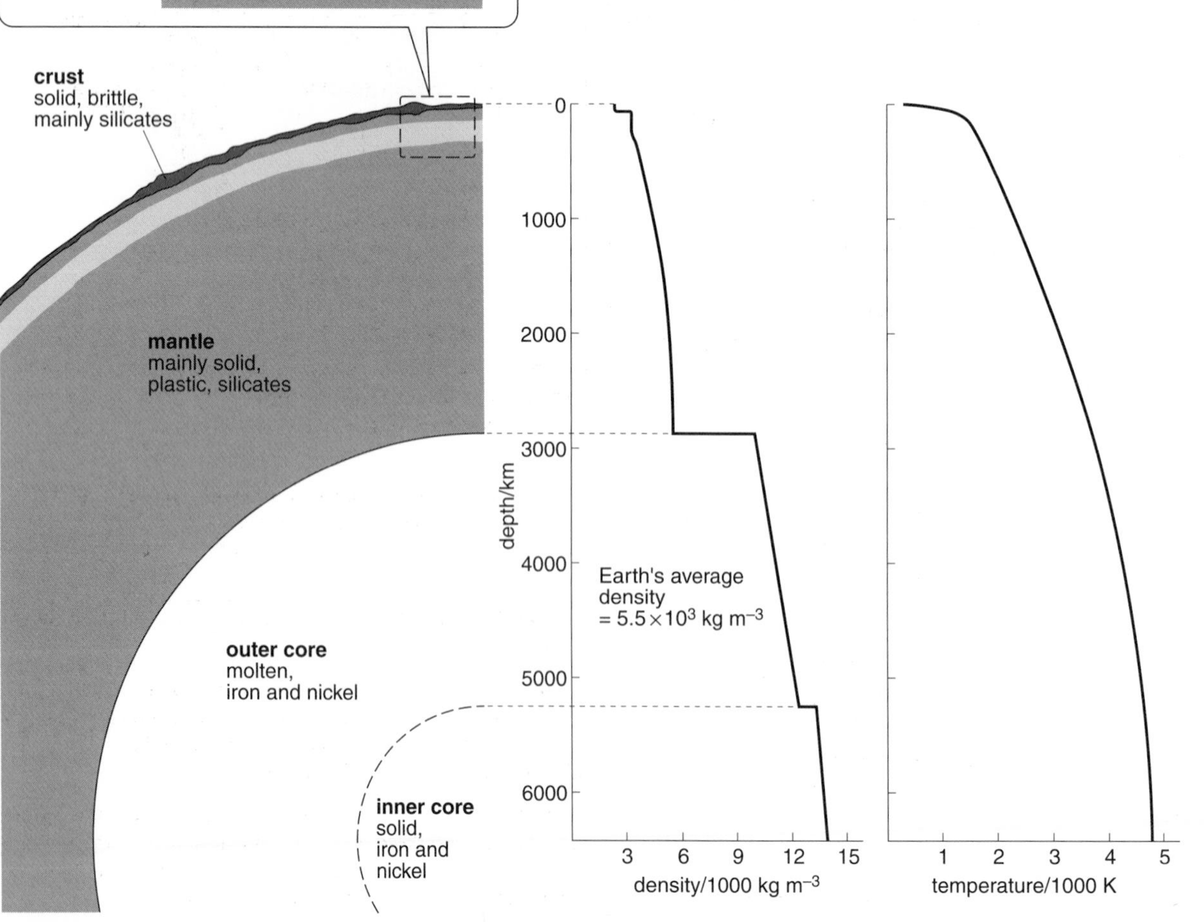

Earth's magnetism The Earth has a weak magnetic field. However, the Earth's core is above the Curie temperature (see C7), so cannot be a permanent magnet. The field is thought to be due to currents generated by the circulation of molten metal in the outer core. The Earth's magnetic axis is inclined at about 12° to its spin axis, but 'wobbles' slightly. Magnetic surveys of rocks indicate that there have been several complete pole reversals in the past.

Plates The Earth's crust and part of its upper mantle form huge 'rafts', called ***plates***, which 'float' on the material beneath them. Pushed by convection currents which cause creep in the mantle, the plates move against each other. At their boundaries, this can cause 1) mountain building 2) volcanoes, because of the frictional heating 3) earthquakes.

Mountains have an increased thickness of crust beneath them. This means that the crust floats in a state of equilibrium, called ***isostasy***. As higher material is worn away by erosion, the crust underneath rises to compensate.

Seismic waves

Read B22 first.

When stresses build up in rocks because of plate movements, the rocks may fracture and release strain energy. The result is an earthquake, which sends ***seismic waves*** through the Earth. These include:

P (primary) waves These are longitudinal waves. They travel through solid rock and molten material.

S (secondary) waves These are transverse waves. They are slower than P waves and cannot travel through molten material.

Note:
- P and S waves travel faster through denser rock, so density changes in the Earth cause refraction.

Seismic waves are recorded using a ***seismograph*** in which sensors detect vibrations transmitted to a suspended mass. The paths of the waves can be worked out from their travel times to different detectors around the world.

Note:
- S waves do not travel through the Earth's core, which suggests that part of this must be molten.

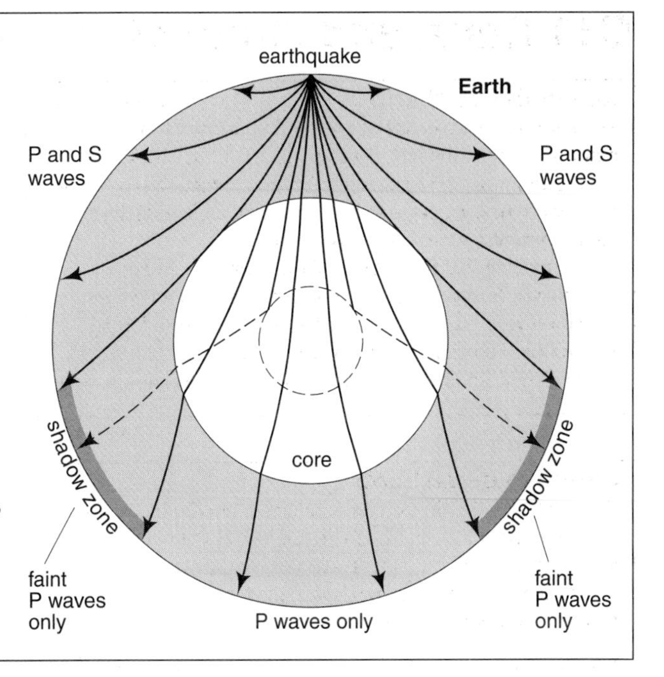

Structure of the atmosphere

Air is mainly nitrogen (78%) and oxygen (21%), with much smaller amounts of other gases, including carbon dioxide (0.03%), and variable amounts of water vapour.

Note:
- Hydrogen and helium escaped from the atmosphere early in its formation when it was still hot. Their faster molecules had speeds that exceeded the Earth's escape speed (see B9 and B30).

The atmosphere can be divided into four main layers, with temperature changes marking their boundaries. (The boundary heights vary with latitude, season, and other factors.)

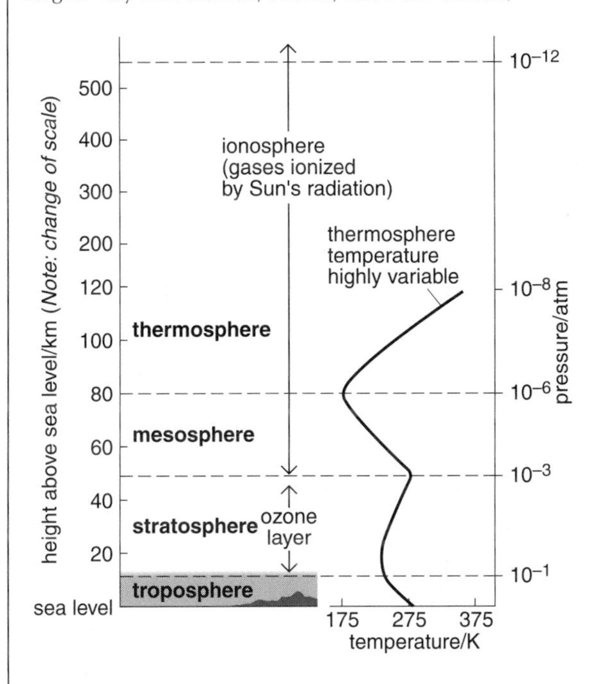

Pressure variations with height Atmospheric pressure p decreases with height h above sea level. For an 'ideal' atmosphere at constant temperature:

$$p = p_0 e^{-kh}$$

where k is a constant and p_0 is the pressure at the surface.

The dynamic atmosphere

Being 'square on' to the Sun's radiation, the equator receives more radiant power per m^2 than regions to the north and south. Hot air rising above the equator creates huge convection currents in the atmosphere, called ***cells.*** These, and the Earth's rotation, give the Earth its wind belts.

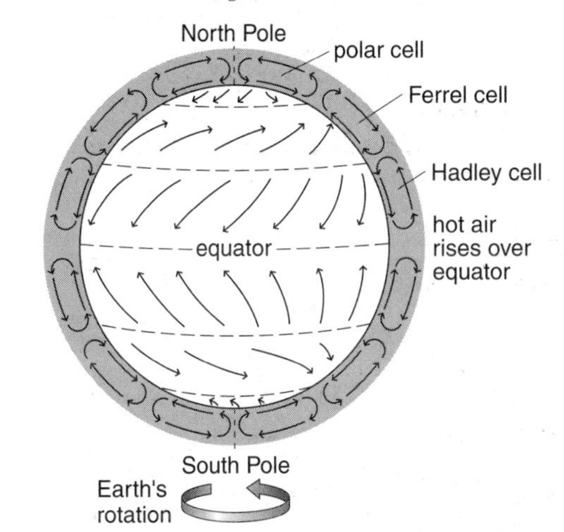

Winds blowing from the equator veer away from a north-south line. This is called the ***Coriolis effect***. It is due to the motion of the air relative to the rotating Earth.

Note:
- The Earth also has ocean currents which are driven by convection, winds, and the Coriolis effect.

Troposphere Weather effects mostly occur in this layer which contains the bulk of the atmosphere.

Ozone layer The stratosphere contains ozone gas. Biologically, it is important because it absorbs most of the harmful ultraviolet radiation arriving from the Sun. (The absorbed energy warms the stratosphere.)

Ozone (O_3) is an unstable form of oxygen. It is constantly being made and destroyed by chemical processes in the atmosphere. However, pollutants such as CFCs upset the balance by increasing the rate of destruction.

C12 Energy and the environment – 1

Energy for the Earth

The Earth's prime source of energy is ***solar radiation*** (radiation from the Sun). Its effects include:

- Maintaining temperatures on Earth
- Maintaining winds, ocean currents, and weather systems
- Maintaining plant and animal life
- Maintaining atmospheric composition
- Millions of years ago, supplying the energy now stored in fossil fuels (e.g. oil, natural gas, and coal).

Non-solar energy

Heat from inside Earth

Energy in nuclear fuels

Tidal energy (due to Moon's gravitational pull)

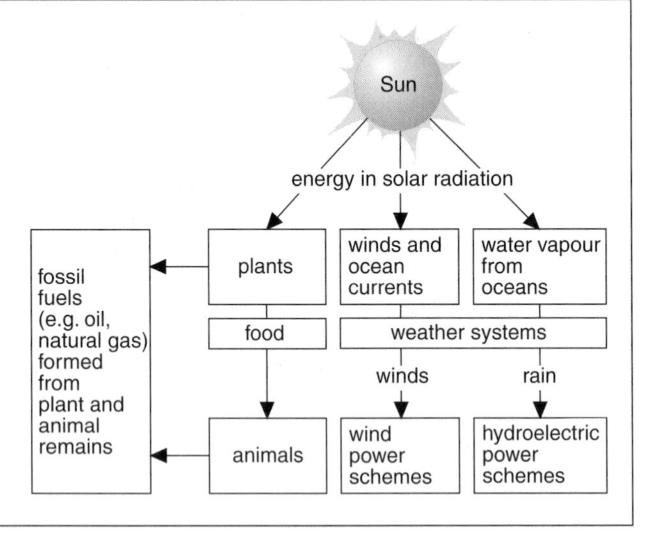

Maintaining atmospheric composition

Animals take in oxygen. They use it to 'burn up' their food and obtain energy. This process is called ***respiration*** and it produces carbon dioxide and water. (Burning fossil fuels also produces carbon dioxide and water.)

Plants take in carbon dioxide and water. With these, they make food using energy from sunlight. This process is called ***photosynthesis*** and it gives out oxygen.

Note:

- Plants also use oxygen for respiration. But overall, they make more oxygen than they consume.
- For photosynthesis, plants absorb light at the red and blue ends of the visible spectrum. They transmit or reflect green light, which is why they look green.

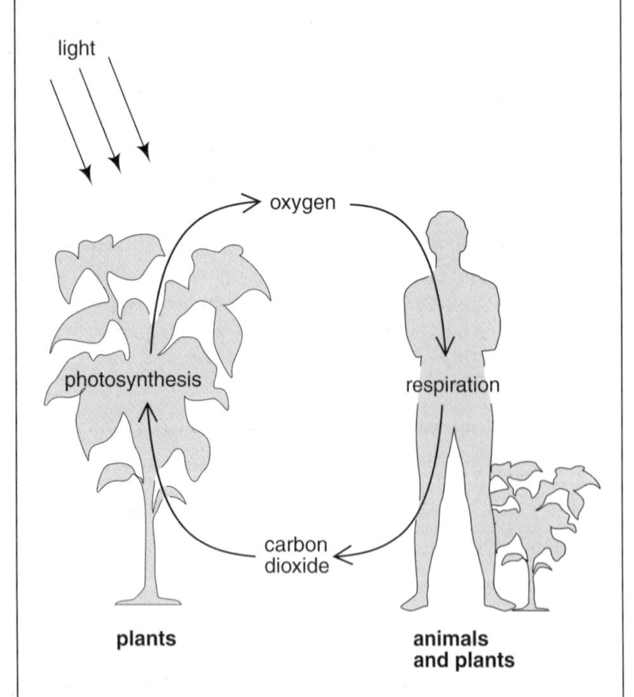

Together, plants and animals maintain the amounts of oxygen and carbon dioxide in the atmosphere. By various chemical processes, some nitrogen is also incorporated in the bodies of living organisms, but this is recycled.

Water vapour and rising air

Below, water vapour in a container is cooled. With reduced molecular motion, some molecules have stuck together, i.e. some vapour has condensed to form liquid. The vapour density is now the maximum possible for that temperature: the space is ***saturated*** with vapour. The vapour and liquid are in a state of ***dynamic equilibrium***: vapour continues to condense, but the liquid evaporates at the same rate.

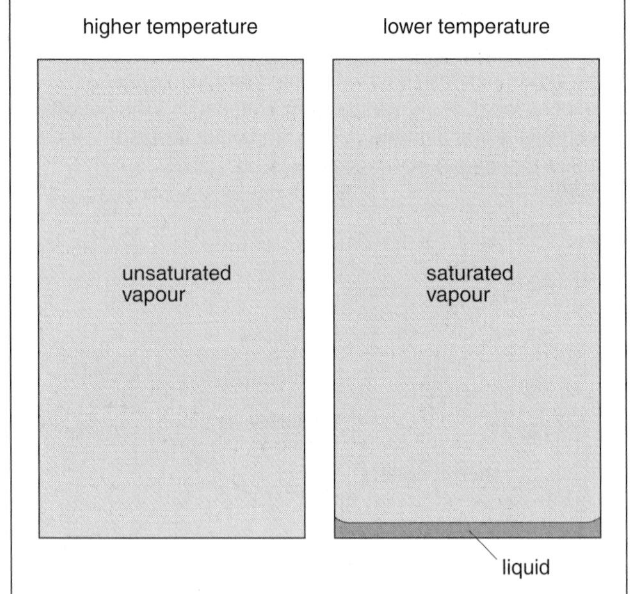

The temperature to which an unsaturated vapour must be cooled to become saturated is called its ***dew point***. If unsaturated vapour in the atmosphere is cooled beneath its dew point, the condensation is seen as millions of tiny droplets (clouds, fog, and mist), or as dew on the ground.

Rising air If warm, dry air rises above the ground, it expands adiabatically and cools (see B29). The fall in temperature is about 1 °C per 100 m of height gain. This is called the ***dry adiabatic lapse rate.***

If unsaturated air rises, it eventually cools beneath its dew point and becomes saturated. So clouds form. With saturated air, the lapse rate is reduced because the vapour releases latent heat as it condenses.

Water balance

Overall, the rate at which water evaporates from the oceans and land regions is equal to the rate at which water is returned by precipitation (rain, snow, and hail). On average, there is a ***water balance***. However, at any given time, each region may have an imbalance – in which case, water is either going into storage or coming out of it.

The oceans are the main water storage system. Others include the polar ice caps, soil, plants, and porous rocks. Underground water-bearing rocks are called ***aquifers***. Water can stay locked away in them for thousands of years.

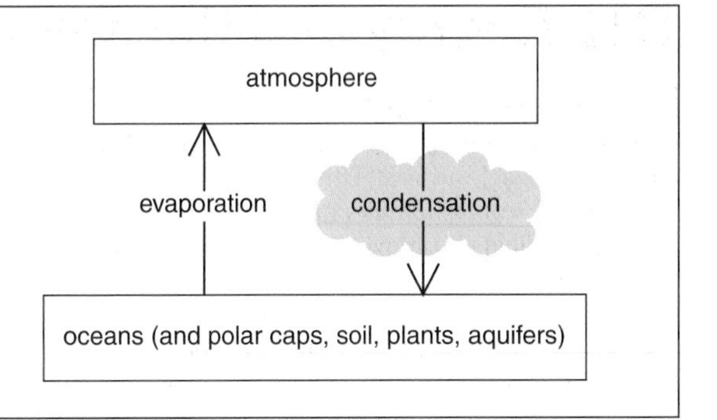

Solar constant

This is the amount of solar energy arriving at the Earth's outer atmosphere per second per square metre (at right angles to the radiation). It is equal to 1.35 kW m^{-2}.

- About 25% of the incoming solar radiation is reflected back into space by the atmosphere and clouds. It does not reach the Earth's surface.
- The amount of solar energy per second striking each square metre of the surface, depends on the time of day, season, atmospheric conditions, and latitude. For example, the radiation reaching region B on the right is spread over a larger area than that reaching A.

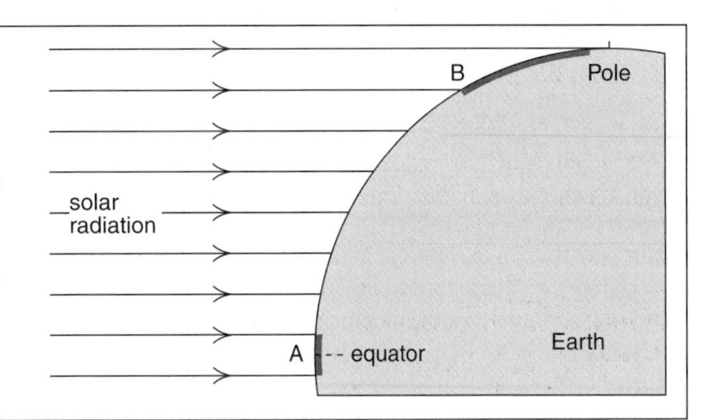

The natural greenhouse effect

Read B31 first.

The Earth gains energy from solar radiation, and loses it by emitting radiation into space. But overall, the *rates* of energy gain and loss are the same. This is another example of dynamic equilibrium.

If the Earth had no atmosphere, its average surface temperature would be about –18 °C. However, the 'heat trapping' effect of the atmosphere, called the ***greenhouse effect***, means that dynamic equilibrium occurs at about 15 °C. The raised temperature is caused like this:

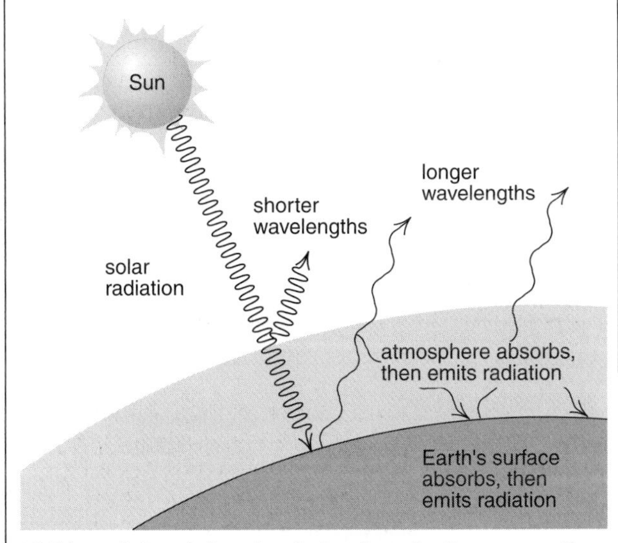

Visible and short-infrared radiation from the Sun pass easily through the atmosphere and warm the Earth's surface. However, being cooler than the Sun, the surface radiates back at longer infrared wavelengths (see B31). Some of these wavelengths are absorbed by molecules of water vapour and carbon dioxide in the atmosphere. These then emit infrared in all directions - including downwards. So the atmosphere and surface are both warmed, and dynamic equilibrium is reached at a higher temperature.

Global warming

By burning fossil fuels, industrial societies are putting carbon dioxide into the atmosphere at a faster rate than plants can absorb it. This is adding to the greenhouse effect and may be causing ***global warming***. In the past 100 years, the average global temperature has risen by almost 1°C.

- Though often called the 'greenhouse effect', global warming is an *addition* to the natural greenhouse effect.
- Extra carbon dioxide may not be the only cause of global warming. Global temperatures have always fluctuated.
- Other 'greenhouse gases', include methane (from paddy fields, animal waste, and oil and gas fields), and CFCs.

The increase in carbon dioxide in the atmosphere is less than half the extra emitted. Possible reasons are:

- With extra carbon dioxide in the air, plant growth is increased, so more of the gas is absorbed.
- Some carbon dioxide dissolves in the oceans.

Future effects of global warming These cannot be predicted with any certainty. Melting of polar ice may cause a rise in sea level. Evaporation from the oceans will increase, so some regions may get more rain. But shifts in climate may mean that some regions are drier.

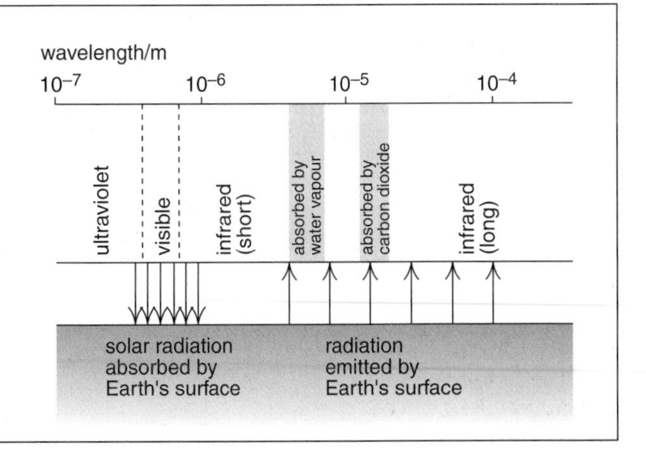

C13 Energy and the environment – 2

Using fossil fuels

Industrial societies get over 90% of their energy by burning oil, natural gas, and coal. However, these fossil fuels took millions of years to form in the ground. They are effectively ***non-renewable*** and supplies are ***finite*** (limited).

Resources of fossil fuels are the total quantities known to exist in the Earth.

Reserves are the quantities which could now be extracted commercially. They are less than resources.

World reserves (1993): energy/10^{20} J	
oil	20
natural gas	6
coal	200

Future consumption This will decide how long reserves will last. It is difficult to predict, but will be affected by:
- the increase in world population
- economic growth in developed countries
- industrialization of developing countries
- efficiency of fuel use
- levels of building insulation

Problems from fossil fuels Major problems include:
- atmospheric pollution, and risk of global warming
- risk of marine pollution from oil
- economic debt in developing countries which import oil.

Power stations: efficiency of fuel use

As with all heat engines, the efficiency of a fuel-burning power station is limited by the second law of thermodynamics (see B28). With additional energy losses (e.g. frictional), the efficiency is reduced to about 40%. So more heat is produced (60%) than electrical energy.

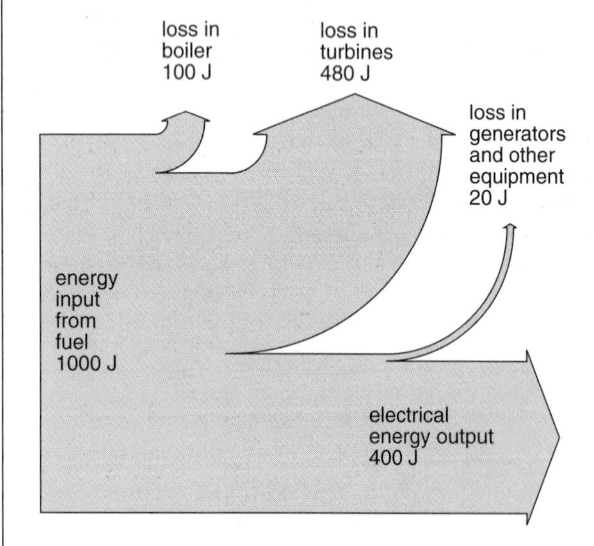

Above, you can see what happens to each 1000 J of energy released by burning fuel in a typical power station. A diagram like this is called a ***Sankey diagram***. Amounts of energy are represented by the widths of the arrows.

Combined heat and power (CHP) In a fuel-burning power station, waste heat produces slightly-warmed cooling water. By running the power station at *reduced* generating efficiency, it is possible to supply the local district with water hot enough for heating systems. In a CHP scheme like this, the *overall* efficiency of fuel use is greatly improved.

Pumped storage

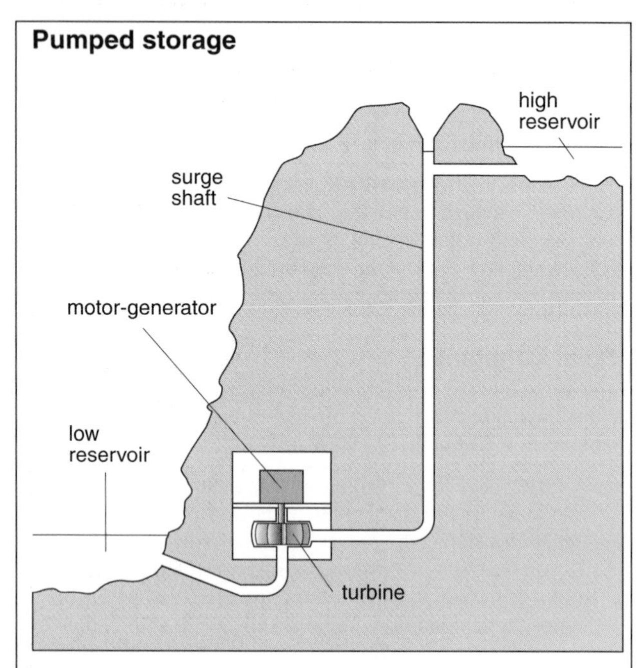

The electricity supply industry has to respond instantly to changes in demand for mains power. A ***pumped storage scheme*** aids this process by acting as an energy store. When demand is high, water flows from the top reservoir and turns the turbines which drive the generators. When the demand is low, the generators are used as motors. Power is taken from stations with spare generating capacity, and water is pumped back up to the top reservoir.

Calculating power output The following calculation assumes that gravitational PE is converted into electrical energy with an efficiency of 100%. If a mass m of water flows from the top reservoir in time t and loses a height h:

electrical energy output = loss of PE = mgh

Dividing by t gives:

electrical power output = mgh/t

Note:
- In practice, the efficiency is, typically, about 75%.

Heat pumps

In a refrigerator, heat is absorbed when a coolant evaporates, and given out at the back when the vapour is condensed by compression. Work is done by the compressor.

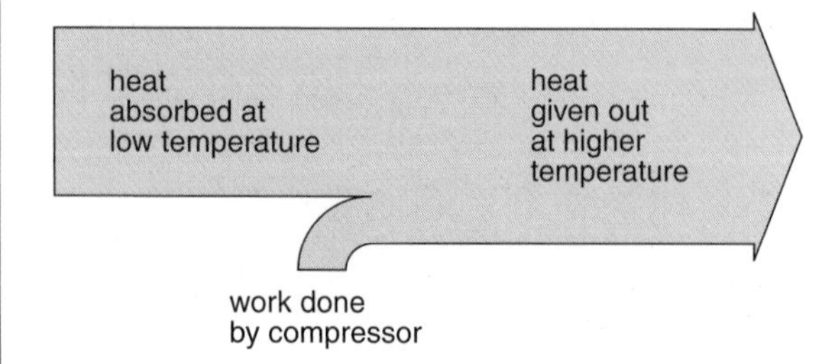

A refrigerator is a ***heat-pump*** - a heat engine (see B28) in reverse. Work is done *on* it in order to transfer heat from a *low* temperature source to a *higher* temperature sink.

Some heating systems use heat pumps. The building is heated by cooling the air, ground, or nearby stream outside. Much less energy is needed than is given out as heat. But the disadvantages are that 1) the local environment is affected 2) the system works *less* well on a *cold* day.

Energy (in kWh) and power

For practical reasons, energy is sometimes measured in units other than the joule (J). For example:

1 ***kilowatt hour*** (kWh) is the energy supplied when delivered at the rate of 1 kW (i.e. 1000 J s^{-1}) for 1 hour.

energy = power × time (see A2)

So: 1 kWh = 1000 J s^{-1} × 3600 s = 3.6×10^6 J

The main alternatives to fossil fuels

Scheme	Details
hydroelectric	Rainwater fills lake behind dam. Flow of water from lake drives generators.
tidal	Lake behind dam fills and empties with tides. Water flow drives generators.
nuclear	See B34.
solar	See panel on right.
wind	See panel below.
biofuel	Wood (for burning) Methane gas from plant and animal waste Alcohol (fuel) produced from sugar cane
geothermal	Using hot water from natural geysers and springs in volcanic areas. Hot rocks underground used to produce steam for turbines in power station.

Scheme	Renewable energy	Fuel costs	Greenhouse gas emissions
hydroelectric	YES	NO	NO
tidal	YES	NO	NO
nuclear	NO	YES	NO
solar	YES	NO	NO
wind	YES	NO	NO
biofuel	YES	YES	YES*
geothermal	YES	NO	NO

* With managed crops, there is no overall addition to global warming because of the carbon dioxide absorbed.

Solar power

Solar power systems make *direct* use of solar radiation. This is done in two main ways:

Solar cells These use the ***photovoltaic effect***: a small voltage is generated when light falls on a slice of doped semiconductor. Such cells are expensive and their efficiency of energy conversion is normally less than 20%.

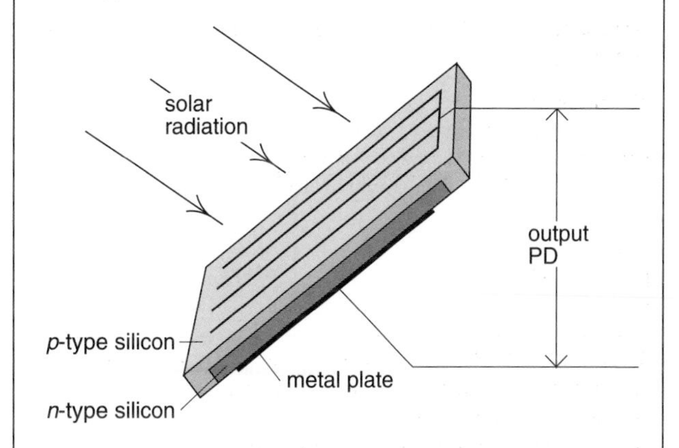

Solar panels These use the heating effect of solar radiation – for example, to pre-warm the water in a domestic hot water system.

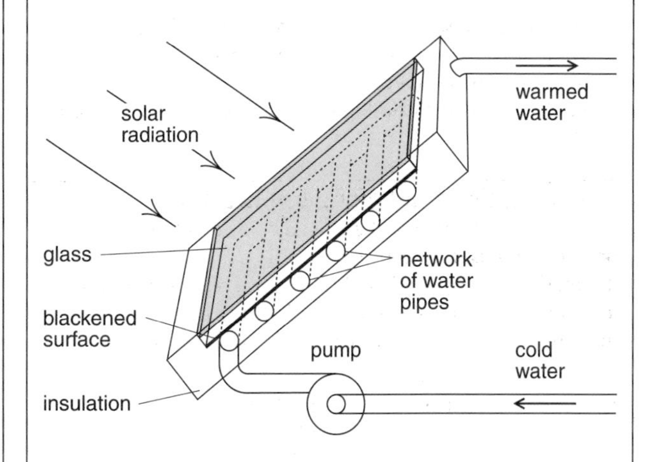

The maximum amount of available energy per second per square metre of panel is equal to the solar constant less corrections for atmospheric absorption, cloud cover, latitude, and angle of panel to the incoming radiation.

Wind power

Generators driven by wind turbines ('windmills') are called ***aerogenerators***. The largest ones have power outputs of about 7 MW – compared with over 3000 MW for a large fuel-burning station. For increased power from one site, aerogenerators are grouped together in ***wind farms***.

Calculating power output The following calculation assumes that the wind loses all its velocity v when striking the turbine blades and transfers all its KE to them.

In the diagram on the right, all the air in the shaded region will transfer its KE to the blades in time t. As this air has a volume of Avt, its mass is $A\rho vt$, so:

KE of air $= \frac{1}{2} \times \text{mass} \times v^2 = \frac{1}{2} \times A\rho vt \times v^2 = \frac{1}{2} A\rho v^3 t$

If the energy conversion efficiency is 100%, this KE is also the electrical energy output. So dividing by t gives:

electric power output $= \frac{1}{2} A\rho v^3$

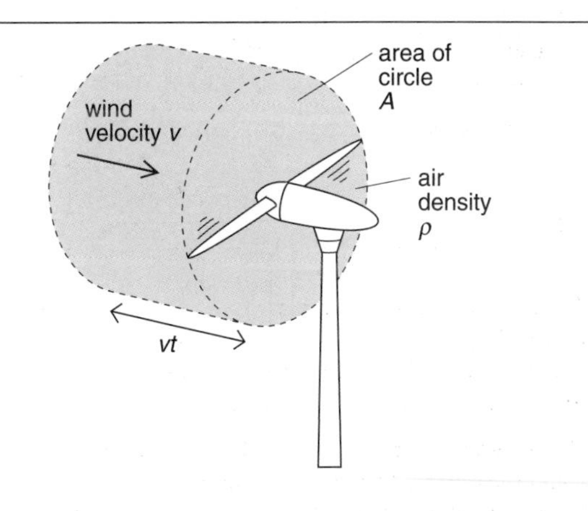

Note:

- In practice, a turbine cannot extract all the wind's KE, and there are other energy losses as well. Overall, the efficiency is reduced to about 40% or less.

C14 Cars and aircraft in motion

Traction forces

Read B5 and B6 first.

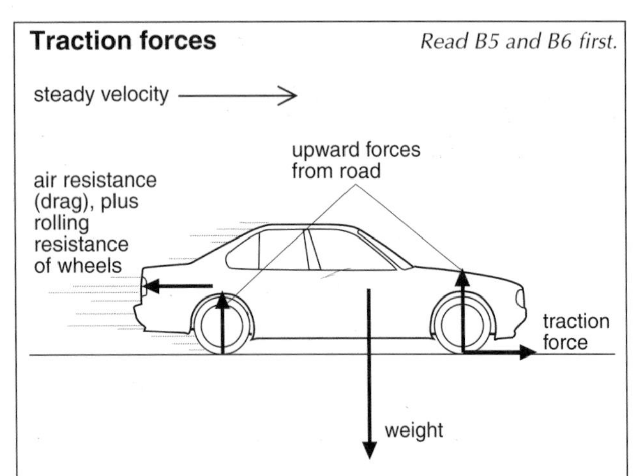

The car above is maintaining a steady velocity, so the forces on it must be balanced (i.e. in equilibrium). Also, the car has no rotational motion, so the moments of the forces about any point must be balanced.

The wheels driven by the engine exert a rearward force on the road, so the road exerts an equal forward force on the wheels – and therefore on the car. This ***traction force*** is provided by friction between the tyres and the road.

Note:

- The traction force is limited by the maximum frictional force that is possible before wheel slip occurs.

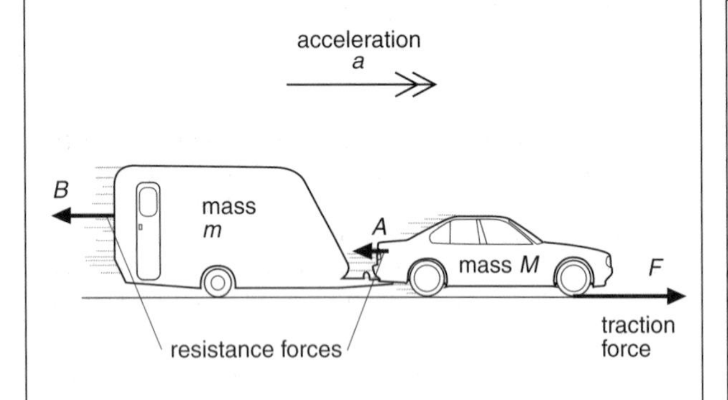

The car above is pulling a caravan. It is accelerating because the horizontal forces on it are unbalanced. (*For simplicity, the balanced vertical forces have not been shown.*)

Treating the car and caravan as a single object:

$$\text{acceleration} = a = \frac{\text{resultant force}}{\text{total mass}} = \frac{F - (A + B)}{M + m}$$

The traction force F' on the caravan comes from the car's tow bar. To calculate this force, it is best to start by drawing another diagram for the caravan alone, as on the right.

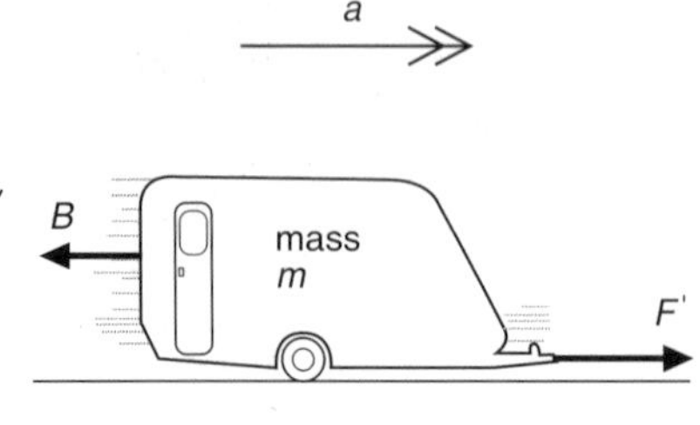

As the caravan has the same acceleration a as the car:

$$\text{resultant force on caravan} = F' - B = \text{mass of caravan} \times \text{acceleration} = ma$$

So:

$$F' = ma + B$$

Cornering

Read B8 first.

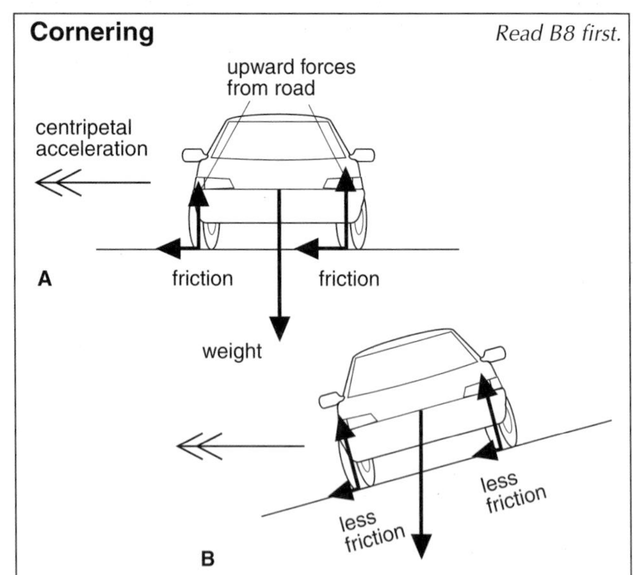

In A, a car is cornering on a flat road. Sideways frictional forces on the tyres provide the centripetal force needed.

In B, the car is cornering on a banked road. The upward forces from the road now have horizontal components. These provide some of the centripetal force required, so less sideways friction on the tyres is needed.

Braking

Car brakes are operated hydraulically (see B26).

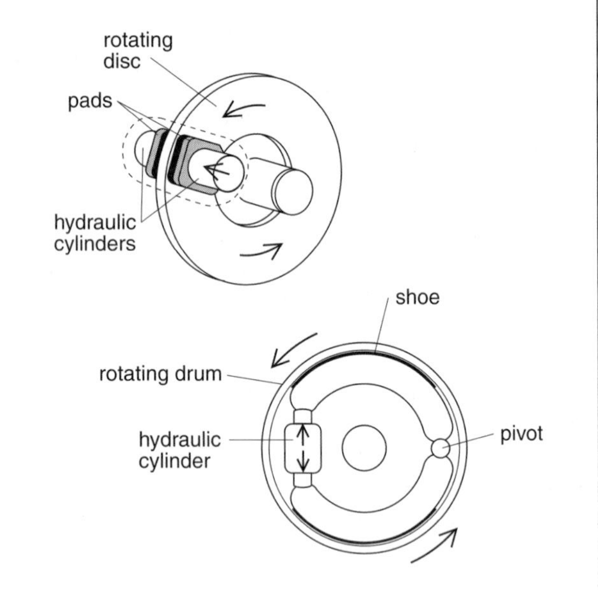

In a ***disc brake***, two friction pads are pushed against a steel disc which rotates with the wheel. In a ***drum brake***, two curved friction strips, called ***shoes***, are pushed against the inside of a steel drum which rotates with the wheel.

When the brakes are applied, the wheels exert a forward force on the road, so the road exerts an equal backward force on the wheels – and therefore on the vehicle. The braking force is limited by the maximum frictional force that is possible before skidding occurs.

Energy dissipation During braking, the car's kinetic energy is transferred into internal energy in the brakes. So the brakes heat up. The energy transferred Q and the temperature rise ΔT are linked by $Q = mc\Delta T$ (see B28).

Aircraft propulsion

Read B6 first.

To move forward, an aircraft pushes a mass of gas backwards so that, by Newton's third law, there is an equal forward force on the aircraft. Here are two ways of producing a backward flow of gas:

Jet engine Air is drawn in at the front by a large fan, and pushed out at the back. Exhaust gases are also ejected, at a higher speed.

Propeller This is driven by the shaft of a jet engine or piston engine. Its blades are angled so that air is pushed backwards as it rotates.

Note:

- *Momentum problem* in B6 shows how to calculate the thrust (force) of a rocket engine. The same principles can be applied to a jet engine or propeller.

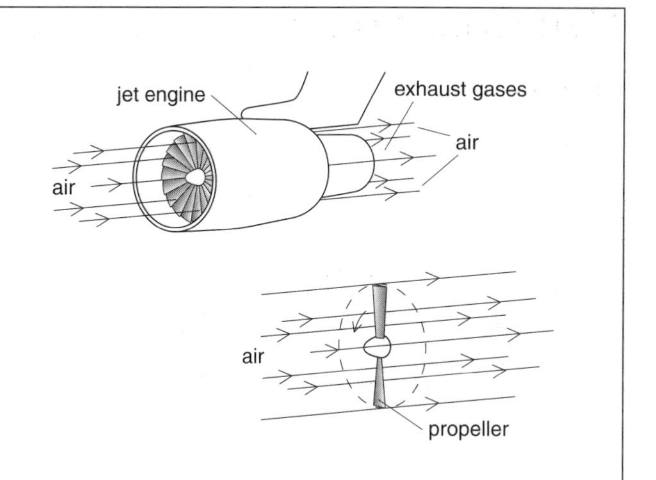

Lift and drag

Read C8 first.

A wing is an ***aerofoil*** - a shape which produces more lift than drag. For a wing of horizontal area S moving at velocity v through air of density ρ, the lift F_L is given by:

$$F_L = \frac{1}{2} S C_L \rho v^2 \qquad (1)$$

where C_L is the lift *coefficient* of the aerofoil section.

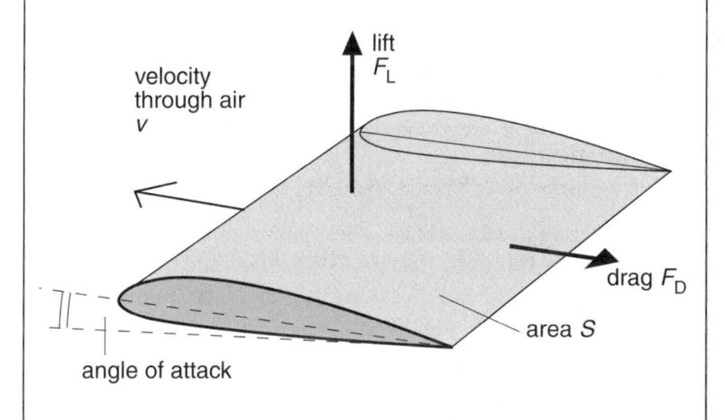

Angle of attack The value of C_L depends on this angle (shown above). Up to a certain limit, increasing the angle of attack increases C_L and, therefore, increases the lift.

For level flight, the lift must balance the aircraft's weight (see B6). If the speed decreases, then according to the above equation, the lift would also decrease if there were no change in C_L. To maintain lift, the pilot must pull the nose of the aircraft up slightly to increase the angle of attack.

Stalling If the angle of attack becomes too high, the airflow behind the wing becomes very turbulent and there is a sudden loss of lift. The wing is ***stalled***:

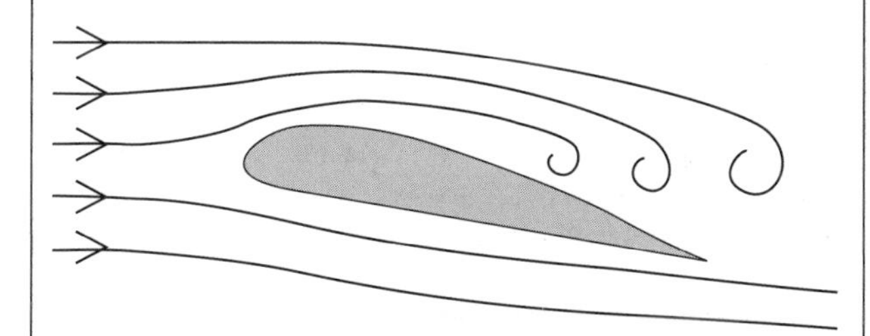

Linking lift and drag Equation (1) is similar in form to that for drag in C8: $F_D = \frac{1}{2} A C_D \rho v^2$. Lift and drag are related. If the lift on an aerofoil increases, so does the drag.

Helicopters

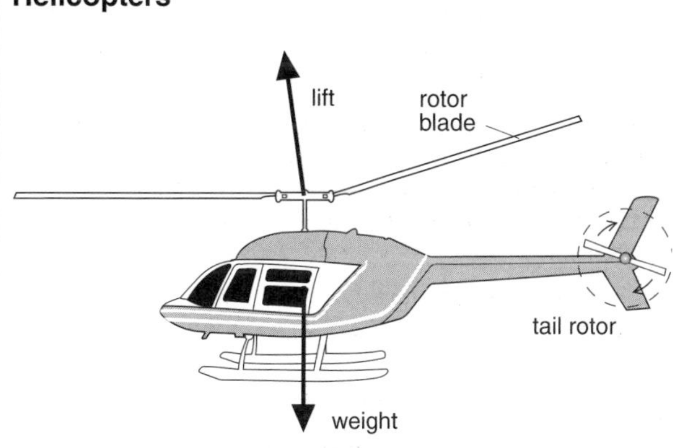

A helicopter's rotor blades are aerofoils. Their motion creates the airflow needed for lift. Each blade is hinged at the rotor hub so that it can move up and down, and there is a lever mechanism for varying its angle of attack. By making each blade rise and fall as it goes round, the plane of the rotor can be tilted to give the horizontal component of force needed for forwards, backwards, or sideways motion.

As the engine exerts a torque on the rotor, there is an equal but opposite torque on the engine. The tail rotor balances this torque and stops the helicopter spinning round.

Hovercraft

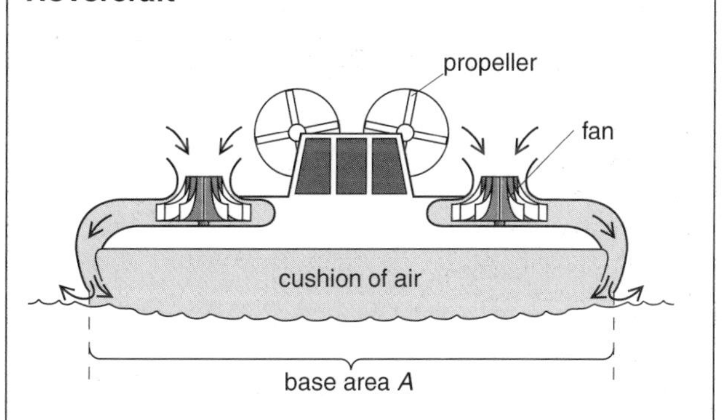

A hovercraft is supported by a 'cushion' of air. If its base area is A, and the trapped air has an excess pressure Δp above atmospheric pressure, then the upward force on the hovercraft is $\Delta p\, A$. This balances the weight. Air is constantly leaking from under the hovercraft. The fans maintain excess pressure by replacing the lost air.

C15 Electronics – 1

Parts and process

Read B15 and B16 first.

Electronic circuits handle small, changing electric currents. The changes are called ***signals***. The diagram below shows the main parts of a basic electronic system.

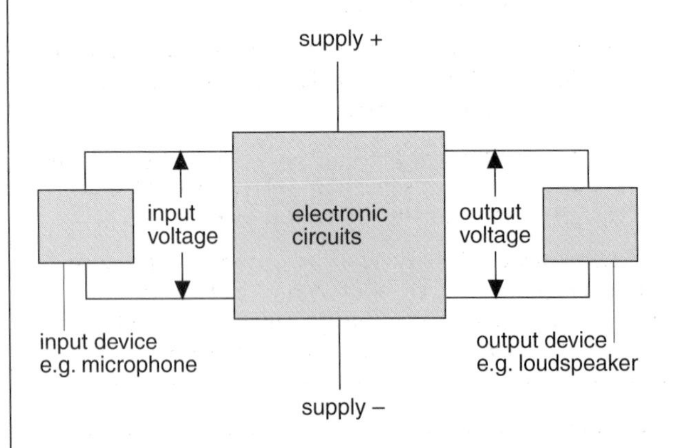

Note:

- Devices which change signals from one form to another (e.g. sound to electrical) are called ***transducers***.
- Input signals can be very weak. But by means of electronic circuits, they can control output signals which can be much stronger. The output power is provided by the supply (usually low voltage DC).

Two possible functions of electronic circuits are described below.

Switching Depending on the input signals received, the output voltage is either HIGH (close to the supply voltage) – or LOW (zero), so the output device is either ON or OFF.

Amplification The output signals are an amplified (magnified) version of the input signals. For example, very low voltage AC from a microphone causes a higher voltage AC output for a loudspeaker.

The ***voltage gain*** of an amplifier is defined like this:

$$\text{voltage gain} = \frac{\text{output voltage}}{\text{input voltage}}$$

Note:

- In electronics, the term 'voltage' is commonly used for potential, PD, and EMF.

The key component in electronics is the ***transistor***. It can amplify or act as a switch. An ***integrated circuit (IC)***, in a package as on the right, may have thousands of transistors and other components formed on a single chip of silicon.

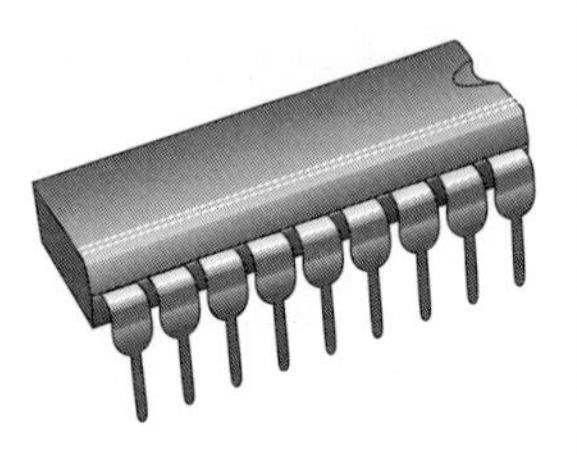

Input devices

Input transducers (e.g. microphones) are called ***sensors***. They must be linked to the circuit in such a way that any change they detect (e.g. a pulse of sound) causes a change in input voltage.

Sensors generating a voltage These include some microphones, and those light sensors that work like solar cells (see C13). Ideally, the voltage is in proportion to the external change causing it.

Sensors with varying resistance These include:

- light-dependent resistors (LDRs) (see A4),
- thermistors (temperature-dependent: see A4, B15),
- strain gauges (resistance changed by stretching).

To produce the necessary voltage change, the sensor forms one part of a ***potential divider*** (see B16). For example, when light falls on the LDR below, its resistance falls. The LDR therefore takes a smaller share of the supply voltage, so the voltage *V* falls.

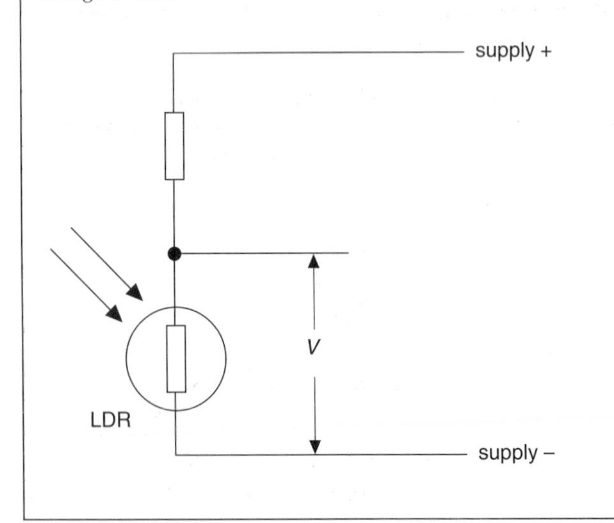

Output devices

These include loudspeakers, buzzers, LEDs, and relays.

Light-emitting diodes (LEDs) These emit light when a small current passes through. They can be used as indicator lamps to show the presence of an output voltage. Like all diodes, they only conduct in one direction (see A4 and B15).

To avoid damage, a resistor must be placed in series with an LED to limit the current through it.

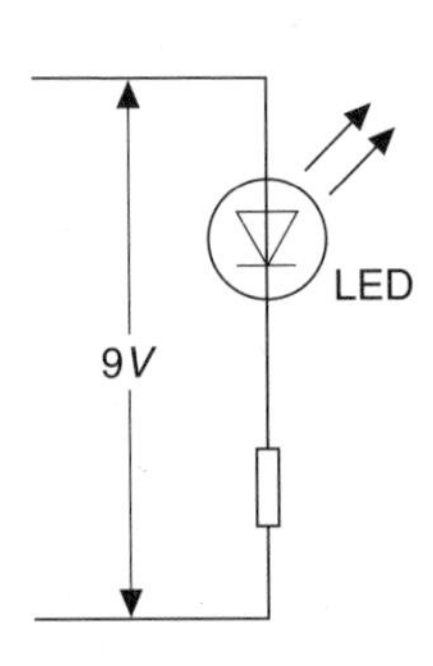

The LED on the right can take a current of 0.01 A, which produces a 2 V drop across it. If a circuit's output voltage is 9 V, there needs to be a 7 V voltage drop across the resistor, so its resistance should be 7/0.01 = 700 Ω.

Relays These are electromagnetic switches. A small current activates an electromagnet. This closes (or opens) a switch which can control the flow of a larger current in a separate circuit, e.g. a circuit with a mains heater or motor in it.

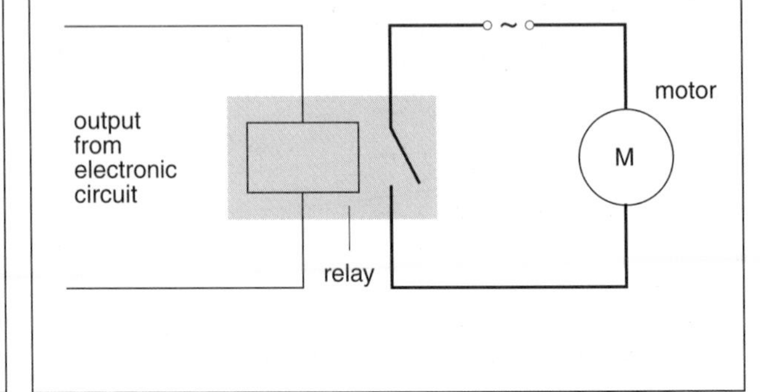

Impedances and matching

Resistance is one form of impedance (see B20). The microphone and loudspeaker below each have impedance. The amplifer has ***input impedance*** and ***output inpedance*** rather as a battery has internal resistance (see B16).

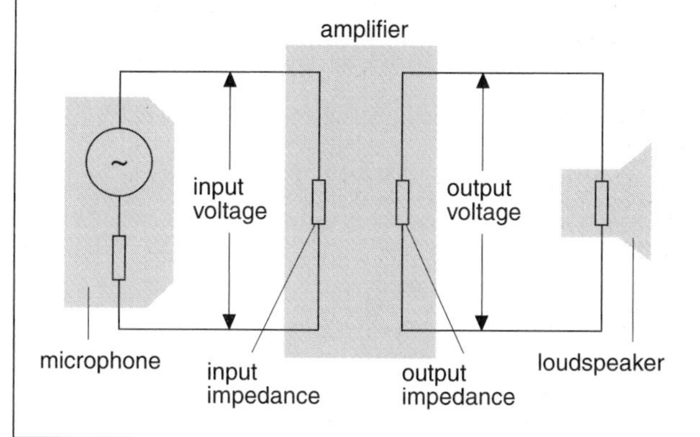

In the diagram, the various impedances are represented by resistors in the input and output circuits.

In each circuit, it is the *higher* impedance that has the *higher* voltage drop across it. So:

- **For maximum input voltage**, the microphone's impedance should be as *low* as possible.
- **For maximum output voltage**, the loudspeaker's impedance should be as *high* as possible. However, this gives a very low output current and almost no sound!
- **For maximum output power**, the loudspeaker's impedance should be the *same* as the output impedance. (Output voltage × output current is then at its highest.)

A ***transformer*** can be used to match impedances and give maximum power transfer. A transformer with an impedance Z in its primary circuit is equivalent to an impedance of $Z(N_2/N_1)^2$. (See A5 for diagram and equation symbols.)

The operational amplifier (op amp)

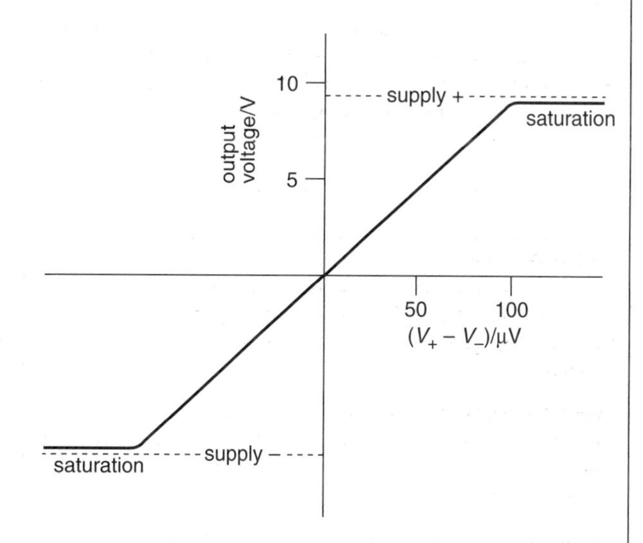

This IC has one output and *two* inputs. It amplifies the *difference* between the two input voltages. It is a ***differential amplifer***.

- If $V_+ > V_-$ the output voltage is positive (+).
- If $V_+ < V_-$ the output voltage is negative (–).
- If $V_+ = V_-$ the output voltage is zero.

If only *one* input is in use (and the other is at zero voltage):

- A *positive* (+) voltage on the ***inverting input*** causes a *negative* (–) output voltage,
- A *positive* (+) voltage on the ***non-inverting input*** causes a *positive* (+) output voltage.

Note:

- The + and – signs on the inputs show whether they invert or not. They do *not* indicate + or – voltage.

Power supply A three-terminal DC supply is required, giving 0 V (earth) and typically, ±9 V. The supply connections are often excluded from diagrams.

Op amp features These include:

- An extremely high voltage gain, typically around 10^5, though less at high frequencies,
- A very high input impedance (e.g. 10^{12} Ω),
- A very low output impedance (e.g. 10^2 Ω).

To reduce gain, op amps are used with a resistor or wire linking the output to one input (see C16). This is called a ***closed loop***. (The op amp above has an ***open loop***.)

The graph above is for an open-loop op amp.

Note:

- The output voltage cannot exceed the supply voltage.
- The amplification is *linear*, provided the output voltage is not close to the supply voltage,
- At saturation, the output and input voltages are no longer in proportion, so the output is *distorted*.

Advantages of reducing gain These include the following:

- Input signals can be stronger without causing saturation and, therefore, distortion.
- The gain is less affected by temperature changes.
- The ***bandwidth*** is greater, i.e. the gain is constant over a wider range of input frequences (see below).

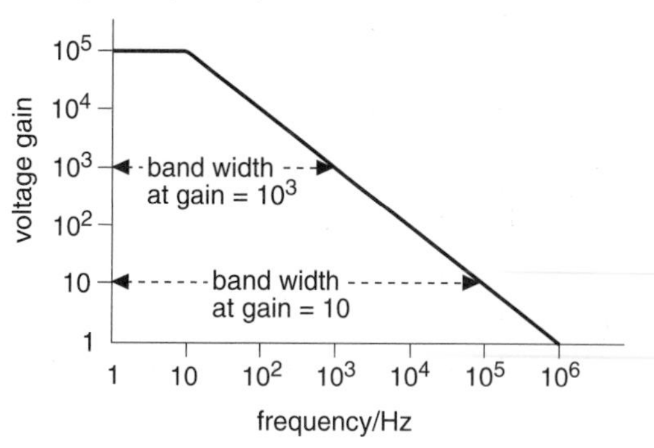

C16 Electronics – 2

Op amp as an inverting amplifier

The amplifier circuit on the right uses a closed loop to feed back a set fraction of the output voltage to the inverting input. This is called ***negative feedback*** because the signal being fed back partly cancels the input signal.

To calculate the amplifier's closed-loop voltage gain (V_{out}/V_{in}), the following assumptions are made:

- The op amp is not saturated. It has such a high open-loop gain that the voltage difference between its inverting and non-inverting inputs must be negligible. Therefore P is effectively at 0 V. (P is called a ***virtual earth***.)
- The current through P is negligible. Therefore, the current through R_f is the same as through R_i (see B16):

If I is the current through R_f and R_i:
voltage drop across $R_f = IR_f$
voltage drop across $R_i = IR_i$

But if P is at 0 V:
voltage drop across $R_f = 0 - V_{out} = -V_{out}$
voltage drop across $R_i = V_{in} - 0 = V_{in}$

From the above, it follows that $V_{out}/V_{in} = -R_f/R_i$

So: $$\text{closed-loop voltage gain} = -\frac{R_f}{R_i}$$

From the closed-loop voltage gain equation below:

- An *inverting* amplifier has a *negative* gain.
- The gain does not depend on the characteristics of the op amp. It is set by the values of R_f and R_i. For example, if $R_f = 200\ \text{k}\Omega$ and $R_i = 20\ \text{k}\Omega$, the gain $= -200/20 = -10$.

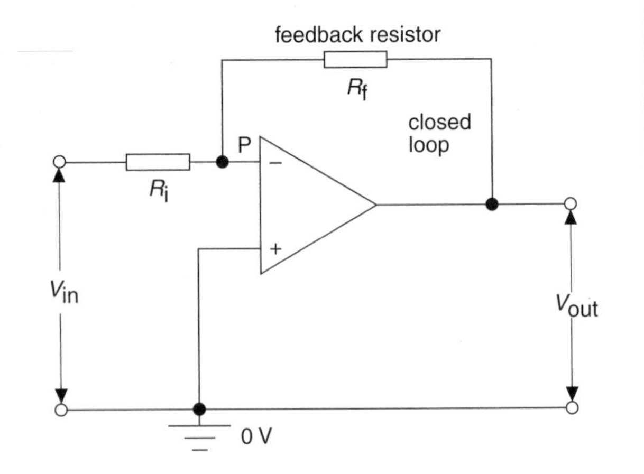

Op amp as a non-inverting amplifier

In the circuit on the right, the input signal goes to the non-inverting input, and the potential divider provides negative feedback. With the same assumptions as above:

$$\text{closed-loop voltage gain} = 1 + \frac{R_f}{R_i} \qquad (1)$$

A non-inverting amplifier has a much higher input impedance than the inverting type. This is useful, for example, where a high-impedance microphone is connected to the input (see *Impedances and matching* in C15).

Voltage follower This is a non-inverting amplifier in which R_f is zero (i.e. a direct connection) and R_i is infinite (i.e. removed). In this case, the gain is 1, so the output voltage is the same as the input voltage. However, the output impedance is much less than the input impedance, which makes the circuit useful for impedance matching.

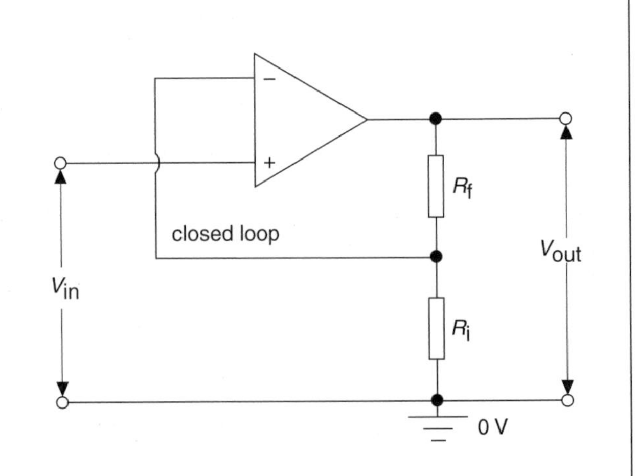

Op amp as a comparator

On the right, the LED is switched on automatically when darkness falls. The switching is done by an op amp which *compares* the voltages from two potential dividers:

V_- is fixed by the ratio of R_2 to R_1.
V_+ varies with the resistance of the LDR
There is no feedback, so a small difference between V_- and V_+ saturates the op amp, causing maximum output voltage.

In bright light, the LDR has a low resistance, so V_+ is low, and less than V_-. The op amp is saturated, but its output voltage is negative, so the LED cannot conduct.

As the light intensity falls, the resistance of the LDR rises, and so does V_+. When $V_+ > V_-$, the op amp saturates in the opposite direction. The output voltage is now positive, so the LED conducts and lights up.

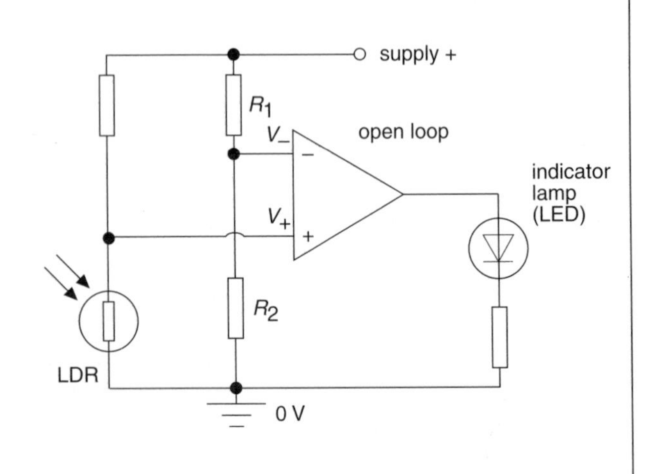

Logic gates

These are electronic switches, with one output and one or more inputs. A typical logic IC has several gates on the same chip, and needs a DC supply providing +5 V and 0 V.

Each input is made either HIGH (e.g. +5 V) or LOW (0 V). As a result, the output is either HIGH or LOW – depending on the type of gate and its input state(s).

The outputs produced by different inputs are shown in a ***truth table*** (as below). The output and input states are represented by the ***logic numbers*** 1 (HIGH) and 0 (LOW).

NOT gate (inverter)

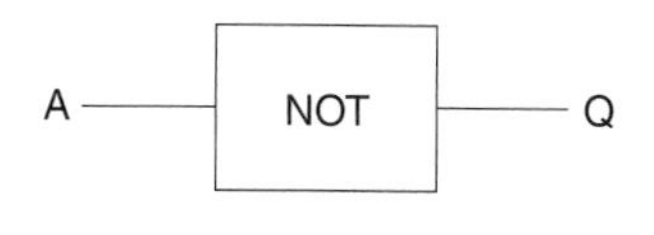

A	Q
0	1
1	0

The ouput is HIGH if the input is *NOT* HIGH, and vice versa.

AND gate

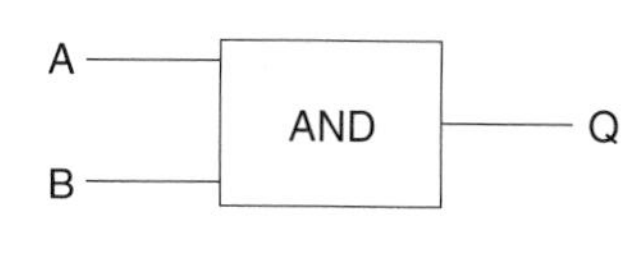

A	B	Q
0	0	0
0	1	0
1	0	0
1	1	1

The output Q is only HIGH if inputs A *AND* B are HIGH.

OR gate

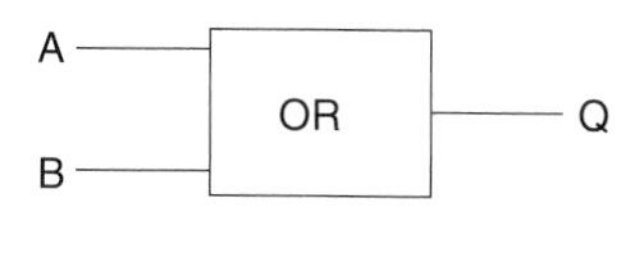

A	B	Q
0	0	0
0	1	1
1	0	1
1	1	1

The output Q is HIGH if input A *OR* input B is HIGH, or both are HIGH.

Exclusive-OR gate

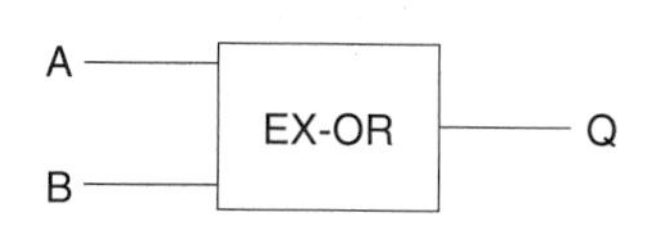

A	B	Q
0	0	0
0	1	1
1	0	1
1	1	0

The output Q is HIGH if input A *OR* input B is HIGH, but *not* if both are HIGH.

Using gates

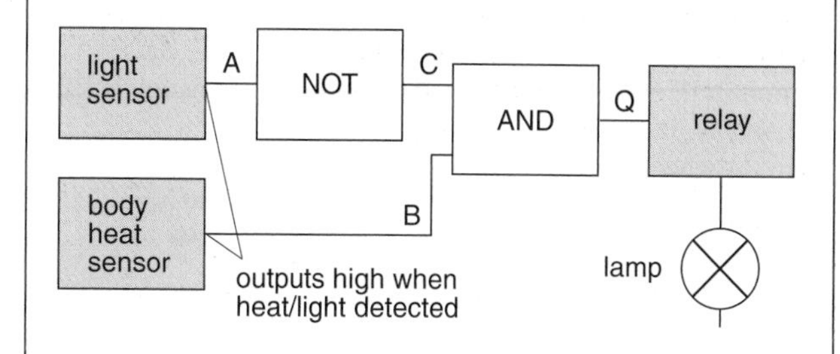

A	B	C	Q
0	0	1	0
0	1	1	1
1	0	0	0
1	1	0	0

Above, gates control a security lamp. The truth table shows that the lamp is only ON if it is dark *and* someone is approaching.

As the gate's output voltage and current are low, a relay is needed to switch the lamp on and off.

NAND and other gates

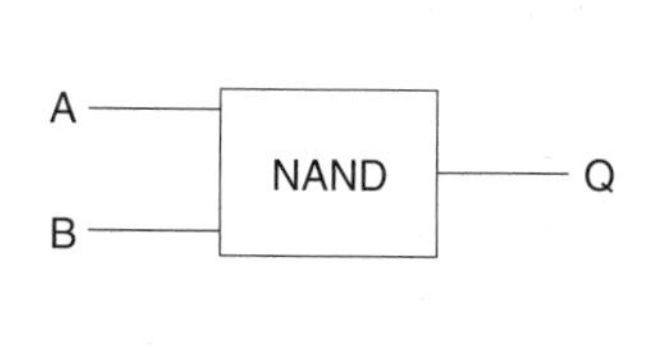

A	B	Q
0	0	1
0	1	1
1	0	1
1	1	0

A ***NAND gate*** is equivalent to an AND gate followed by a NOT gate.

A ***NOR gate*** is equivalent to an OR gate followed by a NOT gate. Its output is that of an OR gate *inverted*.

An ***exclusive-NOR gate*** is equivalent to an exclusive-OR gate followed by a NOT gate.

Made from NAND gates

All gates can be made from NAND (or NOR) gates. e.g:

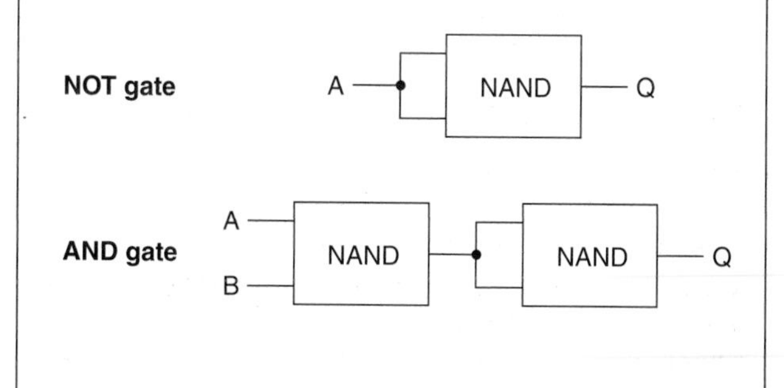

C17 Telecommunications

Telecommunications systems

Telecommunications systems (e.g. radio, TV, and telephone) send information from one place to another using electric currents or electromagnetic radiation. The information being sent may be sounds, pictures, or computer data.

- The ***channel of communication*** may be radio waves, microwave beam, metal cable, or optical fibre.
- Signals for sounds (e.g. speech) are called ***audio*** signals.

Analogue and digital

Analogue signals In an electronic circuit, these produce a voltage which varies continuously over a range of values. The radio system shown below is handling analogue signals.

Digital signals These are pulses, produced because a circuit's output voltage is either HIGH or LOW. They can be represented by the logical numbers 1 and 0 (see C16). The advantages of using them are described on the next page.

Radio communication

The principle of simple radio system is shown below:

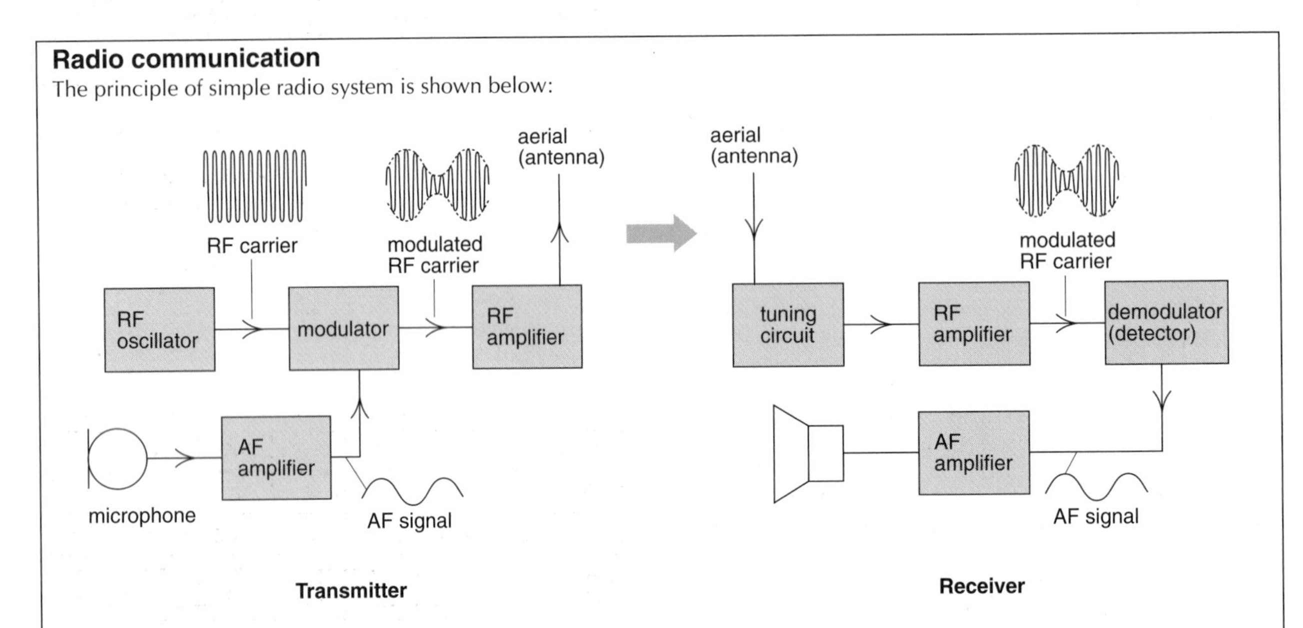

Carrier Radio frequencies (e.g. 1 MHz) are much higher than audio frequencies (e.g. 1 kHz). The principle of radio transmission is to produce a steady radio signal called the carrier, and then ***modulate*** (vary) it with the audio signal.

Modulation The system above uses ***amplitude modulation (AM)***: the amplitude of the carrier is varied by the audio signal. In ***frequency modulation (FM)***, the frequency of the carrier is varied, one advantage being that the signal is less affected by interference.

Bandwidth Mathematically, a carrier of frequency f_c, amplitude modulated at a frequency f_m, is equivalent to a pure sine wave of frequency f_c, with two ***side frequencies*** of $f_c + f_m$ and $f_c - f_m$ (i.e. at the carrier frequency $\pm f_m$).

Speech and music contains a variety of frequencies, mainly between 50 Hz and 4.5 kHz, so a modulated carrier normally has two bands of side frequencies, called ***sidebands***. The frequency range occupied by the signal is the ***bandwidth***.

- A radio station needs a bandwidth of about *twice* its AF range. In the UK, the bandwidth used for AM is 9 kHz.

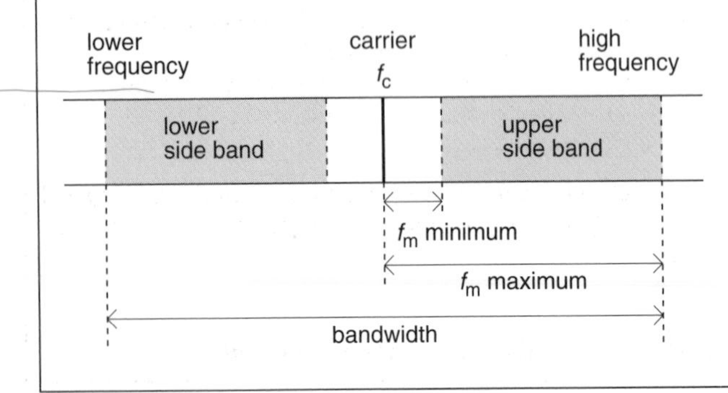

Tuning circuit Each radio station broadcasts at its own carrier frequency. The tuning circuit uses a resonant circuit (see B20) to select the incoming frequency required.

Demodulation The demodulator removes the ***RF*** (radio frequency) part of the signal, and passes on only the ***AF*** (audio frequency) part. The key component in demodulation is the diode. This rectifies (see B20) the RF signal so that only its 'forward' parts are left, as pulses of varying amplitude. The AF signal is recreated from these.

Frequencies used for radio communication

Frequency band		Examples of uses
30 kHz – 300 kHz	low (LF)	long wave radio
300 kHz – 3 MHz	medium (MF)	medium wave radio
3 MHz – 30 MHz	high (HF)	short wave radio
30 MHz – 300 MHz	very high (VHF)	FM radio
300 MHz – 3 GHz	ultra high (UHF)	TV
1 GHz – 30 GHz	microwave	telephone and TV links satellite links, radar

How radio waves travel

Despite the curvature of the Earth's surface, radio waves can travel between places which are a long way apart.

Ground (surface) waves These follow the Earth's surface. Low frequencies travel furthest (up to 1000 km).

Sky waves These are reflected by the ionosphere (see C11) and the Earth. They are mostly high frequency waves.

Space waves These are waves with frequencies above 30 MHz. They are not reflected by the ionosphere. They can only be used for 'line of sight' (i.e. straight) communication, but their range can be extended by a satellite link.

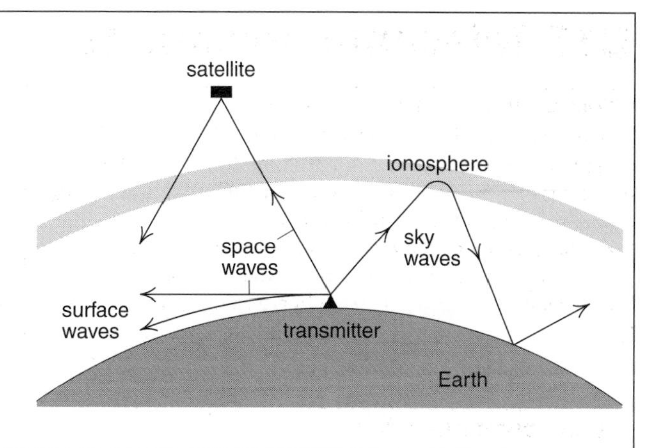

Digital transmission

Most telephone systems use digital transmission between exchanges. Audio signals from one telephone are converted from analogue to digital form, transmitted, and then changed back into analogue signals for the other telephone.

To convert the analogue signal on the right into a digital signal, it is ***sampled*** by measuring the voltage level at regular intervals of time. The levels are then changed into ***binary*** codes, consisting only of 0s and 1s, and these are transmitted as a sequence of pulses. The process is called ***pulse code modulation (PCM)***. Reversing the process produces the analogue signal again.

- Telephone systems normally use 256 voltage levels. Each requires an 8-bit binary code, e.g. 10011001.
- The ***sampling rate*** needs to be at least *twice* the highest frequency in the signal being sampled. Telephone systems normally use a sampling rate of 8000 Hz, i.e. the signal is being sampled every 1/8000 s.

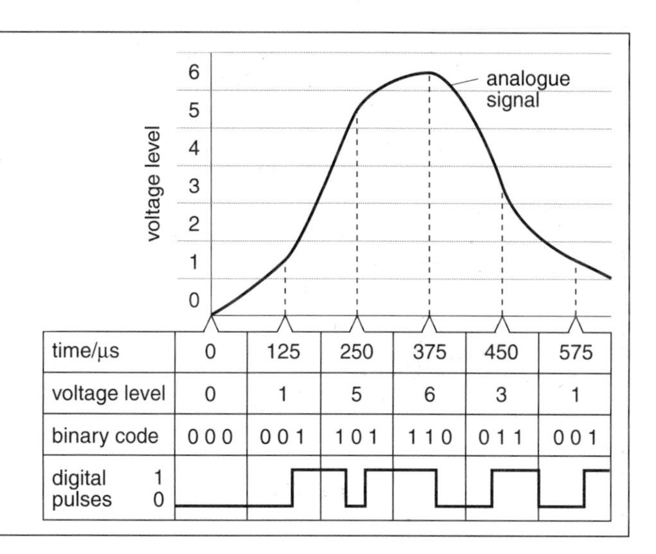

time/µs	0	125	250	375	450	575
voltage level	0	1	5	6	3	1
binary code	0 0 0	0 0 1	1 0 1	1 1 0	0 1 1	0 0 1

Advantages of digital transmission

Regeneration Signals lose power as they travel along a cable. They are also affected by ***noise*** (additions caused by electrical interference and thermal activity). To restore their power and quality, digital signals can be amplified and 'cleaned up' at intervals by ***regenerators***. (Analogue signals can be amplified by ***repeaters***, but unfortunately, the noise is amplified as well.)

Data handling Computers operate digitally, so digital transmission is ideal for long-distance computer links.

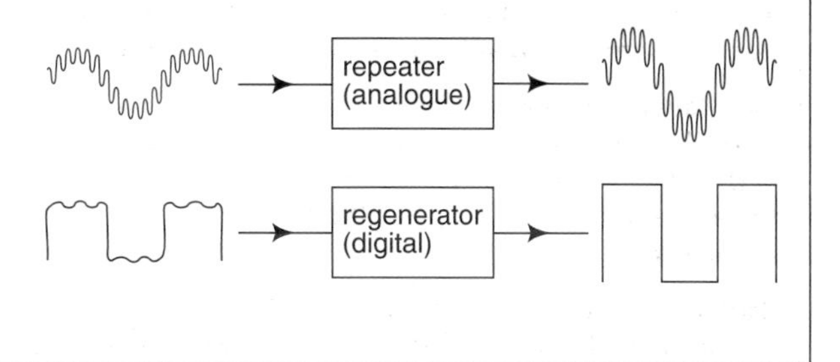

Power losses and gains

Signals lose power as they travel along a cable. The effect is called ***attenuation***. Repeaters or regenerators compensate by increasing the power.

In telecommunication, the unit used for measuring power change is the ***decibel (dB)*** (see also C9). If P_o is the power input into a cable and P is the power output:

$$\text{power increase in dB} = 10 \log_{10} (P/P_o)$$

So, if the power input is 200 mW and the power output is 2 mW, the power increase = $10 \log_{10}(2/200) = -20$ dB. In this case, there is a power *loss* of 20 dB.

Note:

- The attenuation caused by a cable is often expressed in dB per km.
- dB changes can be added algebraically. If there is a power loss of 20 dB in a cable, followed by a power gain of 15 dB in a repeater, the overall power loss is 5 dB.

Optical fibres

Read B22 first.

Optical fibres carry infrared pulses from a laser or LED. At the far end, these are detected by a sensor (a photodiode).

For transmitting signals, optical fibre cables have many advantages over metal cables and radio waves:

- They are ideal for digital transmission,
- They have a much higher signal-carrying capacity,
- They are free of noise and crosstalk (signals crossing over from one fibre or wire to the next),
- They offer better security, e.g. they cannot be 'tapped',
- They are thinner and lighter than metal cables,
- Attenuation is low.

Attenuation Infrared is absorbed as it passes along an optical fibre. If P_o is the power input, P is the power output, and x is the length of the fibre:

$$P = P_o e^{-\alpha x}$$

where α is the ***linear attenuation coefficient***.

C18 Turning points

Waves and particles

Read B22 and B35 first.

Corpuscles or waves? Newton suggested that light might be made up of high-speed 'corpuscles' (particles). Huyghens (in 1680) proposed an alternative wave theory which satisfactorily accounted for reflection and refraction.

The wave theory could not explain how 'empty' space could transmit waves. So it was argued that space must be filled with an invisible medium, called the ***ether***.

The corpuscular theory predicted that light should speed up when passing from air to water. The wave theory predicted the opposite. In 1862, the speed of light in water was measured and found to be less than in air.

Electromagnetic waves Maxwell's electromagnetic theory (1864) predicted that oscillating charges should emit waves which would travel through an electromagnetic field at a speed of $1/\sqrt{\varepsilon_0\mu_0}$ (= speed of light). Later (in 1888), Hertz demonstrated the existence of radio waves.

Note:

- Maxwell's theory is an example of a ***classical*** theory – one that does not deal with quantum effects.

Black body radiation The graph shows the energy distribution in a black body's spectrum (see B31). The dotted line is the distribution predicted by classical theory. In classical theory, oscillating particles are assumed to emit waves continuously, over a continuous range of energies. But at higher frequencies, there is a huge discrepancy between the predicted and experimental results. This is known as the ***ultraviolet catastrophe***.

Quantum theory This was proposed by Planck (in 1900). It solved the black body spectrum problem by restricting energy changes to multiples of hf. Later, it led to the concepts of the ***photon*** and ***wave-particle duality***.

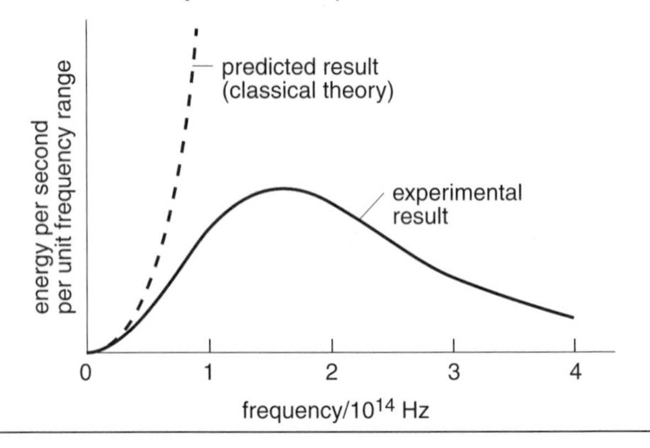

The special theory of relativity

Looking for the ether As the Earth moves through space, the ether should flow past it. In 1887, Michelson and Morley tried to detect this flow with an ***interferometer***:

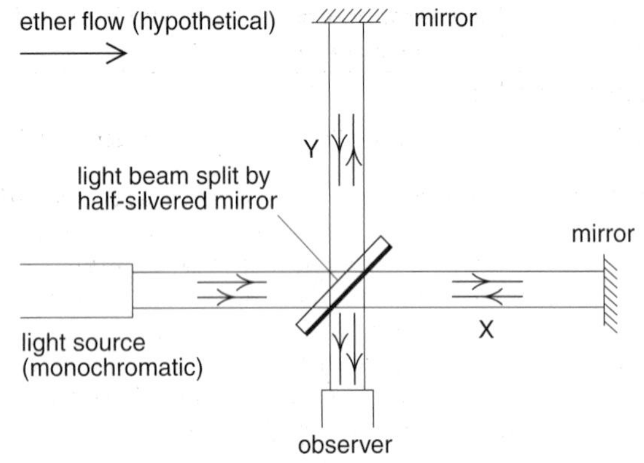

Beams X and Y recombine to form an interference pattern (see B23). If there is an ether flow as above, X's travel time should be slightly longer than normal. But when the apparatus is rotated 90°, Y's travel time should be slightly longer than normal, so the interference pattern should shift. No shift was detected. All experiments indicated that the measured velocity of light in a vacuum is *invariant* (always the same).

Postulates Einstein rejected the idea of absolute motion through space: motion could only be relative to the observer's ***frame of reference***. He developed his ***special theory of relativity*** (1905) from the following two postulates (assumptions):

1. Physical laws (e.g. the laws of motion) are the same in all *inertial* (unaccelerated) frames of reference.
2. The speed of light in a vacuum has the same measured value in all inertial frames of reference.

Deductions From these postulates, Einstein deduced that length and time measurements could not be absolute. They must depend on the relative motion of the observer. Some results of his mathematical analysis are given on the right.

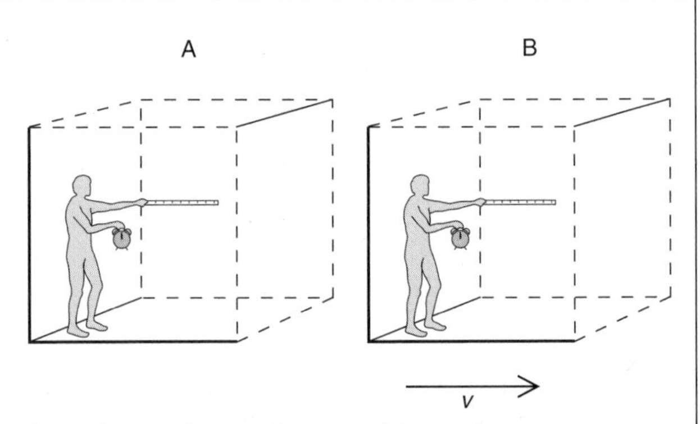

Above, frame B has a velocity v relative to frame A.

- An event in B takes time t_0 when measured by an observer in the same frame. This is its ***proper time***. But to an observer in A, the same event takes time t, where:

$$t = \frac{t_0}{\sqrt{1 - v^2/c^2}}$$

(c = speed of light in a vacuum)

Note: $t > t_0$. To the observer in A, a clock in B runs slow: there is ***time dilation*** (enlarging).

- If an object in frame B has a ***proper length*** l_0 (in the v direction) its length as observed from A is given by:

$$l = l_0\sqrt{1 - v^2/c^2}$$

Note: $l < l_0$. To the observer in A, the object in B is shortened: there is ***length contraction***.

- The object's mass as observed from A also depends on v:

$$m = \frac{m_0}{\sqrt{1 - v^2/c^2}}$$

Note: $m > m_0$. As v increases, m increases. When $v = c$, m is infinite, and so is the KE. This effectively makes the speed of light a universal speed limit.

- Observed increases in mass and energy are linked by the equation $\Delta E = \Delta mc^2$ (see B34).

Discovering the electron

Read B21 first.

Cathode rays 19th century experiments with electric discharges through gases at very low pressure (as below) indicated that invisible rays were travelling from the cathode to the anode in the discharge tube. These were called ***cathode rays***. Perrin (in 1895) demonstrated that they were negatively (–) charged.

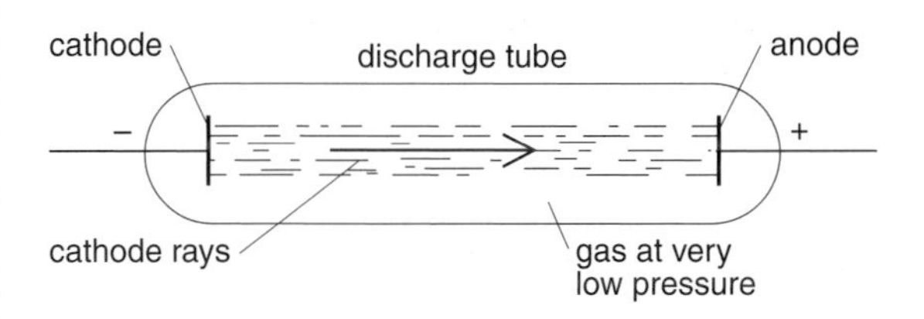

Specific charge (charge/mass) J. J. Thomson suggested that cathode rays were particles, which he called ***electrons***. In 1897, he measured their specific charge (e/m_e). A modern version of his experiment is shown below:

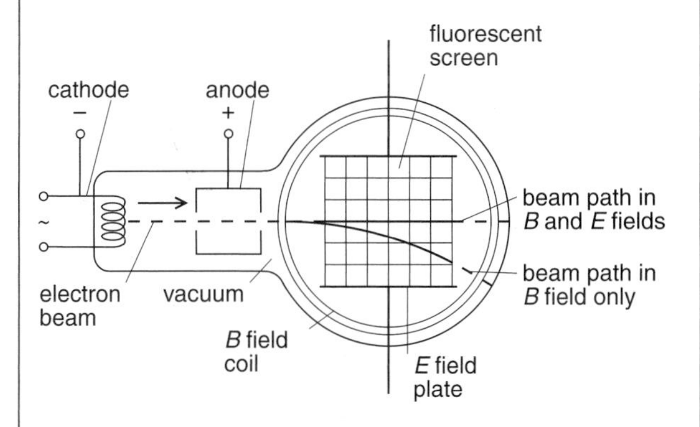

The electron beam is deflected by a magnetic field (B), then restored to a straight path using an electric field (E).

When the magnetic field alone is acting:

$Bev = m_e v^2/r$

So: $e/m_e = v/rB$ (quantities defined as in B21)

With r and B measured, e/m_e can be calculated if v is known. When the electric and magnetic forces on the electron beam are equal, $Bev = Ee$. So $v = E/B$.

Electronic charge *e* Millikan (in 1909) observed oil droplets as they fell at terminal velocity through air, then measured the *change* in terminal velocity (Δv) which occured when a droplet gained charge (q) and a vertical electric field (E) was applied. In this case, electric force = Eq.

So: $Eq = 6\pi\eta a\Delta v$ (see C8)

giving $q = 6\pi\eta a\Delta v /E$

(a was deduced from terminal velocity measurements when E was zero). Millikan took hundreds of measurements and found that q was always a multiple of a basic charge e.

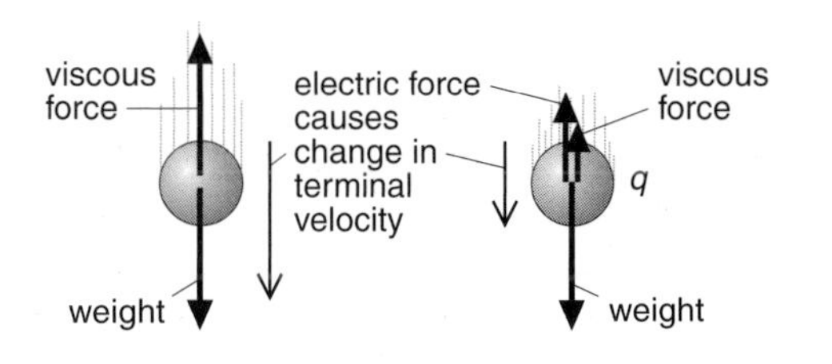

Lowering temperatures

Read B27 – B31 first.

Predicting absolute zero The expansion of gases was investigated by Charles (in 1787) and Gay-Lussac (in 1802). Their results suggested that all gases should have zero volume at –273.15 °C, now called ***absolute zero***.

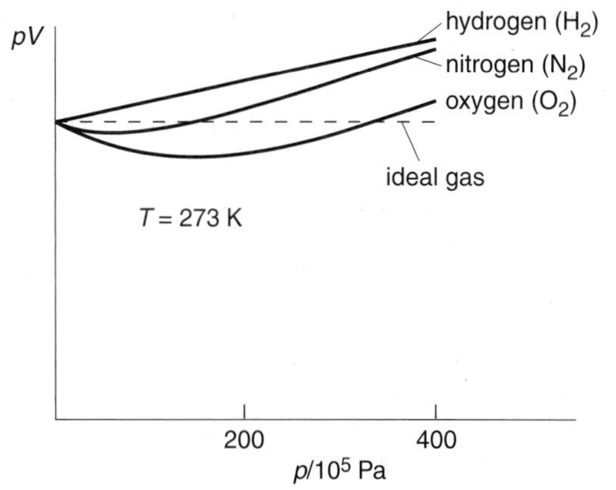

Real and ideal gases Real gases deviate from Boyle's law because 1) of intermolecular forces 2) the molecules themselves occupy a finite volume. The graph shows how pV varies with p for three gases. A gas's ***Boyle temperature*** is the temperature at which pV is most nearly constant.

In an ideal gas, the molecules occupy zero volume and there are no intermolecular forces. Cooling an ideal gas would never liquefy it. It would remain a gas at absolute zero.

Gases and vapours A real gas can be liquefied by compressing it – provided it is beneath its ***critical temperature***. The pressure needed to liquefy it at this temperature is the ***critical pressure***. A gas below its critical temperature is called a ***vapour*** (see also C12).

Critical temperatures		
helium 5 K	hydrogen (H_2) 33 K	oxygen 155 K

The Joule-Kelvin effect Below, a gas expands as it is passed through a porous plug. For an ideal gas, there would be no change in temperature. However, with most real gases, there is a slight *decrease* in temperature, because work is done against intermolecular attractions at the expense of the molecules' KE. The effect (discovered in 1852) only produces cooling below a gas's ***inversion temperature.*** Above this, intermolecular repulsions cause slight heating.

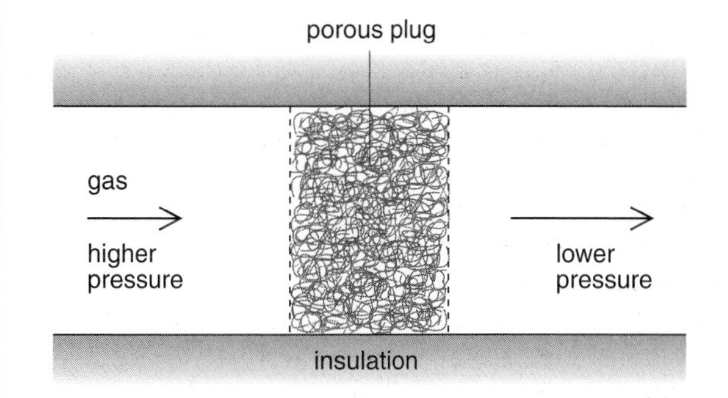

Liquefying gases Techniques for this can make use of:
- the cooling effect of evaporation,
- the cooling effect of adiabatic expansion,
- the cooling effect of a Joule-Kelvin expansion.

Superconductivity at low temperatures: see B15.

Superfluids Near absolute zero, liquid helium loses all viscosity. The effect, called ***superfluidity***, occurs below the ***lamda point*** (2.172 K for ^{4}He; 0.000 93 K for ^{3}He).

INDEX

*If a reference is given in **bold**, you should look this up first.*

A

absolute zero 10, **70**, 74, 123
absorption spectrum 87
AC *see* alternating current
acceleration 6, **22-23**
  centripetal 33
  of free fall 7, **23**
accommodation (eye) 105
activity (nuclear) 82-83
adiabatic expansion 75
aerofoil 103, 115
aircraft 115
alloys 100
alpha
  decay 81
  particles 81, **82**
  scattering 80
alternating current 15, 53, **54-57**
alternator 15, 53
amorphous solids 66,100
ampere 12, **51**
amplifiers 116-118
  inverting and non-inverting 118
  operational 117-118
amplitude 16
amplitude modulation (AM) 120
analogue signals 120-121
angular velocity **32**, 37
anode 58
antinodes 63
antiparticles 81, **89**
aperture 65
Archimedes' principle 69
astigmatism 105
astronomical unit (AU) 92
astrophysics 92-95
atmosphere, Earth's 109
atmospheric pressure 68, 109
atoms 10, **80-81**
  bonds between 98
atomic mass 80
attenuation
  of signals 121
  of X-rays 106
audio signals 120
Avogadro constant **18**, 77
Avodadro's law 77

B

back EMF 53
background radiation 82
  cosmic 96
bandwidth (op amp) 117
bandwidth (radio) 120
barometer 68
baryons 90-91
becquerel 82
bending 67
Bernouilli's equation 103
beta
  decay 81
  particles 81, **82**
big bang 96-97
binary stars 95
binding energy 84-85
biofuels 113
Biot-Savart law 51
black body radiation **79**, 93, 122
black holes 95
body, human 104-105
Bohr's model of atom 87
boiling 11
Boltzmann constant 77
bonding energy 98
bonds 98
bosons **91**, 97
Boyle temperature 123
Boyle's law **74**, 77
brakes 114
Brewster's law 61
Brownian motion 76
bubble chamber 89
bulk strain 98

C

capacitance 44-45
capacitors 44-45
  in AC circuits 55-57
carbon dating 83
carbon dioxide in atmosphere 110-111
carbon-fibre reinforced plastic 100
carrier waves 120
CAT scanning 106
cathode 58
  rays 58, **123**
cells (convection) 109
cells, solar 113
Celsius scale 10, **70**
centre of buoyancy 69
centre of gravity 7, **26**
centripetal force **33**, 36
cepheid variables 94
chain reaction 85
channel (communication) 120
charge 12, **42-46**, 90
charge-coupled device (CCD) 65, **92**
Charles's law 74
circular motion 32-33
  in gravitational field 36
  in magnetic field 58-59
coercivity 101
coherent light 62
coherent optical fibres 106
coil
  field in 51
  induced EMF in 53
  torque on 50
collisions 30-31
colour 17, 62
  vision 105
combined heat and power 112
comparator 118
components (vector) 25
composites 100
conductance 47
conduction (thermal) 11, **78-79**
conductivity (electrical) **47**, 79
conductivity (thermal) 78-79
conductors (electrical) 12, 47, **101**
conservation
  of energy 8
  laws for particles 90
  of momentun 29
constant volume gas thermometer 71
convection 11, 79
Coriolis effect 109
cosmic background 96
cosmological principle 96
cosmology 96-97
coulomb 12
Coulomb's law 42
couples 27
covalent bonds 98
creep 67
critical
  angle 61
  density of Universe 97
  pressure 123
  size 127
  temperature 123
CRO 59
crystal structures 99
crystalline solids 66, 99
Curie temperature 101
current 12-13, **46**
  magnetic effect 14-15

D

damping 39, 41
dark matter 96
dB 105, 121
de Broglie wavelength 87
decay (of charge) 45
decay, radioactive 81-84
defects in crystals 99
DC 15
decibel 105, 121
density 7, 68
  of Earth 108
  of Universe 97
detectors
  astronomical 92
  nuclear radiation 82
  particle 82, **89**
diamagnetism 101
dielectric 44, 101
diffraction 16
  electron 87
  grating 63
  light 62-63
diffusion 76
digital signals 120-121
dimensions 19
diode 13, **46**
  light-emitting 116
  in rectification 57
dioptre 105
direct current 15
dislocations 99
dispersion 17
displacement 6
  angular 32
domains 101
doping 47, **101**
Doppler effect **93**, 96, 107
dose, radiation 107
drag 102-103, 115
drift chamber 89
drift speed (electrons) 46

E

Earth
- age 108
- atmosphere 109
- magnetism 108
- structure 108

earthquakes 109
eddy currents **52**, 56
efficiency 9
- of power stations 112
- thermodynamic 73
- of transformer 56

elastic deformation and limit 66-67
electric fields 42-44
- effect on electrons **58**, 123
- effect on nuclear radiations 82

electric potential 42-43
electric motor **15**, 53
electromagnet 14
electromagnetic force 90
electromagnetic induction 15, **52-53**
electromagnetic spectrum 17
electromagnetic waves **17**, 60, 122
electromotive force 12
- in battery 49
- induced 15, **53**

electron microscope 87
electronics 116-119
electrons 10
- charge on 46, 80, 123
- deflection of 58
- discovery 123
- energy levels in atom 87, 101
- free 10, **46-47**, 78
- specific charge (e/m_e) 59, **123**

electronvolt 58
elementary particles 88-91
elements 10, **80-81**
EMF see electromotive force
force emission spectrum 17
endoscope 106
energy 8-9
- binding 84-85
- in black body spectrum 79, 122
- bonding 98
- in capacitor 44
- conservation 8
- electrical 47, 113
- internal 8, **72-73**
- kinetic 9, **30-31**
- and mass **84**, 88
- nuclear 84-85
- potential (*mgh*) 8
- quantum **86-87**, 122
- reserves and resources 112
- rest 88
- schemes 113
- strain 67, 98
- types 8

energy levels (electron) 87, 101
engine, petrol 75
equilibrium
- of forces 25, **27**
- thermal 70

escape speed 35
ether 122
evaporation 11, **78**, 104
exchange particles 91
excited state 87
eye 105

F

farad 44
Faraday's law of
- electromagnetic induction 52

fatigue 67
feedback 118
ferroelectric crystals 101
ferromagnetism 101
fibre optics *see* optical fibres
fields
- electric 42-44
- gravitational 34-35
- magnetic 14, **50-53**

fission, nuclear 85
Fleming's left-hand rule **14**, 58
flotation 69
fluid flow **102-103**, 115
flux (magnetic) 52-53
flux density (magnetic) 50-51
focus 64
force 7
- electric 42-43
- gravitational **34-36**, 90
- and motion 28-33
- nuclear **88**, 90
- particles 91
- traction 114
- turning effect 26-27
- as vector 24-25

fossil fuels 112
fractures (in solids) 67
free electrons 10, **46-47**, 78, 98
frequency 16
- of AC 54
- radio 120
- of rotation 32
- of waves 61

frequency modulation (FM) 120
friction 114
fuels
- fossil 112
- nuclear 85

fundamental forces **90**, 96
fusion, nuclear 85
- in Sun and stars 95

fusion, specific
- latent heat of 73

G

g 7, **23**
- variations 108

gain (voltage) 116-118
galaxies **92**, 96-97
gamma camera 107
gamma rays 17, **82-83**
gas
- constant (molar) 75
- equations 74-75
- ideal 74-75
- laws 74
- particles in 10, **76-77**
- properties 74-77
- real 74, 123
- work done by 75

gates, logic 119
Geiger-Müller tube 82
geostationary orbit 36
geothermal energy scheme 113
glass 67, 100
glass-reinforced plastic 100
global warming **111**, 112-113
gluon 91
G-M tube 82
grains (metals) 100
grand unified theories 90
gravitation, Newton's law of 34
gravitational field strength 7, **34-35**, 43
- variations in *g* 108

gravitational potential 35
greenhouse effect 111

H

hadrons **90-91**, 97
half-life (discharge) 45
half-life radioactive 83
- biological 107

half-thickness 106
Hall probe 50
hearing 105
heat 8, 10-11, 70, **72-73**
- transfer 11, **78-79**

heat capacity 72
heat pump 112
helicopters 115
henry 53
hertz 16
Hertzsprung-Russell diagram 94-95
Hooke's law **66**, 98
hovercraft 115
Hubble constant 96-97
Hubble law 94, **96**
hydraulics 68
hydroelectric energy scheme 113
hypothermia 104
hysteresis (magnetic) 101
hysteresis (rubber) 67

I

ideal gas **74-75**, 123
images (lenses and mirrors) 64-65
impedance 56-57
- matching 117

impulse **28**, 41
indicator diagrams 75
induced charge 12
induced magnetism 14
inductor 53
- in AC circuits 55-57

inflation (of Universe) 96-97
infrared **17**, 79, 111, 121
- thermometer 71

insulators (electrical) 12, **101**
insulators (thermal) 11
integrated circuit (IC) 116
intensity (radiation) **61**, 82
intensity level (sound) 105
interference 62
internal energy 8, **72-73**
internal resistance 49
inversion temperature 123
inverter 119
ionic bonds 98
ionization 82, 87
ionosphere 109, 121
ions 10, 98
- deflection of 59

isostasy 108
isothermal expansion 75
isotopes 10, **80**

J

joints (bones) 104
joule 8
Joule-Kelvin effect 123

K

Kelvin scale 10, **70**
Kepler's third law 36
kilowatt hour 113
kinetic theory 76-77
kinetic energy 9, **30**
- in collisions 30-31
- rotational 37
- in SHM 39

Kirchhoff's laws 48

L

lapse rate 110
laser 106, 121
latent heat 11, **73**
LDR **13**, 116
LED 116
lenses 64-65
  correcting 105
Lenz's law 52
leptons **90**, 97
lift 103, 115
light 17, **60-65**
  speed of 17, **60**, 84
light-dependent resistor **13**, 116
light-emitting diodes 116
light-year 92
linear accelerator 89
liquids
  particles in 10
  pressure in 7, **68-69**
logic gates 119
loudness 17
luminosity of stars 93

M

magnetic fields 14, **50-53**
  effect on electrons 58-59
  effect on nuclear radiations 82
magnetic flux 52-53
magnetic flux density 50-51
magnetic properties 101
magnetic resonance imaging (MRI) 106
magnetism, Earth's 108
magnets 14, 101
magnification 64-65
magnitudes of stars 93
mains (AC) 54, 57
manometer 69
mass 7, 18
  and energy **84**, 88
materials 66-67, **98-101**
mass defect 84
Maxwell's screw rule 14
medical physics 104-107
mesons 90-91
metabolic rate 104
metals
  bonding in 98
  electrical conduction in 47
  stretching 66-67
  strengthening 100
micrometer 21
microwaves 17, 120
Millikan's experiment 123
modulation 120
molar gas constant 75
molar heat capacity 72
mole 18
molecule 76, 98
moment of inertia 37
moments 7, **26-27**
momentum (linear) 28-29, 88
  conservation of 29
monochromatic light 62
motion
  circular 32-33
  equations of 22-23
  graphs 22, **40-41**
  laws of 28-29
  linear **22-23**, 37
  rotational 37
  simple harmonic **38-39**, 41
moons 36, 92
muscles 104

N

nebula 94
neutrino 81, 89, **90**
neutron 10, 80, **90-91**
  in fission 85
  mass 80
neutron stars 95
Newton's laws of motion 28-29
nodes 63
nuclear
  fission 85
  fuel 85
  fusion 85, 95
  radiation 81-85
  reactions **81**, 84-85
  reactors 85
  safety 85
nucleon number 10, 80
nucleus 10, **80-81**
  stability of 81
nuclide 80

O

ohm 13
Ohm's law 13, **46**
Olber's paradox 96
operational amplifier 117-118
optical fibres 17, **61**
  medical use 106
  in telecommunications 121
orbits 36
oscilloscope 59
oxygen in atmosphere 109, 110
ozone layer 109

P

parallax 94
paramagnetism 101
parsec 92
particle accelerators 89
particles, elementary 88-91
pascal 7
path difference (optical) 62
PD *see* potential difference
pendulum 38
period 32, 38
permeability 51
permittivity 42, 44
phase (AC) 54-56
phases of matter 11
photoelectric effect 86
photon 17, 82, **86-87**, 91
photosynthesis 110
photovoltaic effect 113
piezoelectric effect **101**, 107
pitch 17
Planck's constant 86
planets 36, 92
plates (Earth's) 108
plastic deformation 66-67
plastics 66, **100**
Poiseuille's equation 102
polarization of dielectrics 101
polarization of molecules 98
polarization in waves 61
pollution 112
polycrystalline solids 66
polymers 66
positive holes 101
positron 81, 89
potential
  electric 42-43
  gravitational 35
potential difference 12-13, **43-44**
  across battery 49
  in circuits 12-13, **48-49**
potential energy
  atom separation 98
  mgh 8
  neutron separation 88
potential divider **49**, 116
power 9
  and velocity 31
power (electrical) **13**, 47
  in AC circuits 54-56
  in/from battery 49
  factor 56
power of lens 105
power stations 57, 112-113
pressure 7
  atmospheric 68, 109
  law for gases 74
  in liquids 66-69
  kinetic theory of 77
  in moving fluids 102-103
prisms 17, 65
proton 10, 80, 89, **90-91**
  mass 80
proton number 80-81
pulsars 95
pulse code modulation 121
pumped storage 112

Q

quantum energy 86, 122
quantum mechanical tunnelling 88
quantum numbers 90
quarks **91**, 97
quasars 95

R

radar astronomy 93
radian 19, **32**
radiation
  background 82
  black body **79**, 93, 122
  doses 107
  electromagnetic **17**, 60
  from nucleus 81-85
  thermal 11, **79**, 93
radio waves 17, **120-121**
radioactive decay 81-84
  law 83
radioisotopes 83, 107
radiotherapy 106
reactance 55
reactions, nuclear **81**, 84-85
reactor, nuclear 85
rectification 57
red giant 95
red shift **93**, 96
reflection 16, **64**
  total internal 17, **61**, 65
  of waves 16
refraction 16, 60
refractive index 60-61
refrigerator 112
regenerator 121
relativity 84, 88, **122**
relay 116
remanence 101
repeater 121
resistance 13, **46**
  in AC circuits 54, 56
  internal 49
  thermometers 71
resistivity 47
resistors, series and parallel 13, **48**
resolving power **65**, 87, 93

resonance 39
 in air column 63
 in RCL circuits 57
respiration 104, 110
rest mass 84
resultant 24
Reynolds' number 102
RMS *see* root mean square
rocks, dating 83
root mean square
 current 54
 PD 54
 speed (molecules) 76-77
rotation 37
rubber, stretching 67
Rutherford's atomic model 80

S

sampling rate 121
Sankey diagram 112
saturated vapour 110
scalars 9
scanning
 CAT and MRI 106
 ultrasound 107
seismic waves 109
self-induction 53
semiconductors 12, 47, 101
semicrystalline solids 66, 100
sensors 116
shear strain 98
SHM **38-39**, 41
SI units 18
sidebands 120
simple harmonic motion **38-39**, 41
smoothing 30
Snell's law 60
Solar System 92
solids
 particles in 10
 properties and structure 66-67, 98-101
sound waves 17
specific charge (electron) 59
specific heat capacity 11, **72**
specific latent heat 73
spectrum
 absorption and emission 87
 black body 79
 electromagnetic 17
 of Sun, stars 87, 93
speed 6
 of light 17, **60**, 84
 of sound 17
stability 27, 69
stacking faults 99
stars 94-95
Stokes' law 102
strain **66-67**, 98
 energy 67
strangeness 90
streamline flow 102
stress **66-67**, 98
strong nuclear force 10, **88**, 90, 91
Sun
 energy from 110
 life cycle 95
 spectrum of 87
 structure 95
superconductivity 47
superposition (waves) 62
sweating 104
switching (electronic) 116, **118-119**
synchrotron 89

T

telecommunications 120-121
telescopes
 optical **65**, 91-93
 others (e.g. radio) 92-93
temperature 10, **70-71**
 control in body 104
 and kinetic theory 77
 thermodynamic 70
terminal velocity **41**, 102
tesla 50
thermal
 conductivity 78-79
 radiation 11, **79**
 reactor (nuclear) 85
thermionic emission 58
thermistor 13, **46-47**, 71, 116
thermocouple 71
thermodynamics
 first law **72,** 75
 second law 73
 zeroth law 70
thermometers 70-71
thermoplastics 100
thermosets 100
tidal energy scheme 113
time constant 45
torque 27
 on coil 50
total internal reflection 17, **61**
tracers (radioactive) 83, **107**
traction forces 114
transducers 107, **116**
transformer 15, **56-57**, 117
transistor 116
transition termperature
 glass 100
 superconductors 47
transmutation (nuclear) 81
truth tables 119
tuning 120
turbulent flow **102**, 115

U

U-values 79
ultrasound 107
ultraviolet 17
 catastrophe 122
uncertainties 20
uncertainty principle 91
unified atomic mass unit 80
units 18
Universe 92, **96-97**
 models of 97

V

van der Waals' bonds 98
vaporization
 specific latent heat of 73
vapour 123
variables 21
vectors 6, 9, **24-25**
 in AC 56-57
velocity 6, **22-23**
 terminal **41**, 102
Venturi meter 103
vernier 21
virtual image 64
virtual particles 91
viscosity 102
voltage *see* potential difference and electromotive force
voltage follower 118

W

water balance 111
water vapour in atmosphere 110
watt 9
wave-particle duality 87
wavelength 16, **61**
 electron 87
 measurement (light) 62-63
waves 16-17, **60-63**
 electromagnetic **17**, 60
 light 17
 longitudinal and transverse 16
 progressive 16
 radio 120-121
 seismic 109
 sound 17
 stationary 63
weak force 90, 91
Weber 52
weight 7
weightlessness 36
white dwarf 95
Wien's law 93
wind belts 109
wind power 113
work 8, **30**, 41
 conversion into heat 73
work function 86
work hardening 100

X

X-ray binary stars 95
X-rays 17, **106**

Y

yield point 66-67
Young's modulus 67

Physical data

Physical quantity	*Symbol*	*Value*
speed of light in a vacuum	c	2.998×10^{8} m s^{-1}
permittivity of free space	ε_o	8.854×10^{-12} F m^{-1}
permeability of free space	μ_o	$4\pi \times 10^{-7}$ H m^{-1}
proton rest mass	m_p	1.673×10^{-27} kg
neutron rest mass	m_n	1.675×10^{-27} kg
electron rest mass	m_e	9.110×10^{-31} kg
proton charge	e	1.602×10^{-19} C
electron charge	$-e$	-1.602×10^{-19} C
	(minus sign often omitted)	
specific charge: electron	e/m_e	1.759×10^{11} C kg^{-1}
Planck constant	h	6.626×10^{-34} J s
gravitational constant	G	6.672×10^{-11} N m^{2} kg^{-2}
Avogadro constant	N_A	6.022×10^{23} mol^{-1}
universal molar gas constant	R	8.314 J K^{-1} mol^{-1}
Boltzmann constant	k	1.381×10^{-23} J K^{-1}
absolute zero		0 K, –273.15 °C
standard atmospheric pressure		1.013×10^{5} Pa
kilowatt hour	kW h	3.600×10^{6} J
electronvolt	eV	1.602×10^{-19} J
unified atomic mass unit	u	1.661×10^{-27} kg
	(energy equivalent: 931.5 MeV)	
acceleration of free fall (mean, at Earth's surface)	g, g_o	9.807 m s^{-2}
mass of Earth		5.976×10^{24} kg
mass of Sun		1.989×10^{30} kg
mass of Moon		7.350×10^{22} kg
equatorial radius of Earth		6.378×10^{6} m
mean distance of Earth from Sun		1.496×10^{11} m
mean distance of Moon from Earth		3.844×10^{8} m
solar constant		1.352×10^{3} W m^{-2}
astronomical unit	AU	1.496×10^{11} m
parsec	pc	3.086×10^{16} m
light year	ly	9.461×10^{15} m